PRENTICE HALL
TeacherEXPRESS™
Plan · Teach · Assess

Lab
zone™

XPLORER offers many aids to help you plan your instruction time, whether regular class periods or
...uling. Section-by-section lesson plans for each chapter include suggested times for Student Edition
...acherExpress™ and the Lab zone™ Easy Planner CD-ROM will help you manage your time electronically.

Pacing Chart

	PERIODS	BLOCKS		PERIODS	BLOCKS
Solar Astronomer	1	$\frac{1}{2}$	**Chapter 4 Stars, Galaxies, and the Universe**		
1 Earth, Moon, and Sun			Chapter 4 Project: *Star Stories*	Ongoing	Ongoing
Project: *Track the Moon*	Ongoing	Ongoing	1 Tech & Design: Telescopes	3	$1\frac{1}{2}$
Space	3	$1\frac{1}{2}$	2 Characteristics of Stars	2	1
ng Physics: Gravity and Motion	1	$\frac{1}{2}$	3 Lives of Stars	1	$\frac{1}{2}$
Eclipses, and Tides	4	2	4 Star Systems and Galaxies	2	1
Moon	1	$\frac{1}{2}$	5 The Expanding Universe	1	$\frac{1}{2}$
Review and Assessment	1	$\frac{1}{2}$	Chapter 4 Review and Assessment	1	$\frac{1}{2}$
2 Exploring Space			Interdisciplinary Exploration: Journey to Mars	2	1
Project: *Space Exploration Vehicle*	Ongoing	Ongoing			
...ce of Rockets	3	$1\frac{1}{2}$			
...ce Program	1	$\frac{1}{2}$			
...g Space Today	1	$\frac{1}{2}$			
...esign: Using Space Science on Earth	3	$1\frac{1}{2}$			
Review and Assessment	1	$\frac{1}{2}$			
3 The Solar System					
Project: *Model of the Solar System*	Ongoing	Ongoing			
...ng the Solar System	2	1			
	2	1			
...er Planets	3	$1\frac{1}{2}$			
...er Planets	3	$1\frac{1}{2}$			
...Asteroids, and Meteors	1	$\frac{1}{2}$			
...ng Life Science: ...Life Beyond Earth?	1	$\frac{1}{2}$			
Review and Assessment	1	$\frac{1}{2}$			

Astronomy: Teacher's Edition
 W9-BMG-081

Contents in Brief

Teacher's Edition

*See Program
Component List
on page ii*

Student Edition

Complete Table of Contents vi

Prentice Hall Science Explorer

Series Tables of Contents

Life Science

The Nature of Science and Technology
1. What Is Science?
2. The Work of Scientists
3. Technology and Engineering

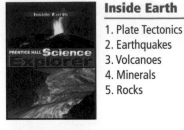

From Bacteria to Plants
1. Living Things
2. Viruses and Bacteria
3. Protists and Fungi
4. Introduction to Plants
5. Seed Plants

Animals
1. Sponges, Cnidarians, and Worms
2. Mollusks, Arthropods, and Echinoderms
3. Fishes, Amphibians, and Reptiles
4. Birds and Mammals
5. Animal Behavior

Cells and Heredity
1. Cell Structure and Function
2. Cell Processes and Energy
3. Genetics: The Science of Heredity
4. Modern Genetics
5. Changes Over Time

Human Biology and Health
1. Bones, Muscles, and Skin
2. Food and Digestion
3. Circulation
4. Respiration and Excretion
5. Fighting Disease
6. The Nervous System
7. The Endocrine System and Reproduction

Environmental Science
1. Populations and Communities
2. Ecosystems and Biomes
3. Living Resources
4. Land, Water, and Air Resources
5. Energy Resources

Earth Science

Inside Earth
1. Plate Tectonics
2. Earthquakes
3. Volcanoes
4. Minerals
5. Rocks

Earth's Changing Surface
1. Mapping Earth's Surface
2. Weathering and Soil Formation
3. Erosion and Deposition
4. A Trip Through Geologic Time

Earth's Waters
1. Earth: The Water Planet
2. Freshwater Resources
3. Ocean Motions
4. Ocean Zones

Weather and Climate
1. The Atmosphere
2. Weather Factors
3. Weather Patterns
4. Climate and Climate Change

Astronomy
1. Earth, Moon, and Sun
2. Exploring Space
3. The Solar System
4. Stars, Galaxies, and the Universe

Physical Science

Chemical Building Blocks
1. Introduction to Matter
2. Solids, Liquids, and Gases
3. Elements and the Periodic Table
4. Exploring Materials

Chemical Interactions
1. Atoms and Bonding
2. Chemical Reactions
3. Acids, Bases, and Solutions
4. Carbon Chemistry

Motion, Forces, and Energy
1. Motion
2. Forces
3. Forces in Fluids
4. Work and Machines
5. Energy
6. Thermal Energy and Heat

Electricity and Magnetism
1. Magnetism
2. Electricity
3. Using Electricity and Magnetism
4. Electronics

Sound and Light
1. Characteristics of Waves
2. Sound
3. The Electromagnetic Spectrum
4. Light

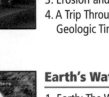

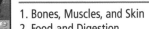

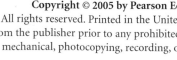

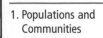

Teacher's Edition

Astronomy

PRENTICE HALL Science Explorer

PEARSON
Prentice Hall

Needham, Massachusetts
Upper Saddle River, New Jersey

Copyright © 2005 by Pearson Education, Inc., publishing as Pearson Prentice Hall, Upper Saddle River, New Jersey 07458.

Pearson Prentice Hall™ is a trademark of Pearson Education, Inc.
Pearson® is a registered trademark of Pearson plc.
Prentice Hall® is a registered trademark of Pearson Education, Inc.
Lab zone™ is a trademark of Pearson Education, Inc.

Planet Diary® is a registered trademark of Addison Wesley Longman, Inc.

Discovery Channel School® is a registered trademark of Discovery Communications, Inc., used under license. The Discovery Channel logo is a trademark of Discovery Communications, Inc.

SciLinks® is a trademark of the National Science Teachers Association. The SciLinks® service includes copyrighted materials and is owned and provided by the National Science Teachers Association. All rights reserved.

Science News® is a registered trademark of Science Services, Inc.

ISBN 0-13-181129-0

Research-Based and Proven to Work

As the originator of the small book concept in middle school science, and as the nation's number one science publisher, Prentice Hall takes pride in the fact that we've always listened closely to teachers. In doing so, we've developed programs that effectively meet the needs of your classroom.

As we continue to listen, we realize that raising the achievement level of all students is the number one challenge facing teachers today. To assist you in meeting this latest challenge, Prentice Hall has combined the very best author team with solid research to create a program that meets your high standards and will ensure that no child is left behind.

With Prentice Hall, you can be confident that your students will not only be motivated, inspired, and excited to learn science, but that they will also achieve the success needed in today's environment of the No Child Left Behind (NCLB) legislation and testing reform.

On the following pages, you will read about the key elements found throughout *Science Explorer* that truly set this program apart and ensure success for you and your students.

> As we continue to listen, we realize that raising the achievement level of all students is the number one challenge facing teachers today.

A Science Program Backed by Research

In developing Prentice Hall *Science Explorer*, we used research studies as a central, guiding element. Research on *Science Explorer* indicated key elements of a textbook program that ensure students' success: support for reading and mathematics in science, consistent opportunities for inquiry, and an ongoing assessment strand. This research was conducted in phases and continues today.

1. Exploratory: Needs Assessment

Along with periodic surveys concerning state and national standards as well as curriculum issues and challenges, we conducted specific product development research, which included discussions with teachers and advisory panels, focus groups, and quantitative surveys. We explored the specific needs of teachers, students, and other educators regarding each book we developed in Prentice Hall *Science Explorer*.

2. Formative: Prototype Development and Field-Testing

During this phase of research, we worked to develop prototype materials. Then we tested the materials by field-testing with students and teachers and by performing qualitative and quantitative surveys. In our early prototype testing, we received feedback about our lesson structure. Results were channeled back into the program development for improvement.

3. Summative: Validation Research

Finally, we conducted and continue to conduct long-term research based on scientific, experimental designs under actual classroom conditions. This research identifies what works and what can be improved in the next revision of Prentice Hall *Science Explorer*. We also continue to monitor the program in the market. We talk to our users about what works, and then we begin the cycle over again. The next section contains highlights of this research.

A Science Program With Proven Results

In a year-long study in 2000–2001, students in six states using Prentice Hall *Science Explorer* outscored students using other science programs on a nationally normed standardized test.

The study investigated the effects of science textbook programs at the eighth-grade level. Twelve eighth-grade science classes with a total of 223 students participated in the study. The selected classes were of similar student ability levels.

Each class was tested at the beginning of the school year using the TerraNova CTBS Basic Battery Plus, and then retested at the end of the school year. The final results, shown in the graph, show a significant improvement in test scores from the pre-test to the post-test evaluation.

• All tests were scored by CTB/McGraw-Hill, the publisher of the TerraNova exam. Statistical analyses and conclusions were performed by an independent firm, Pulse Analytics, Inc.

In Japan, Lesson Study Research has been employed for a number of years as a tool for teachers to improve their curriculum. In April 2003, Prentice Hall adapted this methodology to focus on a lesson from this edition. Our goal was to test the effectiveness of lesson pedagogy and improve it while in the program development stage. In all three classrooms tested, student learning increased an average of 10 points from the pre- to the post-assessment.

• Detailed results of these studies can be obtained at **www.PHSchool.com/research.**

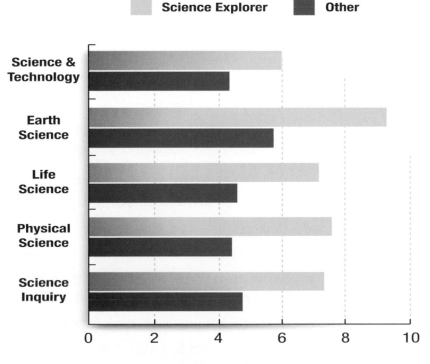

Foundational Research: Inquiry in the Science Classroom

"How do I know if my students are inquiring?" "If students are busy doing lots of hands-on activities, are they using inquiry?" "What is inquiry, anyway?" If you're confused, you are not alone. Inquiry is the heart and soul of science education, with most of us in continuous pursuit of achieving it with our students!

Defining Science Inquiry

What is it? Simply put, inquiry is the intellectual side of science. It is thinking like a scientist—being inquisitive, asking why, and searching for answers. The National Science Education Content Standards define inquiry as the process in which students begin with a question, design an investigation, gather evidence, formulate an answer to the original question, and communicate the investigative process and results. Since it is often difficult to accomplish all this in one class period, the standards also acknowledge that at times students need to practice only one or two inquiry components.

Understanding Inquiry

The National Research Council in Inquiry and the National Science Education Standards (2000) identified several "essential features" of classroom inquiry. We have modified these essential features into questions to guide you in your quest for enhanced and more thoughtful student inquiry.

1. *Who asks the question?* In most curricula, these focusing questions are an element given in the materials. As a teacher you can look for labs that, at least on a periodic basis, allow students to pursue their own questions.

2. *Who designs the procedures?* To gain experience with the logic underlying experimentation, students need continuous practice with designing procedures. Some labs in which the primary target is content acquisition designate procedures. But others should ask students to do so.

3. *Who decides what data to collect?* Students need practice in determining the data to collect.

4. *Who formulates explanations based upon the data?* Students should be challenged to think—to analyze and draw conclusions based on their data, not just copy answers from the text materials.

5. *Who communicates and justifies the results?* Activities should push students not only to communicate but also to justify their answers. Activities also should be thoughtfully designed and interesting so that students want to share their results and argue about conclusions.

Making Time for Inquiry

One last question—Must each and every activity have students do all of this? The answer is an obvious and emphatic "No." You will find a great variety of activities in *Science Explorer*. Some activities focus on content acquisition, and thus they specify the question and most of the procedures. But many others stress in-depth inquiry from start to finish. Because inquiry is an intellectual pursuit, it cannot merely be characterized by keeping students busy and active. Too many students have a knack for being physically but not intellectually engaged in science. It is our job to help them engage intellectually.

Michael J. Padilla, Ph.D.
Program Author of *Science Explorer*
Professor of Science Education
University of Georgia
Athens, Georgia

"Because inquiry is an intellectual pursuit, it cannot merely be characterized by keeping students busy and active."

Evaluator's Checklist

Does your science program promote inquiry by—

✔ Enabling students to pursue their own questions

✔ Allowing students to design their own procedures

✔ Letting students determine what data are best to collect

✔ Challenging students to think critically

✔ Pushing students to justify their answers

Inquiry in *Science Explorer*

Science Explorer offers the most opportunities to get students to think like a scientist. By providing inquiry opportunities throughout the program, *Science Explorer* enables students to enhance their understanding by participating in the discovery.

Student Edition Inquiry

Six lab and activity options are included in every chapter, structured from directed to open-ended—providing you the flexibility to address all types of learners and accommodate your class time and equipment requirements. As Michael Padilla notes, some activities focus on content acquisition, and thus the question and most of the procedures are specified. But many others stress in-depth inquiry from start to finish. The graph below shows how, in general, inquiry levels are addressed in the Student Edition.

Science Explorer encourages students to develop inquiry skills across the spectrum from teacher-guided to open-ended. Even more opportunities for real-life applications of inquiry are included in Science & Society, Science & Technology, Careers in Science, and Interdisciplinary Exploration features.

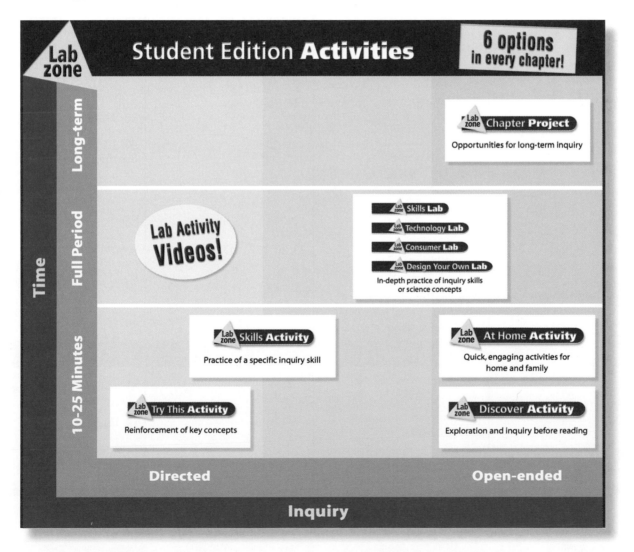

Inquiry Skills Chart

SCIENCE EXPLORER provides comprehensive teaching, practice, and assessment of science skills, with an emphasis on the process skills necessary for inquiry. This chart lists the skills covered in the program and cites the page numbers where each skill is covered.

Basic Process SKILLS

	Student Text: Projects and Labs	Student Text: Activities	Student Text: Caption and Review Questions	Teacher's Edition: Extensions
Observing	14–15, 28–29, 46–47, 117	42, 78, 84, 118, 126, 145	31, 49, 76, 95, 98, 105	20, 42, 78, 84, 126, 145
Inferring	14–15, 28, 46–47, 83, 125, 134–135	20, 40, 43, 48, 88, 104, 121, 128, 148	36, 54, 59, 62, 77, 89, 99, 101, 109, 156	10, 18, 20, 21, 40, 48, 86, 88, 104, 121, 128, 143, 148
Predicting	14–15, 134–135	10, 75, 76, 138, 150	13, 19, 36, 52, 114, 133, 140, 153	10, 22, 30, 75, 138
Classifying	29	94	68, 101, 114, 133, 147	49, 94
Making Models	14, 28–29, 71, 102–103	6, 24, 98, 129, 141	114, 150	6, 8, 11, 12, 19, 24, 25, 26, 74, 90, 98, 122, 127, 129, 141, 145
Communicating	15, 29, 63, 83, 103, 135	109		40, 49, 51, 55, 59, 61, 75, 87, 89, 105, 109, 119, 133, 137
Measuring	71		133	130
Calculating	71, 134–135	50	32, 36, 127, 147, 156	9, 50
Creating Data Tables	46			81
Graphing	63, 83			18, 43

Advanced Process SKILLS

	Student Text: Projects and Labs	Student Text: Activities	Student Text: Caption and Review Questions	Teacher's Edition: Extensions
Posing Questions				41
Developing Hypotheses	102–103	16, 30		12, 16, 30
Designing Experiments	47, 102–103		62	12

Advanced Process SKILLS (continued)

	Student Text: Projects and Labs	Student Text: Activities	Student Text: Caption and Review Questions	Teacher's Edition: Extensions
Controlling Variables	63			
Forming Operational Definitions	63	108		108
Interpreting Data	63, 83, 135	76, 80	77, 114	80, 120, 123
Drawing Conclusions	15, 29	53, 58, 72, 76, 90, 136, 150	52, 77, 114	43, 53, 58, 72, 136

Critical Thinking SKILLS

Comparing and Contrasting	5, 71		13, 27, 33, 36, 45, 56, 57, 62, 67–68, 77, 82, 91, 96, 101, 107, 113–114, 124, 133, 140, 156	7, 10, 21, 25, 55, 61, 85, 87, 95, 98, 104, 121
Applying Concepts	5, 39, 117		7, 19, 36, 60, 68, 77, 110, 111, 114, 124, 129, 130, 133, 137, 140, 147, 156	86, 120
Interpreting Diagrams, Graphs, Photographs, and Maps	71, 117		11, 12, 19, 21, 22, 25, 26, 27, 36, 42, 44, 45, 68, 73, 74, 77, 81, 85, 97, 119, 131, 132, 138, 142, 145, 156	11, 17, 22, 24, 31, 51, 73, 79, 81, 95, 97, 111, 121, 131, 139, 144
Relating Cause and Effect	5		10, 13, 27, 33, 45, 52, 62, 68, 82, 91, 107, 111, 140, 153, 156	23, 79, 144
Making Generalizations	5, 39	18	68, 111, 114	9
Making Judgments	39		57, 68	110
Problem Solving	39			61

Informational Organizational SKILLS

Concept Maps			35, 155	34, 43, 66, 112
Compare/Contrast Tables				98
Venn Diagrams				
Flowcharts				88
Cycle Diagrams				

The *Science Explorer* program provides additional teaching, reinforcement, and assessment of skills in the *Inquiry Skills Activities Book* and the *Integrated Science Laboratory Manual*.

A National Look at Science Education

Project 2061 was established by the American Association for the Advancement of Science (AAAS) as a long-term project to improve science education nationwide. A primary goal of Project 2061 is to define a "common core of learning"—the knowledge and skills we want all students to achieve. Project 2061 published *Science for All Americans* in 1989 and followed this with Benchmarks for Science Literacy in 1993. Benchmarks recommends what students should know and be able to do by the end of grades 2, 5, 8, and 12. Project 2061 clearly states that *Benchmarks* is not a curriculum but a tool for designing successful curricula.

The National Research Council (NRC) used *Science for All Americans* and *Benchmarks* to develop the National Science Education Standards (NSES), which were published in 1996. The NSES are organized into six categories (Content, Teaching, Assessment, Professional Development, Program, and System) to help schools establish the conditions necessary to achieve scientific literacy for all students.

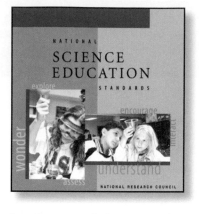

Michael Padilla, the program author of *Science Explorer,* guided one of six teams of teachers whose work led to the publication of *Benchmarks.* He also was a contributing writer of the National Science Education Standards. Under his guidance, *Science Explorer* has implemented these standards through its inquiry approach, a focus on student learning of important concepts and skills, and teacher support aligned with the NSES teaching standards.

Neither *Benchmarks* nor the NSES requires a single, uniform national curriculum, and in fact there is a great diversity nationwide in science curricula. The correlations that follow are designed to help you use the *Science Explorer* program to meet your particular curriculum needs.

Meeting the National Science Education Standards

EARTH, MOON, AND SUN

Science as Inquiry (Content Standard A)

● **Communicate scientific procedures and explanations** Students present their observations of the moon, using words, charts, and drawings. (*Chapter Project*)

● **Identify questions that can be answered through scientific investigations** Students observe the moon and look for patterns in its motions and changing appearance. (*Chapter Project*)

Physical Science (Content Standard B)

● **Motions and forces** Students use Newton's laws to explain orbital motion. (*Gravity and Motion*)

Earth and Space Science (Content Standard D)

● **Earth in the solar system** Earth has day and night and the moon has phases because of relative motions of Earth and the moon in the Solar system. Gravity explains the phenomena of the tides. (*Earth in Space; Gravity and Motion; Phases, Eclipses, and Tides; Earth's Moon*)

EXPLORING SPACE

Science as Inquiry (Content Standard A)

● **Use appropriate tools and techniques to gather, analyze, and interpret data** Students build a space exploration vehicle and test insulating materials. (*Chapter Project, Skills Lab*)

Physical Science (Content Standard B)

● **Motions and forces** Students learn how rockets work. (*The Science of Rockets*)

Science and Technology (Content Standard E)

● **Design a solution or product** Students design a space exploration vehicle. (*Chapter Project*)

● **Abilities of technological design** The space program includes many examples of both the successes and limitations of technology. (*The Space Program*)

A National Look at Science Education (continued)

Science in Personal and Social Perspectives (Content Standard F)

● **Science and technology in society** Space spinoffs have improved the quality of life on Earth. (*Using Space Science on Earth*)

THE SOLAR SYSTEM

Science as Inquiry (Content Standard A)

● **Develop descriptions, explanations, predictions, and models using evidence** Students design scale models of the Solar system and investigate the relationship between a planet's orbital speed and its distance from the sun. (*Chapter Project, Design Your Own Lab*)

Earth and Space Science (Content Standard D)

● **Structure of the Earth system** Earth's structure is the basis for understanding the structure of other planets. (*The Inner Planets*)

● **Earth in the solar system** The heliocentric model of the solar system is the basis for our modern understanding. (*The Inner Planets*)

Science in Personal and Social Perspectives (Content Standard F)

● **Risks and benefits** Space exploration has many benefits but is very costly and risky. (*Science and Society*)

History and the Nature of Science (Content Standard G)

● **History of science** The struggle that occurred when society changed from a geocentric to a heliocentric model of the solar system is an example of the development of a scientific paradigm. (*Observing the Solar System*)

STARS, GALAXIES, AND THE UNIVERSE

Science as Inquiry (Content Standard A)

● **Use mathematics in all aspects of scientific inquiry** Astronomers use parallax to determine the distance to nearby stars. (*Characteristics of Stars, Skills Lab*)

Physical Science (Content Standard B)

● **Properties and changes of properties in matter** Matter can emit and absorb radiation of many different wavelengths. (*Telescopes*)

Science and Technology (Content Standard E)

● **Abilities of technological design** In order to better understand telescopes as a tool of astronomy, students construct a simple telescope. (*Technology Lab*)

Science in Personal and Social Perspectives (Content Standard F)

● **History of science** The tools of astronomy have changed dramatically since Galileo first looked at the sky with his telescope. (*Telescopes*)

Note: To see how the Benchmarks are supported by *SCIENCE EXPLORER,* go to **PHSchool.com.**

Reading Comprehension in the Science Classroom

Q&A

Q: Why are science texts often difficult for students to read and comprehend?

A: In general, science texts make complex literacy and knowledge demands on learners. They have a more technical vocabulary and a more demanding syntax, and place a greater emphasis on inferential reasoning.

Q: What does research say about facilitating comprehension?

A: Studies comparing novices and experts show that the conceptual organization of experts' knowledge is very different from that of novices. For example, experts emphasize core concepts when organizing knowledge, while novices focus on superficial details. To facilitate comprehension, effective teaching strategies should support and scaffold students as they build an understanding of the key concepts and concept relationships within a text unit.

Q: What strategies can teachers use to facilitate comprehension?

A: Three complementary strategies are very important in facilitating student comprehension of science texts. First, guide student interaction with the text using the built-in strategies. Second, organize the curriculum in terms of core concepts (e.g., the **Key Concepts** in each section). Third, develop visual representations of the relationships among the key concepts and vocabulary that can be referred to during instruction.

Nancy Romance, Ph.D.
Professor of Science Education
Florida Atlantic University
Fort Lauderdale, Florida

"Effective teaching strategies should support and scaffold students as they build an understanding of the key concepts and concept relationships within a text unit."

Reading Support in *Science Explorer*

The latest research emphasizes the importance of activating learners' prior knowledge and teaching them to distinguish core concepts from less important information. These skills are now more important than ever, because success in science requires students to read, understand, and connect complex terms and concepts.

Before students read—
Reading Preview introduces students to the key concepts and key terms they'll find in each section. The **Target Reading Skill** is identified and applied with a graphic organizer.

During the section—
Boldface Sentences identify each key concept and encourage students to focus on the big ideas of science.

Reading Checkpoints reinforce students' understanding by slowing them down to review after every concept is discussed.

Caption Questions draw students into the art and photos, helping them connect the content to the images.

After students read—
Section Assessment revisits the **Target Reading Skill** and encourages students to use the graphic organizer.

Each review question is scaffolded and models the way students think, by first easing them into a review and then challenging them with increasingly more difficult questions.

Evaluator's Checklist

Does your science program promote reading comprehension with—

✔ Text structured in an outline format and key concepts highlighted in boldface type

✔ Real-world applications to activate prior knowledge

✔ Key concepts, critical vocabulary, and a reading skill for every section

✔ Sample graphic organizers for each section

✔ Relevant photos and carefully constructed graphics with questions

✔ Reading checkpoints that appear in each section

✔ Scaffolded questions in section assessments

Math in the Science Classroom

Why should students concern themselves with mathematics in your science class?

Good science requires good data from which to draw conclusions. Technology enhances the ability to measure in a variety of ways. Often the scientist must measure large amounts of data, and thus an aim of analysis is to reduce the data to a summary that makes sense and is consistent with established norms of communication—i.e., mathematics.

Calculating measures of central tendency (e.g., mean, median, or mode), variability (e.g., range), and shape (graphic representations) can effectively reduce 500 data points to 3 without losing the essential characteristics of the data. Scientists understand that a trade-off exists between precision and richness as data are folded into categories, and so margins of error can be quantified in mathematical terms and factored into all scientific findings.

Mathematics is the language used by scientists to model change in the world. Understanding change is a vital part of the inquiry process. Mathematics serves as a common language to communicate across the sciences. Fields of scientific research that originated as separate disciplines are now integrated, such as happened with bioengineering. What do the sciences have in common? Each uses the language of mathematics to communicate about data and the process of data analysis. Recognizing this need, *Science Explorer* integrates mathematics practice throughout the program and gives students ample opportunity to hone their math skills.

Clearly, mathematics plays an important role in your science classroom!

William Tate, Ph.D.
Professor of Education and
Applied Statistics and
Computation
Washington University
St. Louis, Missouri

> "Mathematics is the language used by scientists to model change in the world."

Integrated Math Support

In the Student Edition
The math instruction is based on principles derived from Prentice Hall's research-based mathematics program.

Sample Problems, Math Practice, Analyzing Data, and a Math Skills Handbook all help to provide practice at point of use, encouraging students to Read and Understand, Plan and Solve, and then Look Back and Check.

Color-coded variables aid student navigation and help reinforce their comprehension.

In the Teacher's Edition
Math teaching notes enable the science teacher to support math instruction and math objectives on high-stakes tests.

In the Guided Reading and Study Workbook
These unique worksheets help students master reading and enhance their study and math skills. Students can create a record of their work for study and review.

Evaluator's Checklist

Does your science program promote math skills by—

✔ Giving students opportunities to collect data

✔ Providing students opportunities to analyze data

✔ Enabling students to practice math skills

✔ Helping students solve equations by using color-coded variables

✔ Using sample problems to apply science concepts

Technology and Design

Technology and Design in the Science Classroom

Much of the world we live in is designed and made by humans. The buildings in which we live, the cars we drive, the medicines we take, and often the food we eat are products of technology. The knowledge and skills needed to understand the processes used to create these products should be a component of every student's basic literacy.

Some schools offer hands-on instruction on how technology development works through industrial arts curricula. Even then, there is a disconnect among science (understanding how nature works), mathematics (understanding data-driven models), and technology (understanding the human-made world). The link among these fields of study is the engineering design process—that process by which one identifies a human need and uses science knowledge and human ingenuity to create a technology to satisfy the need. Engineering gives students the problem-solving and design skills they will need to succeed in our sophisticated, three-dimensional, technological world.

As a complement to "science as inquiry," the National Science Education Standards (NRC, 1996) call for students at all age levels to develop the abilities related to "technology as design," including the ability to identify and frame a problem and then to design, implement, and evaluate a solution. At the 5–8 grade level, the standards call for students to be engaged in complex problem-solving and to learn more about how science and technology complement each other. It's also important for students to understand that there are often constraints involved in design as well as trade-offs and unintended consequences of technological solutions to problems.

As the *Standards for Technological Literacy* (ITEA, 2000) state, "Science and technology are like conjoined twins. While they have separate identities they must remain inextricably connected." Both sets of standards emphasize how progress in science leads to new developments in technology, while technological innovation in turn drives advances in science.

Ioannis Miaoulis, Ph.D.
President
Museum of Science
Boston, Massachusetts

"Engineering gives students the problem-solving and design skills they will need to succeed in our sophisticated, three-dimensional, technological world."

Evaluator's Checklist

Does your science program promote technology and design by—

✔ Incorporating technology and design concepts and skills into the science curriculum

✔ Giving students opportunities to identify and solve technological design problems

✔ Providing students opportunities to analyze the impact of technology on society

✔ Enabling students to practice technology and design skills

Technology and Design in *Science Explorer*

How often do you hear your students ask: "Why do I need to learn this?" Connecting them to the world of technology and design in their everyday life is one way to help answer this question. It is also why so many state science curricula are now emphasizing technology and design concepts and skills.

Science Explorer makes a special effort to include a technology and design strand that encourages students to not only identify a need but to take what they learned in science and apply it to design a possible solution, build a prototype, test and evaluate the design, and/or troubleshoot the design. This strand also provides definitions of technology and engineering and discusses the similarities and differences between these endeavors and science. Students will learn to analyze the risks and benefits of a new technology and to consider the tradeoffs, such as safety, costs, efficiency, and appearance.

In the Student Edition

Integrated Technology & Design Sections

Sections throughout *Science Explorer* specifically integrate technology and design with the content of the text. For example, students not only learn how seismographs work but also learn what role seismographs play in society and how people use the data that are gathered.

Technology Labs

These labs help students gain experience in designing and building a device or product that meets a particular need or solves a problem. Students follow a design process of Research and Investigate, Design and Build, and Evaluate and Redesign.

Chapter Projects

Chapter Projects work hand-in-hand with the chapter content. Students design, build, and test based on real-world situations. They have the opportunity to apply the knowledge and skills learned to building a product.

Special Features

This technology and design strand is also reflected in Technology & Society and Science & Society features as well as Technology & History timelines. These highly visual features introduce a technology and its impact on society. For example, students learn how a hybrid car differs from a traditional car.

Assessment in the Science Curriculum

No Child Left Behind clearly challenges school districts across the nation to raise expectations for all students with testing of student achievement in science beginning in 2007–2008.

A primary goal of NCLB is to provide classroom teachers with better data from scientifically valid assessments in order to inform instructional planning and to identify students who are at risk and require intervention. It has been a common practice to teach a science lesson, administer a test, grade it, and move on. This practice is a thing of the past. With the spotlight now on improving student performance, it is essential to use assessment results as a way to identify student strengths and challenges. Providing student feedback and obtaining student input is a valuable, essential part of the assessment process.

Assessment is a never-ending cycle, as is shown in the following diagram. Although you may begin at any point in the assessment cycle, the basic process is the same.

An important assessment strategy is to ensure that students have ample opportunities to check their understanding of skills and concepts before moving on to the next topic. Checking for understanding also includes asking appropriate, probing questions with each example presented. This enables students and teachers to know whether the skills or concepts being introduced are actually understood.

Eileen Depka
Supervisor of Standards
and Assessment
Waukesha, Wisconsin

"Meeting the NCLB challenge will necessitate an integrated approach to assessment with a variety of assessment tools."

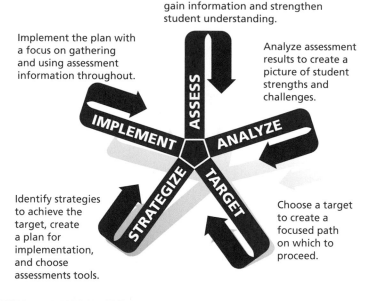

Use a variety of assessment tools to gain information and strengthen student understanding.

Implement the plan with a focus on gathering and using assessment information throughout.

Analyze assessment results to create a picture of student strengths and challenges.

IMPLEMENT ASSESS ANALYZE

STRATEGIZE TARGET

Identify strategies to achieve the target, create a plan for implementation, and choose assessments tools.

Choose a target to create a focused path on which to proceed.

Evaluator's Checklist

Does your science program include assessments that—

✔ Are embedded before, during, and after lesson instruction

✔ Align to standards and to the instructional program

✔ Assess both skill acquisition and understanding

✔ Include meaningful rubrics to guide students

✔ Mirror the various formats of standardized tests

Assessment in *Science Explorer*

Science Explorer's remarkable range of strategies for checking progress will help teachers find the right opportunity for reaching all their students.

The assessment strategies in *Science Explorer* will help both students and teachers alike ensure student success in content mastery as well as high-stakes test performance. A wealth of opportunities built into the Student Edition help students monitor their own progress. Teachers are supported with ongoing assessment opportunities in the Teacher's Edition and an easy-to-use, editable test generator linked to content objectives. These integrated, ongoing assessment tools assure success.

Especially to support state and national testing objectives, Prentice Hall has developed test preparation materials that model the NCLB approach.

- **Diagnostic Assessment** tools provide in-depth analysis of strengths and weaknesses, areas of difficulty, and probable underlying causes that can help teachers make instructional decisions and plan intervention strategies.

- **Progress Monitoring** tools aligned with content objectives and state tests provide ongoing, longitudinal records of student achievement detailing individual student progress toward meeting end-of-year and end-of-schooling grade level, district, or state standards.

- **Outcomes** tools that mimic state and national tests show whether individual students have met the expected standards and can help a school system judge whether it has made adequate progress in improving its performance year by year.

Caption Questions enhance critical thinking skills

Reading Checkpoints reinforce students' understanding

Scaffolded Section Assessment Questions model the way students think

Comprehensive Chapter Reviews and Assessment provide opportunities for students to check their own understanding and practice valuable high-stakes test-taking skills

Exam*View*®, Computer Test Bank CD-ROM provides teachers access to thousands of modifiable test questions in English and Spanish

Test Preparation Blackline Masters and Student Workbook include diagnostic and prescription tools, progress-monitoring aids, and practice tests that help teachers focus on improving test scores.

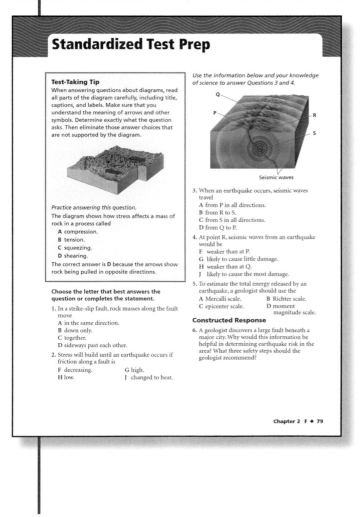

Master Materials List

SCIENCE EXPLORER offers an abundance of activity options in the Student Edition so you can pick and choose those that suit your needs. Prentice Hall has worked with Neo/SCI Corporation to develop Consumable Kits and Nonconsumable Kits that precisely match the needs of the SCIENCE EXPLORER labs. Use this Master Materials List or the Materials Ordering CD-ROM to help order your supplies. For more information on materials kits for this program, contact your local Prentice Hall sales representative or Neo/SCI Corporation at 1-800-526-6689 or **www.neosci.com**.

Consumable Materials

Description	Textbook Section(s)	Quantity per class	Description	Textbook Section(s)	Quantity per class
Acetate grid, 6/sheet	1-1(Lab)	1	*Pen	2-4(DIS), 4-2(Lab)	5
Antacid tablet	2-1(TT)	5	*Pen, space	2-4(DIS)	5
Aluminum foil roll, 12" × 25'	4-1(TT)	1	*Pencil	1-1(Lab), 1-3(Lab), 1-3(SA), 3-1(TT), 3-5(DIS),4-4(DIS)	25
Bag, plastic, 8" × 12"	2-1(Lab), 3-5(TT)	10			
Baking soda, 454 g	3-4(SA)	1			
Ball, plastic foam, 8 cm	1-1(Lab), 1-3(Lab), 3-4(SA)	15	*Pencils, colored, pkg/4	4-2(Lab)	5
			*Penny	1-2(DIS), 1-3(DIS)	130
Balloon, large	2-1(DIS), 2-1(Lab), 4-5 (DIS)	35	Peppercorn, 30g	3-4(SA)	1
			Petroleum jelly, pack	3-5(TT)	5
*Blanket, cloth, piece	2-4(Lab)	5	Pipe cleaner	4-4(TT)	10
Blanket, foil, piece	2-4(Lab)	5	*Poster board	2-1(Lab)	5
*Bottle, plastic, 2L	2-1(Lab)	5	Pushpin	3-1(TT)	10
*Box, corrugated	4-2(Lab)	5	*Quarter	1-3(DIS), 3-4(DIS)	10
Bulb, 100-watt	4-2(Lab)	1	Rubberband, assorted, 1.5 oz.	2-4(Lab)	1
Bulb, 150-watt	1-1(DIS), 1-3(Lab)	5	Sand, white, fine, 3 lb	1-4(DIS)	1
*Cardboard, 20 cm × 28 cm	3-2(DIS), 3-1(TT)	10	Spoon, plastic	3-6(DIS)	5
Cellophane, roll	3-3(TT)	1	String, ball	3-1(TT), 3-4(Lab), 3-5(DIS), 3-5(TT)	1
Cotton ball, pkg/100	2-4(Lab)	1			
Craft stick	1-1(TT)	20	Sugar, granulated, 454 g	3-6(DIS)	1
Cup, paper, 7 oz.	2-1(TT)	5	Tape, cellophane	2-1(TT), 2-4(Lab)	1
Cup, plastic, 7 oz.	1-2(Lab)	5	Tape, masking, roll	2-1(Lab), 3-2(DIS), 3-3(TT), 3-4(SA), 4-1(TT), 4-2(Lab), 4-4(DIS)	1
Film canister with snap lid	2-1(TT)	5			
*Foam, piece	4-1(Lab)	5			
*Graph paper, sheet	3-2(Lab)	5	Tape, transparent	4-1(Lab)	1
*Marker, permanent	4-5(DIS)	5	Toothpick, pkg/250	1-1(Lab), 3-4(SA)	1
Microscope slides, pkg/72	3-5(TT)	1	*Transparency, overhead	3-4(SA)	5
Modeling clay, white, 1 lb	2-1(Lab), 3-5(DIS)	1	Tube, cardboard, large	4-1(Lab)	5
Paper clip, box/100	2-1(Lab), 4-2(Lab)	4	Tube, cardboard, small	4-1(Lab)	5
*Paper, sheet	1-3(SA), 1-3(Lab), 1-1(Lab), 2-1(TT), 3-1(TT), 3-2(DIS), 3-3(DIS), 3-3(TT), 4-2(Lab), 4-4(DIS)	75	Yeast, dry baking, 7 g	3-6(DIS)	5

KEY: CP: Chapter Project; **DIS:** Discover; **SA:** Skills Activity; **TT:** Try This; **Lab:** Skills, Consumer, Design Your Own, & Technology and * items are school supplied.

Quantities based on five groups of six students per class.

Master Materials List

Nonconsumable Materials

Description	Textbook Section(s)	Quantity per class	Description	Textbook Section(s)	Quantity per class
Basin, plastic	1-4(DIS)	5	Marble, 1"	1-4(DIS)	5
Beaker, 600 mL	2-4(Lab)	5	Marble, 1/2"	1-4(DIS)	5
*Binoculars, pair	3-2(DIS)	5	Marble, 5/8"	1-4(DIS)	5
*Bowl	3-6(DIS)	5	Meter stick, 1/2, plain	1-1(TT), 3-4(SA), 3-4(Lab), 4-1(Lab), 4-2(Lab)	5
*Calculator	4-2(Lab)	5			
*Clamp, utility	3-2(DIS)	5	*Microscope	3-5(TT)	5
Compass	1-1(CP), 1-1(TT)	5	Objective lens, 15 cm focal length	4-1(Lab)	10
*Drill, electric	2-4(DIS)	1	Protractor	1-1(Lab)	5
*Drill, hand	2-4(DIS)	1	*Pump, tire	2-1(Lab)	1
Eyepiece lens, 5 cm focal length	4-1(Lab)	10	*Radio, small	4-1(TT)	5
*Fan, electric	3-5(DIS)	5	*Ring stand	3-2(DIS)	5
Flashlight	1-1(Lab), 3-1(DIS), 4-2(TT)	10	Rubber stopper, one-hole, pkg/39	3-4(Lab)	5
*Globe	1-1(DIS)	5	Ruler, 15 cm	1-2(DIS), 3-2(Lab), 3-3(Lab), 4-2(Lab)	5
*Goggles, pair	1-4(DIS), 2-1(DIS), 2-1(TT), 3-3(TT)	30	*Scissors	2-1(Lab)	5
Hand lens	4-1(DIS)	5	*Stopwatch	2-1(Lab), 3-4(Lab)	5
Hot glue gun	2-1(Lab)	1	*Table	4-2(Lab)	TK
*Inclinometer	2-1(Lab)	5	Test tube, large, 18 × 150 mm	2-4(Lab)	15
*Jar, glass	3-3(TT)	10	Test tube, small, 17 × 100 mm	2-4(Lab)	15
*Lamp, floor	1-3(Lab)	1	Thermometer, 12", −10°C to 110°C	2-4(Lab), 3-3(TT)	20
*Lamp, table	1-1(DIS), 4-2(Lab)	5	Tube, plastic, 3/16" × 8"	3-4(Lab)	5
Launcher, water rocket	2-1(Lab)	1	*Umbrella	4-1(TT)	5
Magnet, round	3-5(TT)	5	Washer, 1.5"	3-4(Lab)	15
*Map of moon, large	2-2(DIS)	5			

KEY: CP: Chapter Project; **DIS:** Discover; **SA:** Skills Activity; **TT:** Try This; **Lab:** Skills, Consumer, Design Your Own, & Technology and * items are school supplied.

Quantities based on five groups of six students per class.

PRENTICE HALL Science Explorer

Astronomy

Book-Specific Resources

Student Edition
Interactive Textbook
Teacher's Edition
All-in-One Teaching Resources
Color Transparencies
Guided Reading and Study Workbook
Student Edition on Audio CD
Discovery Channel Video
Lab Activity Video
Consumable and Nonconsumable Materials Kits

Program Print Resources

Integrated Science Laboratory Manual
Computer Microscope Lab Manual
Inquiry Skills Activity Books
Progress Monitoring Assessments
Test Preparation Workbook
Test-Taking Tips With Transparencies
Teacher's ELL Handbook
Reading in the Content Area

Program Technology Resources

TeacherExpress™ CD-ROM
Interactive Textbook
Presentation Pro CD-ROM
ExamView®, Computer Test Bank CD-ROM
Lab zone™ Easy Planner CD-ROM
Probeware Lab Manual With CD-ROM
Computer Microscope and Lab Manual
Materials Ordering CD-ROM
Discovery Channel DVD Library
Lab Activity DVD Library
Web Site at PHSchool.com

Spanish Print Resources

Spanish Student Edition
Spanish Guided Reading and Study Workbook
Spanish Teaching Guide With Tests

Acknowledgments appear on page 198, which constitutes an extension of this copyright page.

PEARSON

Prentice Hall

ISBN 0-13-115095-2

2 3 4 5 6 7 8 9 10   08 07 06 05 04

Cover
The Horsehead Nebula is part of a dark cosmic dust cloud that lies in front of a bright red nebula of glowing gas (top). *Valles Marineris,* nicknamed the Grand Canyon of Mars, can be seen from one of Mars's moons in this composite artwork (bottom).

Program Authors

Michael J. Padilla, Ph.D.
Professor of Science Education
University of Georgia
Athens, Georgia

Michael Padilla is a leader in middle school science education. He has served as an author and elected officer for the National Science Teachers Association and as a writer of the National Science Education Standards. As lead author of Science Explorer, Mike has inspired the team in developing a program that meets the needs of middle grades students, promotes science inquiry, and is aligned with the National Science Education Standards.

Ioannis Miaoulis, Ph.D.
President
Museum of Science
Boston, Massachusetts

Originally trained as a mechanical engineer, Ioannis Miaoulis is in the forefront of the national movement to increase technological literacy. As dean of the Tufts University School of Engineering, Dr. Miaoulis spearheaded the introduction of engineering into the Massachusetts curriculum. Currently he is working with school systems across the country to engage students in engineering activities and to foster discussions on the impact of science and technology on society.

Martha Cyr, Ph.D.
Director of K–12 Outreach
Worcester Polytechnic Institute
Worcester, Massachusetts

Martha Cyr is a noted expert in engineering outreach. She has over nine years of experience with programs and activities that emphasize the use of engineering principles, through hands-on projects, to excite and motivate students and teachers of mathematics and science in grades K–12. Her goal is to stimulate a continued interest in science and mathematics through engineering.

Book Author

Jay M. Pasachoff, Ph.D.
Professor of Astronomy
Williams College
Williamstown, Massachusetts

Contributing Writers

W. Russell Blake, Ph.D.
Planetarium Director
Plymouth Community
Intermediate School
Plymouth, Massachusetts

Naomi Pasachoff, Ph.D.
Research Associate
Williams College
Williamstown, Massachusetts

Thomas R. Wellnitz
Science Instructor
The Paideia School
Atlanta, Georgia

Consultants

Reading Consultant

Nancy Romance, Ph.D.
Professor of Science
Education
Florida Atlantic University
Fort Lauderdale, Florida

Mathematics Consultant

William Tate, Ph.D.
Professor of Education and
Applied Statistics and
Computation
Washington University
St. Louis, Missouri

Reviewers

Teacher Reviewers

David R. Blakely
Arlington High School
Arlington, Massachusetts

Jane E. Callery
Two Rivers Magnet Middle
    School
East Hartford, Connecticut

Melissa Lynn Cook
Oakland Mills High School
Columbia, Maryland

James Fattic
Southside Middle School
Anderson, Indiana

Dan Gabel
Hoover Middle School
Rockville, Maryland

Wayne Goates
Eisenhower Middle School
Goddard, Kansas

Katherine Bobay Graser
Mint Hill Middle School
Charlotte, North Carolina

Darcy Hampton
Deal Junior High School
Washington, D.C.

Karen Kelly
Pierce Middle School
Waterford, Michigan

David Kelso
Manchester High School Central
Manchester, New Hampshire

Benigno Lopez, Jr.
Sleepy Hill Middle School
Lakeland, Florida

Angie L. Matamoros, Ph.D.
ALM Consulting, INC.
Weston, Florida

Tim McCollum
Charleston Middle School
Charleston, Illinois

Bruce A. Mellin
Brooks School
North Andover, Massachusetts

Ella Jay Parfitt
Southeast Middle School
Baltimore, Maryland

Evelyn A. Pizzarello
Louis M. Klein Middle School
Harrison, New York

Kathleen M. Poe
Fletcher Middle School
Jacksonville, Florida

Shirley Rose
Lewis and Clark Middle School
Tulsa, Oklahoma

Linda Sandersen
Greenfield Middle School
Greenfield, Wisconsin

Mary E. Solan
Southwest Middle School
Charlotte, North Carolina

Mary Stewart
University of Tulsa
Tulsa, Oklahoma

Paul Swenson
Billings West High School
Billings, Montana

Thomas Vaughn
Arlington High School
Arlington, Massachusetts

Susan C. Zibell
Central Elementary
Simsbury, Connecticut

Safety Reviewers

W. H. Breazeale, Ph.D.
Department of Chemistry
College of Charleston
Charleston, South Carolina

Ruth Hathaway, Ph.D.
Hathaway Consulting
Cape Girardeau, Missouri

Douglas Mandt, M.S.
Science Education Consultant
Edgewood, Washington

Activity Field Testers

Nicki Bibbo
Witchcraft Heights School
Salem, Massachusetts

Rose-Marie Botting
Broward County Schools
Fort Lauderdale, Florida

Colleen Campos
Laredo Middle School
Aurora, Colorado

Elizabeth Chait
W. L. Chenery Middle School
Belmont, Massachusetts

Holly Estes
Hale Middle School
Stow, Massachusetts

Laura Hapgood
Plymouth Community
    Intermediate School
Plymouth, Massachusetts

Mary F. Lavin
Plymouth Community
    Intermediate School
Plymouth, Massachusetts

James MacNeil, Ph.D.
Cambridge, Massachusetts

Lauren Magruder
St. Michael's Country
    Day School
Newport, Rhode Island

Jeanne Maurand
Austin Preparatory School
Reading, Massachusetts

Joanne Jackson-Pelletier
Winman Junior High School
Warwick, Rhode Island

Warren Phillips
Plymouth Public Schools
Plymouth, Massachusetts

Carol Pirtle
Hale Middle School
Stow, Massachusetts

Kathleen M. Poe
Fletcher Middle School
Jacksonville, Florida

Cynthia B. Pope
Norfolk Public Schools
Norfolk, Virginia

Anne Scammell
Geneva Middle School
Geneva, New York

Karen Riley Sievers
Callanan Middle School
Des Moines, Iowa

David M. Smith
Eyer Middle School
Allentown, Pennsylvania

Gene Vitale
Parkland School
McHenry, Illinois

Contents

Astronomy

Reference Section

VIDEO

Enhance understanding through dynamic video.

Preview Get motivated with this introduction to the chapter content.

Field Trip Explore a real-world story related to the chapter content.

Assessment Review content and take an assessment.

Web Links

Get connected to exciting Web resources in every lesson.

SC*LINKS.* **NSTA** Find Web links on topics relating to every section.

Active Art Interact with selected visuals from every chapter online.

Planet Diary® Explore news and natural phenomena through weekly reports.

Science News® Keep up to date with the latest science discoveries.

Experience the complete text-book online and on CD-ROM.

Activities Practice skills and learn content.

Videos Explore content and learn important lab skills.

Audio Support Hear key terms spoken and defined.

Self-Assessment Use instant feedback to help you track your progress.

Activities

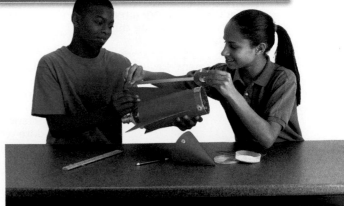

J ● ix

A Solar Astronomer

Inquiry and Astronomy

Astronomer Dr. Leonard Strachan explores the sun's corona using instruments onboard SOHO, the Solar and Heliospheric Observatory. This article describes how he uses inquiry skills such as designing experiments, interpreting data, and forming conclusions in his work. A detailed discussion of the sun occurs in this book, but students can read and learn from these pages before studying this material.

Build Background Knowledge

Experience with Ultraviolet Light

Remind students how painful a sunburn can be. Ask: **What type of radiation causes sunburns?** (*Ultraviolet radiation*) **What is the source of this radiation?** (*The sun*) Tell students that Dr. Strachan studies ultraviolet radiation from the sun to learn about the sun's outer atmosphere.

Introduce the Career

Before students read the feature, allow them to read the title, examine the pictures, and read the captions on their own. Then ask: **What questions came into your mind as you looked at these pictures?** (*Students may suggest questions such as these: How was this image of the sun made? What kinds of instruments are on SOHO? What does a coronagraph spectrometer do?*) Point out to students that just as they have questions about what they are seeing, scientists too have questions about what they observe.

Image of the sun ▶

A Solar Astronomer

Leonard Strachan always knew he wanted to be an astronomer. "The funny thing is: I thought I'd be a nighttime astronomer with a telescope. I'd go up on a mountain and study the stars at night."

But Leonard doesn't study the night sky. "I'm a daytime astronomer. I study the sun." And the instruments he uses are not on a mountaintop. They are on a satellite in space between Earth and the sun. The satellite's name is SOHO—the Solar and Heliospheric Observatory.

"The sun," Leonard says, "doesn't just shine as a steady yellow ball. It's always changing. Every so often the sun shoots out a huge cloud of gas particles into space. Within days the particles crash into Earth's upper atmosphere. They cause auroras: shimmering, glowing light shows in the sky. The particles interfere with radio waves. Pagers and cell phones can stop working. Even our electrical power can be affected. Telecommunications, weather satellites, and military operations are all affected by the space weather caused by the sun."

An instrument on SOHO, the Solar and Heliospheric Observatory (above), generated this image of the sun (top). SOHO is positioned in space between Earth and the sun.

x ◆ J

Background

Facts and Figures The conditions of the solar wind in the region of Earth and the sun is referred to as *space weather*. Because emissions of charged particles in the solar wind change frequently, space weather is quite variable. One of the most notable space weather events is a coronal mass ejection (CME). CMEs are large eruptions of charged gas from the sun's corona. These eruptions are most common during sunspot maximums, but CMEs can occur at any time. SOHO has produced many images of CMEs.

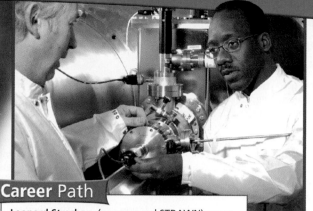

Leonard Strachan (pronounced STRAWN) grew up in an Air Force family, so he traveled a lot as a child. He attended college at the Massachusetts Institute of Technology and received his Ph.D. in astronomy from Harvard University. Since 1991 he has been an Astrophysicist at the Harvard-Smithsonian Center for Astrophysics in Cambridge, Massachusetts. He enjoys giving talks at museums and schools as part of NASA's public outreach program.

Leonard (right) and his co-worker Nigel Atkins are shown here operating an ultraviolet lamp used for testing one of the instruments on SOHO.

Talking With Dr. Leonard Strachan

? How did you become interested in astronomy?

I was hooked from the very beginning. When I was in second grade in Washington, D.C., some high-school students gave a slide presentation on the stars. Later on, I started reading books on astronomy and science fiction. I loved thinking about what it would be like living on Mars or traveling to a black hole or moving at the speed of light. When I was in seventh grade, I asked my dad for an amateur telescope. I'd take it out every clear night and look at the stars.

? What do you study about the sun?

Most of my work involves learning about the solar corona and what causes the solar wind. The corona is the hot outer atmosphere of the sun. Just like Earth has an atmosphere, the sun, too, has an outer layer. But the sun is a ball of glowing gases with no solid surface inside. What we call the "surface" is just the layer where most of the visible light comes from. Most of the mass of the sun is inside that ball of light we can see. Above that is the corona, where it's super hot, about one or two million degrees Celsius.

The corona is so hot that most of the individual atoms in it are split apart. The heating of the corona may also force these particles to fly away from the sun. That stream of particles is called the solar wind. It can go as fast as 800 kilometers per second. It blows past Earth, past all the planets, out beyond the edge of the solar system.

J ◆ 1

Explore the Career

Choose from among the teaching strategies on these pages as you help your students explore the practical application of inquiry skills in the real world.

Help Students Read

Preview Before students read the feature, ask them to preview the headings. Make certain that students understand that the headings are questions and that what follows each heading is an answer. Ask: **Who answered the questions?** *(Dr. Strachan)*

Use Maps Encourage students to learn to use a star chart, such as those at the back of this book. Large poster-size star charts also are available. Have each student, while supervised by an adult, step outside during the evening to identify stars. Students should list each star or constellation that they are able to identify in the night sky. Remind students during this exercise that the sun is also a star.

Connect Culture Remind students that astronomy is one of the oldest sciences. Ancient astronomers often studied the changing movement of the sun across the sky throughout the seasons. Prehistoric people in Britain, for example, likely built Stonehenge as a solar observatory and used it to time events in their lives, such as festivals, anniversaries, and planting times. Ancient cultures, such as the Inca, Maya, and Egyptians, also worshipped the sun as a god. This is not surprising, considering that all living things on Earth depend on the sun's energy. The Romans celebrated a holiday at the winter solstice called *Sol Invictus,* or the Unconquered Sun. This was the time of year that the sun's steady movement south and the gradual shortening of the days ceased. Ask: **Why would ancient people think that the sun is so important?** *(They realized that their crops depended on the sun. They also knew the sun to be a source of warmth and light. If the sun went away, their world would be cold and dark and eventually lifeless.)*

┌ **Background** ─────────

History of Science The existence of the solar wind was theorized in 1958 by Eugene Parker, who was a professor at the University of Chicago. Parker envisioned the solar wind as a natural consequence of the high temperature gas that existed in the sun's corona. Initially rejected by the scientific community, Parker's ideas were confirmed during the next two to three years, when experimental evidence for the solar wind began to be reported.

Research Challenge students to research the sun's corona. After their research, have them work together as a class to describe the corona's position and characteristics.

Show Examples Many coronagraph images are available online. Download some of these images, and show them to students. Help students understand that a disk is blocking most of the sun. Ask: **What is shown surrounding the disk?** (*The sun's corona*) Look with students for interesting coronal features, such as streamers, prominences, and filaments, in the images.

Connect Culture Tell students that the SOHO team includes scientists and engineers from more than 30 different countries. The International Academy of Astronautics awarded the SOHO team its Team Achievement award for 2003.

Discuss Remind students that the SOHO is in an orbit that keeps it almost directly between Earth and the sun. Ask: **Why is it an advantage to be outside Earth's atmosphere?** (*Earth's atmosphere absorbs much of the radiation that SOHO would receive.*) **Why is SOHO able to study the sun constantly?** (*Because it is between the sun and Earth, SOHO always receives sunlight.*)

? Why can't you observe the corona from Earth?

The best way to study the sun is to look at all the light and energy it gives off, not just the visible light that our eyes can see. The photosphere, the surface layer of the sun, gives off mostly visible light. But the corona is hotter. Most of its light is invisible. We can only "see" invisible kinds of light, such as ultraviolet light and x-rays, with special equipment.

The problem is that Earth's atmosphere absorbs most of the sun's ultraviolet light. If you want your instruments to measure the sun's invisible light, you have to be in space, above the atmosphere.

So we go way beyond the atmosphere. That's where our SOHO satellite is. It's always between the sun and Earth so that it can observe the sun 24 hours a day. There are no eclipses and no atmosphere, and you can look at all wavelengths of light. That's the big advantage to being out there.

? What instruments do you use?

The UVCS is an instrument which is both a coronagraph and a spectrometer. A coronagraph is needed to block out the bright disk of the sun so that the much fainter corona can be seen. A spectrometer spreads light out in a spectrum, a pattern of light and dark lines. Different elements in the sun, at different temperatures, have their own special pattern of lines. By looking at the patterns, we can tell what kind of particles are in the corona, how hot they are, even how fast they're going.

? This all happens on SOHO?

Sure. We send commands up every day by radio to point the instrument to specific targets. That takes place at NASA's Goddard Space Flight Center in Maryland. We have three people there who "talk" to the satellite on a daily basis.

Projects like SOHO require people from all over the country, all over the world. In addition to Americans, we have Italians, a Russian, a Chinese, and a Palestinian. It's a really international project. We work and meet with each other all the time.

A model of the Ultraviolet Coronagraph Spectrometer (or UVCS) is shown here with Leonard. The UVCS is one of twelve instruments on the SOHO spacecraft.

Background

Facts and Figures The SOHO orbits a point called L1, which is short for the first Lagrangian point. Lagrangian points are locations in space at which a balance exists between the sun's gravity and Earth's gravity. An object that is stationary at such a point will remain stationary. L1 is one of five Lagrangian points, but the only one that lies directly between Earth and the sun. Therefore, orbiting L1 provides SOHO with constant access to the sun and easy communication with Earth.

This is a composite image made with two of the instruments on SOHO.

? How will you answer your questions?

I plan and analyze observations that can be used to prove whether our theories about the sun are correct. I also work with people who create the theories and others who build the instruments. The instruments are important because without them we would not have the much needed information that tells us what is happening right at the sun.

This work is fascinating. It's something I'd recommend to anybody who likes solving problems. They don't have to be grand problems, like figuring out how the universe began. You look at small things, and piece those small problems together. Eventually you build a bigger picture that helps us understand our universe.

? What are some unanswered questions?

One big question is: What makes the solar corona so hot? At first, it doesn't make sense. The central region of the sun is incredibly hot, about 30 million degrees Celsius. As you move away from the center, the sun's gases cool down so they are only about 6,000 degrees Celsius at the surface. But then, for reasons we don't fully understand, it suddenly rises back to millions of degrees in the corona, above the surface. It's as if your hand became warmer when you moved it away from a fire. You would expect it to get cooler when you move it away. With our UVCS instrument, we can look at the light from individual particles in the corona and maybe find out what's happening.

We want to understand what happens in the corona because the solar wind comes from there. We want to know how the particles in the corona speed up in the solar wind. And in the future, we would like to be able to predict the big explosions in the corona that can cause space weather. It is these explosions that kick out the gas clouds that can disrupt Earth's magnetic field.

Leonard shows a high school student how to find a planet.

Writing in Science

Career Link Leonard says he loved reading science fiction as a boy. He enjoyed imagining what it would be like to live on Mars or travel in space. This energized his desire to learn about science—like understanding how the conditions on Mars came to be. Write a paragraph in which you imagine what it would it be like to live on Mars. Include scientific information in your paragraph.

Go Online
PHSchool.com
For: More on this career
Visit: PHSchool.com
Web Code: cfb-5000

Build Inquiry Skills Encourage each student to write three questions about the sun. After students have written their questions, ask them to suggest a way in which each question could be answered.

Discuss Tell students that the explosions in the sun's corona mentioned in the student text often cause the northern lights to occur. Ask: **What are the northern lights?** (*The northern lights are auroras—shimmering colors that appear in the northern sky.*) **How could explosions in the sun's corona reach Earth?** (*Charged particles are released from the sun and travel to Earth.*) Tell students that when these particles reach Earth, they are carried to the poles by Earth's magnetic field. As the particles collide with atoms and molecules in Earth's upper atmosphere, the colors of the aurora form. Remind students that auroras also form at Earth's south pole.

Writing in Science

Writing Mode Narration
Scoring Rubric
4 Exceeds criteria, includes detailed description of what it would be like to live on Mars and at least three pieces of correct scientific information
3 Meets criteria and includes two pieces of correct information
2 Includes one piece of correct information
1 Is incomplete and inaccurate

Go Online
PHSchool.com
For: More on this career
Visit: PHSchool.com
Web Code: cfb-5000

Students can research this career and others that relate to the study of meteorology.

Chapter at a Glance

PRENTICE HALL
TeacherEXPRESS™
Plan • Teach • Assess

Lab zone Chapter **Project** *Track the Moon*

Technology

Local Standards

All in One Teaching Resources
- Chapter Project Teacher Notes, pp. 38–39
- Chapter Project Student Introduction, pp. 40–41
- Chapter Project Student Worksheets, pp. 42–343
- Chapter Project Scoring Rubric, p. 44

Discovery CHANNEL SCHOOL Video Preview

Section 1 **Earth in Space**

3 periods
1 1/2 blocks

J.1.1.1 Demonstrate how Earth moves in space.
J.1.1.2 Explain what causes the cycle of seasons on Earth.

Go Online *active art*

Section 2 **Gravity and Motion**

1 period
1/2 block

J.1.2.1 Identify what determines the strength of the force of gravity between two objects.
J.1.2.2 Describe two factors that keep the moon and Earth in orbit.

Go Online SCi LINKS™ NSTA

Section 3 **Phases, Eclipses, and Tides**

4 periods
2 blocks

J.1.3.1 Explain what causes the phases of the moon.
J.1.3.2 Describe solar and lunar eclipses.
J.1.3.3 Identify what causes tides.

Go Online *active art*

Section 4 **Earth's Moon**

1 period
1/2 block

J.1.4.1 Describe features found on the moon's surface.
J.1.4.2 Identify some characteristics of the moon.
J.1.4.3 Explain how the moon formed.

Go Online SCi LINKS™ NSTA

Review and Assessment

Test Preparation

All in One Teaching Resources
- Key Terms Review, p. 78
- Transparency J14
- Performance Assessment Teacher Notes, p. 85
- Performance Assessment Scoring Rubric, p. 86
- Performance Assessment Student Worksheet, p. 87
- Chapter Test, pp.88–91

Discovery CHANNEL SCHOOL Video Assessment

Go Online PHSchool.com

Test Preparation Blackline Masters

Lab zone Chapter Activities Planner

For more activities

LAB ZONE Easy Planner CD-ROM

Student Edition	Inquiry	Time	Materials	Skills	Resources
Chapter Project, p. 5	Open-Ended	Ongoing (one month)	**All in One** Teaching Resources See p. 38	Observing, measuring	**Lab zone Easy Planner**
Section 1					
Discover Activity, p. 6	Guided	15 min	Lamp, light bulb, glove	Making models	**Lab zone Easy Planner**
Try This Activity, p. 10	Guided	20 min per day, 5 days	Compass, craft sticks, meter stick	Predicting	**Lab zone Easy Planner**
Skills Lab, pp. 14–15	Guided	Prep 10 min; Class 40 min	Books, flashlight, paper, pencil, protractor, toothpick, acetate sheet, plastic foam ball	Making models, observing, inferring, predicting	**Lab zone Easy Planner Lab Activity Video** **All in One** Teaching Resources Skills Lab: *Reasons for the Seasons*, pp. 52–54
Section 2					
Discover Activity, p. 16	Open-Ended	10 min	Pennies, ruler	Developing hypotheses	**Lab zone Easy Planner**
Section 3					
Discover Activity, p. 20	Guided	10 min	Quarters, pennies	Inferring	**Lab zone Easy Planner**
Skills Activity, p. 24	Guided	15 min	Paper, metric rulers, calculators	Making models	**Lab zone Easy Planner**
Skills Lab, pp. 28–29	Guided	Prep 15 min; Class 40 min	Floor lamp with 150-watt bulb, pencils, plastic foam balls	Making models, observing, inferring	**Lab zone Easy Planner Lab Activity Video** **All in One** Teaching Resources Skills Lab: *A "Moonth" of Phases*, pp. 69–70
Section 4					
Discover Activity, p. 30	Guided	20 min	Plastic basin or mixing bowl about 25 cm across, sand, 3 marbles of different masses, meter stick	Developing hypotheses	**Lab zone Easy Planner**

Section 1 Earth in Space

⏱ *3 periods, 1 1/2 blocks*

Objectives

J.1.1.1 Demonstrate how Earth moves in space.

J.1.1.2 Explain what causes the cycle of seasons on Earth.

Key Terms

• astronomy • axis • rotation • revolution • orbit • calendar • solstice
• equinox

Local Standards

Preteach

Build Background Knowledge

Ask students to estimate the current sunrise and sunset times and to describe how the hours of daylight differ in the summer and in the winter.

Lab zone Discover Activity *What Causes Day and Night?* **L1**

Targeted Print and Technology Resources

All in One Teaching Resources

L2 Reading Strategy Transparency J1: *Using Prior Knowledge*

⊙ **Presentation-Pro CD-ROM**

Instruct

How Earth Moves Use photographs and analogies to help students distinguish rotation and revolution.

The Seasons on Earth Explain why different areas of Earth receive different amounts of heat energy throughout the year.

Lab zone Skills Lab *Reasons for the Seasons* **L2**

Targeted Print and Technology Resources

All in One Teaching Resources

L2 Guided Reading, pp. 47–49
L2 Transparencies J2, J3
L2 Skills Lab: *Reasons for the Seasons*, pp. 52–54

📼 **Lab Activity Video/DVD**
Skills Lab: *Reasons for the Seasons*

PHSchool.com Web Code: cfp-5012

⊙ **Student Edition on Audio CD**

Assess

Section Assessment Questions

↻ Have students use their completed graphic organizers to answer the questions.

Reteach

Use diagrams to review the seasons, and have students describe the tilt of Earth's axis during solstices and equinoxes.

Targeted Print and Technology Resources

All in One Teaching Resources

• Section Summary, p. 46
L1 Review and Reinforce, p. 50
L3 Enrich, p. 51

Section 2 Gravity and Motion

⏱ *1 period, 1/2 block*

Objectives

J.1.2.1 Identify what determines the strength of the force of gravity between two objects.

J.1.2.2 Describe two factors that keep the moon and Earth in orbit.

Key Terms

• force • gravity • law of universal gravitation • mass • weight • inertia
• Newton's first law of motion

Local Standards

Preteach

Build Background Knowledge

Elicit definitions of weight, and explain that weight is related to gravity.

Lab zone **Discover Activity** *Can You Remove the Bottom Penny?* L2

Targeted Print and Technology Resources

All in One Teaching Resources

L2 Reading Strategy Transparency J4: *Asking Questions*

⊙ **Presentation-Pro CD-ROM**

Instruct

Gravity Define the causes of the strength of the force of gravity, and prompt students to analyze the relationship between those factors and gravity.

Inertia and Orbital Motion Help students identify how gravity and inertia keep objects in orbit.

Targeted Print and Technology Resources

All in One Teaching Resources

L2 Guided Reading, pp. 57–58
L2 Transparencies J5, J6

www.SciLinks.org Web Code: scf-0612

⊙ **Student Edition on Audio CD**

Assess

Section Assessment Questions

Have students use their completed graphic organizers to answer the questions.

Reteach

Use diagrams to summarize how objects stay in orbit.

Targeted Print and Technology Resources

All in One Teaching Resources

• Section Summary, p. 56
L1 Review and Reinforce, p. 59
L3 Enrich, p. 60

Section 3 Phases, Eclipses, and Tides

🕐 *4 periods, 2 blocks*

Objectives

J.1.3.1 Explain what causes the phases of the moon.

J.1.3.2 Describe solar and lunar eclipses.

J.1.3.3 Identify what causes the tides.

Key Terms

• phases • eclipse • solar eclipse • umbra • penumbra • lunar eclipse • tide
• spring tide • neap tide

Local Standards

Preteach

Build Background Knowledge

Ask questions to prompt students to describe their observations of the moon.

Lab zone Discover Activity *How Does the Moon Move?* L1

Targeted Print and Technology Resources

All in One Teaching Resources

L2 Reading Strategy Transparency J7: *Previewing Visuals*

⊙ **Presentation-Pro CD-ROM**

Instruct

Motions of the Moon Ask leading questions to help students recognize the relative movements and positions of the moon and Earth.

Phases of the Moon Use a diagram to help students analyze the causes of moon phases.

Eclipses Identify the cause of eclipses, and describe the relative positions of objects in space when one occurs.

Tides Use a diagram to help students visualize how the moon's gravity causes tides.

Lab zone Skills Lab *A "Moonth" of Phases* L2

Targeted Print and Technology Resources

All in One Teaching Resources

L2 Guided Reading, pp. 63–66
L2 Transparencies J8, J9, J10, J11
L2 Skills Lab: *A "Moonth" of Phases,* pp. 69–70

📼 **Lab Activity Video/DVD**
Skills Lab: *A "Moonth" of Phases*

PHSchool.com Web Code: cfp-5013

⊙ **Student Edition on Audio CD**

Assess

Section Assessment Questions

⊙ Have students use their questions and answers from previewing the phases of the moon to answer the questions.

Reteach

Use diagrams to review the phases of the moon and solar and lunar eclipses.

Targeted Print and Technology Resources

All in One Teaching Resources

• Section Summary, p. 62
L1 Review and Reinforce, p. 67
L3 Enrich, p. 68

Section 4 Earth's Moon

🕐 *1 period, 1/2 block*

Objectives

J.1.4.1 Describe features found on the moon's surface.

J.1.4.2 Identify some characteristics of the moon.

J.1.4.3 Explain how the moon formed.

Key Terms

• telescope • maria • craters • meteoroids

Local Standards

Preteach

Build Background Knowledge

Hold up a rock, and elicit students' predictions of the effects of a very large rock hitting Earth.

Lab zone **Discover Activity** *Why Do Craters Look Different From One Another?* **L2**

Targeted Print and Technology Resources

All in One Teaching Resources

L2 Reading Strategy Transparency J12: *Identifying Main Ideas*

⊙ **Presentation-Pro CD-ROM**

Instruct

The Moon's Surface Describe features of the moon and how they formed.

Characteristics of the Moon Compare and contrast the size, density, temperature, atmosphere, and water of Earth to those of the moon.

The Origin of the Moon Use a diagram to summarize the collision-ring theory of how the moon formed.

Targeted Print and Technology Resources

All in One Teaching Resources

L2 Guided Reading, pp. 73–75
L2 Transparency J13

www.SciLinks.org Web Code: scf-0614

⊙ **Student Edition on Audio CD**

Assess

Section Assessment Questions

↻ Have students use their completed graphic organizers to answer the questions.

Reteach

Compare and contrast the properties of the moon and Earth.

Targeted Print and Technology Resources

All in One Teaching Resources

• Section Summary, p. 72
L1 Review and Reinforce, p. 76
L3 Enrich, p. 77

Chapter 1 **Content Refresher**

Section 1 **Earth in Space**

Earth's Rotation Earth's rotation is gradually slowing through time. This change is a result of the pull of the moon's gravity on Earth's tidal bulges. Earth has tides in the solid planet and in its oceans. However, because Earth's ocean-water bulges are larger and more massive, they have a greater effect on slowing Earth's rotation. Because Earth rotates, the tidal bulges are not on a direct line connecting the moon and Earth. The bulge on the side of Earth facing the moon, for example, is ahead of the line connecting Earth and the moon. The moon pulls on this displaced mass and creates tidal friction, which is gradually slowing Earth's rate of rotation. Most of the friction between the water bulges and Earth occurs through tidal currents and other tidal effects. As Earth's rotation slows, angular momentum is transferred to the moon, which moves farther from Earth. Some consequences of Earth's changing rate of rotation include the fact that days were much shorter in the distant past. For example, about 500 million years ago, there were only about 22 hours in a day. Currently, the length of the day on Earth is increasing at a rate of about 2.3 milliseconds per century.

Address Misconceptions

Students may think that the changing distance between Earth and the sun causes seasons as Earth travels in its elliptical orbit. For a strategy for overcoming this misconception, see **Address Misconceptions** in the section titled "Earth in Space."

Ancient Calendars Early cultures, such as the Sumerians of Babylon, used the phases of the moon to make a calendar with 12 lunar months equaling one year. The early Romans also used a calendar that was based on the lunar cycles. This calendar, regulated by high priests, was not very accurate, so the calendar fell out of step with the seasons. By Julius Caesar's time, the summer months were coming in springtime. Caesar adopted the 365 day-a-year calendar developed by the early Egyptians. Additional corrections to the Julian calendar included adding one day every four years. However, this caused the calendar year to be longer than the year as measured by the seasons. As a result, 10 days were dropped from the year 1582. In that year, October 4th was followed by October 15th.

Section 2 **Gravity and Motion**

Perturbation The law of universal gravitation states that every object in the universe exerts a force on every other object. When discussing the effect of the sun's gravitational pull on the orbits of planets, astronomers must take into account perturbation—variances in the expected orbits of planets. These variances are caused by other bodies in the solar system exerting gravitational force on one another. For example, the most massive planet, Jupiter, slows down the orbital period of neighboring Saturn by one week relative to its expected orbital period based on the sun's gravitational pull. The perturbation of Uranus's orbit led astronomers to predict the existence of an eighth planet, which was eventually sighted in 1846 and named Neptune. Similarly, Pluto was discovered as the result of its gravitational effect on Neptune.

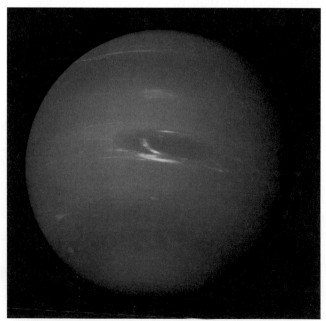

Neptune's existence was predicted before the planet was seen.

Section 3 Phases, Eclipses, and Tides

Earthshine During certain moon phases, such as crescent moon, the remaining, unlit portion of the moon can be seen in dim light. This dimly-lit portion of the moon is illuminated by earthshine, which is light reflected from Earth's surface. Because the moon is almost between Earth and the sun at crescent phases, the effects of earthshine are dramatic. From the moon, Earth would appear almost full. However, a new moon cannot be seen by earthshine. During the new moon phase, the moon is very close in the sky to the sun. Therefore, the sun's bright light makes it impossible to see the new moon.

Eclipses Many people have seen total lunar eclipses, but few people have the opportunity to view a total solar eclipse. The reason is that a total lunar eclipse is visible over at least half of Earth, but a total solar eclipse can be seen only along a narrow path of up to a few hundred miles wide and a few thousand miles long.

Astronomers can accurately predict the dates and times of future eclipses. Because solar eclipses occur when the new moon passes near the plane of Earth's orbit, lunar eclipses frequently occur in the two weeks before or the two weeks after a solar eclipse. Six-and-a-half lunar months later, the full moon may be near the plane of Earth's orbit, so more lunar and solar eclipses can occur. These periods, when the new moon or full moon is near the plane of Earth's orbit, are called *eclipse seasons*.

Section 4 Earth's Moon

Moon Photos The *Apollo* astronauts orbited the moon and photographed its surface. The images confirmed that the far side of the moon, shown in the image at right, is much rougher than the near side and has few maria. Because the moon's crust is thicker on the far side, lava might not have been able to erupt at the surface to form maria.

In 1994 an uncrewed NASA spacecraft, *Clementine*, took images of the moon through different filters specifically chosen to identify different types of minerals on the moon. Using this technology, scientists were able to produce maps showing the moon's minerology. The spacecraft was named in honor of the prospector's daughter in the old song "My Darlin' Clementine."

In 1998 the American *Lunar Prospector* mapped the entire moon from an altitude of only 100 kilometers. The spacecraft found evidence suggesting the existence of ice frozen in the lunar soil near the moon's poles. The ice might exist in permanently shaded regions at the bottom of large craters. The *Lunar Prospector* mission ended when the probe was intentionally crashed into a large crater. It was hoped that the impact would liberate water vapor that could be detected from Earth. However, the results of the test were inconclusive. Recent radar studies suggest that if ice is present in these craters, it does not form a continuous layer.

Help Students Read

Reciprocal Teaching
Modeling Strategies in Combination

Strategy Help students learn to apply the strategies of predicting, questioning, clarifying, and summarizing. Teaching of this strategy should take place over several days, beginning with the teacher modeling and leading students in discussion. The teacher should gradually turn leadership over to the students and become a facilitator, intervening only as needed. Prepare for the reading by choosing a passage of several paragraphs. Make a copy of the paragraphs, and note appropriate places to model the strategies for students.

Example
1. Read a few paragraphs aloud as students follow along silently.
2. Discuss strategies for clarifying meaning and getting past trouble spots in the passage. Engage the group in discussing ways to apply each of the following strategies:
- Predicting what will come next in the text. Remind students to use what they already know about a topic to make connections that will help them understand what comes next.
- Asking "teacherlike" questions to check understanding and to think about what they need to find out.
- Clarifying the meaning of unfamiliar words or concepts.
- Summarizing what has been read.

3. Reread the paragraphs, modeling all four strategies.
4. Continue reading a few paragraphs at a time, discussing and modeling the strategies.
5. Repeat the process with different passages over a few days, gradually turning over the leadership role to students by having them lead the discussion of a portion of the text.
6. When students are comfortable with the strategies, they can lead the entire discussion. Intervene only to get students back on track or to jump-start a discussion.

Astronomy: Teacher's Edition

Contents in Brief

Teacher's Edition

See Program Component List on page ii

Student Edition

Prentice Hall Science Explorer

Series Tables of Contents

Interactive Textbook
- Complete student edition
- Video and audio
- Simulations and activities
- Section and chapter activities

Lab zone Chapter **Project** L3

Objectives
This project will enhance students' observation and measurement skills as they keep track of the moon's appearance and position for one month. After this Chapter Project, students will be able to
- observe the phases of the moon
- measure the direction and altitude of the moon in the sky
- interpret data to explain why the moon has phases
- predict when and where one would expect to see the moon on the basis of analysis of data
- communicate their conclusions to the class

Skills Focus
Observing, measuring, interpreting data, predicting, communicating

Project Time Line one month

All in One Teaching Resources
- Chapter Project Teacher Notes
- Chapter Project Worksheet 1
- Chapter Project Worksheet 2
- Chapter Project Scoring Rubric

Chapter

1

Earth, Moon, and Sun

Chapter Preview

❶ **Earth in Space**
Discover *What Causes Day and Night?*
Try This *Sun Shadows*
Active Art *The Seasons*
Skills Lab *Reasons for the Seasons*

❷ **Gravity and Motion**
Discover *Can You Remove the Bottom Penny?*
Analyzing Data *Gravity Versus Distance*

❸ **Phases, Eclipses, and Tides**
Discover *How Does the Moon Move?*
Active Art *Phases of the Moon*
Active Art *Lunar Eclipses*
Skills Activity *Making Models*
At-Home Activity *Tracking the Tides*
Skills Lab *A "Moonth" of Phases*

❹ **Earth's Moon**
Discover *Why Do Craters Look Different From Each Other?*
At-Home Activity *Moonwatching*

Interactive Textbook

This time-lapse photo shows an eclipse of the moon as it rises over the Golden Gate Bridge in San Francisco.

Developing a Plan
This project requires at least one month to observe all of the phases of the moon. If cloudy weather makes observations difficult, you may wish to extend the observation time.

Possible Materials
Tell students to use a compass to record landmarks around their house in each of the eight major compass directions: N, NE, E, SE, S, SW, W, NW. They can then use these landmarks to orient themselves.

Possible Shortcuts
If the time available is only two to three weeks, begin the project near a new moon to allow students to gather usable data. The moon is most visible in the early evening sky between the new moon and the full moon.

Chapter Project

Track the Moon

How does the moon move across the sky? How does its appearance change over the course of a month? In this project, you will observe how the position and apparent shape of the moon change over time.

Your Goal To observe the shape of the moon and its position in the sky every day for one month

To complete this project, you must

- observe the compass direction in which you see the moon, its phase, and its height above the horizon
- use your observations to explain the phases of the moon
- develop rules you can use to predict when and where you might see the moon each day

Plan It! Begin by preparing an observation log. You will record the date and time of each observation, the direction and height of the moon, a sketch of its shape, and notes about cloud cover and other conditions. Observe the moon every clear night, looking for patterns. Make a map of your observation site on which you will plot the direction of the moon. You can measure the moon's height in degrees above the horizon by making a fist and holding it at arm's length. One fist above the horizon is 10°, two fists are 20°, and so on. On at least one day, compare your observations of the moon an hour or two apart.

Chapter 1 J ◆ 5

Earth, Moon, and Sun

Show the Video Preview to introduce the Chapter Project and to present an overview of the chapter content. Discussion question: **List two methods that ancient people used to tell time by observing the sun and the moon.** *(Sundials and calendars)*

Performance Assessment

The Chapter Project Scoring Rubric will help you evaluate how well students complete the Chapter Project. Share the rubric with students at the beginning of the project so that they will know what is expected. Students will be assessed on

- the quality and consistency of their daily record keeping
- the quality of their graphs and drawings and their analysis of the data
- their ability to find patterns in the data and use these patterns to make predictions
- the level of their understanding as demonstrated in the presentation of their conclusions

Launching the Project

Ask: **On a clear evening, can you always see the moon in the sky?** *(No)* **Can you ever see the moon during the day?** *(Yes)* Encourage students to discuss whether they have seen a relationship between the phase of the moon, such as full or quarter, and how high the moon is in the sky at a particular time of night, such as 8 P.M. Tell students that they will investigate this relationship in the Chapter Project.

Emphasize the importance of recording the data at least three times per day on some days. Explain that it is easier to monitor the movement of the moon by noting its position several times a day rather than only once.

Section 1 — Earth in Space

Objectives

After this lesson, students will be able to

J.1.1.1 Demonstrate how Earth moves in space.

J.1.1.2 Explain the causes of the cycle of seasons on Earth.

Target Reading Skill

Using Prior Knowledge Explain that using prior knowledge helps students connect what they already know to what they are about to read.

Answers

Possible answers:

What You Know

1. The sun's rays heat Earth.

2. Earth has seasons.

3. In the Northern Hemisphere, fall begins in September and spring begins in March.

What You Learned

1. Areas where the sun hits Earth at a more direct angle are generally warmer than areas where the sun's rays are more spread out.

2. The tilt of Earth's axis as it moves around the sun causes seasons.

3. Around March 21 and September 22, day and night are each 12 hours long.

All in One Teaching Resources

• Transparency J1

Preteach

Build Background Knowledge L2

Changes in Daylight

Ask students to estimate what time the sun rises in the morning and sets at night. Tell them the actual times from a daily newspaper. Next, ask students to describe how the number of hours of daylight changes during the winter and summer. *(There are fewer hours of daylight in winter than in summer.)*

Section 1 — Earth in Space

Reading Preview

Key Concepts

• How does Earth move in space?

• What causes the cycle of seasons on Earth?

Key Terms

• astronomy • axis • rotation
• revolution • orbit • calendar
• solstice • equinox

Target Reading Skill

Using Prior Knowledge Your prior knowledge is what you already know before you read about a topic. Before you read, write what you know about seasons on Earth in a graphic organizer like the one below. As you read, write in what you learn.

What You Know
1. The sun's rays heat Earth.
2.

What You Learned
1.
2.

Lab zone — Discover Activity

What Causes Day and Night?

1. Place a lamp with a bare bulb on a table to represent the sun. Put a globe at the end of the table about 1 meter away to represent Earth.

2. Turn the lamp on and darken the room. Which parts of the globe have light shining on them? Which parts are in shadow?

3. Find your location on the globe. Turn the globe once. Notice when it is lit—day—at your location and when it is dark—night.

Think It Over

Making Models What does one complete turn of the globe represent? In this model, how many seconds represent one day? How could you use the globe and bulb to represent a year?

Each year, ancient Egyptian farmers eagerly awaited the flood of the Nile River. For thousands of years, their planting was ruled by it. As soon as the Nile's floodwaters withdrew, the farmers had to be ready to plow and plant their fields along the river. Therefore, the Egyptians wanted to predict when the flood would occur. Around 3000 B.C., people noticed that the bright star Sirius first became visible in the early morning sky every year shortly before the flood began. The Egyptians used this knowledge to predict each year's flood. The ancient Egyptians were among the first people to study the stars. The study of the moon, stars, and other objects in space is called **astronomy.**

FIGURE 1
Ancient Egyptian Farmers
Egyptian farmers watched the sky in order to be prepared to plow and plant their fields.

6 ◆ J

Lab zone — Discover Activity

Skills Focus Making models

Materials lamp, light bulb, globe

Time 15 minutes

Tips Place the bulb at a height approximately level with the globe's equator. Alternatively, use flashlights and have students work in pairs. One student can hold the flashlight steady while the other turns the globe.

L1

Expected Outcome The half of the globe facing the bulb will be lit and will move into shadow as the globe rotates.

Think It Over A complete spin of the globe represents one rotation of Earth on its axis, which equals one day. In the model, one day is five seconds. One possible way to model a year is to carry the spinning globe in a circle around the bulb.

How Earth Moves

Ancient astronomers studied the movements of the sun and the moon as they appeared to travel across the sky. It seemed to them as though Earth was standing still and the sun and moon were moving. Actually, the sun and moon seem to move across the sky each day because Earth is rotating on its axis. Earth also moves around the sun. **Earth moves through space in two major ways: rotation and revolution.**

Rotation The imaginary line that passes through Earth's center and the North and South poles is Earth's **axis.** The spinning of Earth on its axis is called **rotation.**

Earth's rotation causes day and night. As Earth rotates eastward, the sun appears to move westward across the sky. It is day on the side of Earth facing the sun. As Earth continues to turn to the east, the sun appears to set in the west. Sunlight can't reach the side of Earth facing away from the sun, so it is night there. It takes Earth about 24 hours to rotate once. As you know, each 24-hour cycle of day and night is called a day.

Revolution In addition to rotating on its axis, Earth travels around the sun. **Revolution** is the movement of one object around another. One complete revolution of Earth around the sun is called a year. Earth follows a path, or **orbit,** as it revolves around the sun. Earth's orbit is not quite circular. It is a slightly elongated circle, or ellipse.

FIGURE 2
Rotation
The rotation of Earth on its axis is similar to the movement of the figure skater as she spins.

FIGURE 3
Revolution
Earth revolves around the sun just as a speed skater travels around the center of a rink during a race. **Applying Concepts** *What is one complete revolution of Earth around the sun called?*

How Earth Moves

Teach Key Concepts L2
Earth's Rotation and Revolution

Focus Remind students that Earth moves through space in two major ways.

Teach Refer students to the photographs of the skaters in Figures 2 and 3. Point out that the skater who is rotating is moving around her own center. The skater who is revolving is moving around the center of another object—the rink. Ask students to use this analogy to compare and contrast Earth's rotation and revolution. *(Earth's rotation and revolution are similar because both represent types of movement. They are different because rotation is the movement of Earth on its axis, whereas revolution is the movement of Earth around another object—the sun.)*

Apply Have students suggest other examples of rotation and revolution. **learning modality: visual**

Independent Practice L2

All in One Teaching Resources

• Guided Reading and Study Worksheet: *Earth in Space*

⊙ **Student Edition on Audio CD**

Differentiated Instruction

English Learners/Beginning Comprehension: Key Concepts L1 The word pair *rotation* and *revolution* can be confusing. Provide examples such as *rotating* a doorknob (it moves around its center). Relate the expression of someone's life *revolving* around something; for example, "The athlete's life revolved around sports." Point out that sports is the center. Ask students to think of other examples in their native language and translate into English. **learning modality: verbal**

English Learners/Intermediate Comprehension: Key Concepts L2 Have students make a table that compares and contrasts rotation and revolution. **learning modality: verbal**

Monitor Progress L1

Writing Ask each student to write a short paragraph describing either Earth's rotation or Earth's revolution around the sun.

Answer
Figure 3 A year

Modeling Rotation

Materials ring stand, string, tape, turntable (such as a lazy Susan), weight

Time 15 minutes

Focus Tell students that in 1851, a French physicist named Jean Foucault used a pendulum to prove that Earth rotates.

Teach To model Foucault's pendulum, hang a small weight from the arm of a ring stand. Swing the pendulum, and ask students to describe what happens. *(The weight swings back and forth in one plane.)* Next, place the pendulum in the center of the turntable. Mark one side of the turntable with a piece of tape. Swing the pendulum as you slowly spin the turntable. Ask: **What does the turntable represent?** *(Earth rotating on its axis)* **What does the tape represent?** *(A location on Earth)*

Apply Tell students to suppose that this activity models a pendulum at the North Pole. Challenge them to explain how such a model could prove that Earth rotates. *(If a pendulum were swinging above the North Pole, the direction of its swing would appear to make one complete rotation every 24 hours.)* **learning modality: visual**

Help Students Read

Reciprocal Teaching Refer to the Content Refresher, which provides the guidelines for reciprocal teaching. Have students read the section with a partner. One partner reads a paragraph aloud. Then the other partner summarizes the paragraph's contents and explains the main concepts. The partners continue to switch roles with each new paragraph until they have finished the section.

Calendars People of many different cultures have struggled to establish calendars based on the length of time that Earth takes to revolve around the sun. A **calendar** is a system of organizing time that defines the beginning, length, and divisions of a year.

The ancient Egyptians created one of the first calendars. Egyptian astronomers counted the number of days between each first appearance of the star Sirius in the morning. In this way, they found that there are about 365 days in a year.

Dividing the year into smaller parts was also difficult. Early people used moon cycles to divide the year. The time from one full moon to the next is about $29\frac{1}{2}$ days. A year of 12 of these "moonths" adds up to only 354 days. The ancient Egyptian calendar had 12 months of 30 days each, with an extra 5 days at the end.

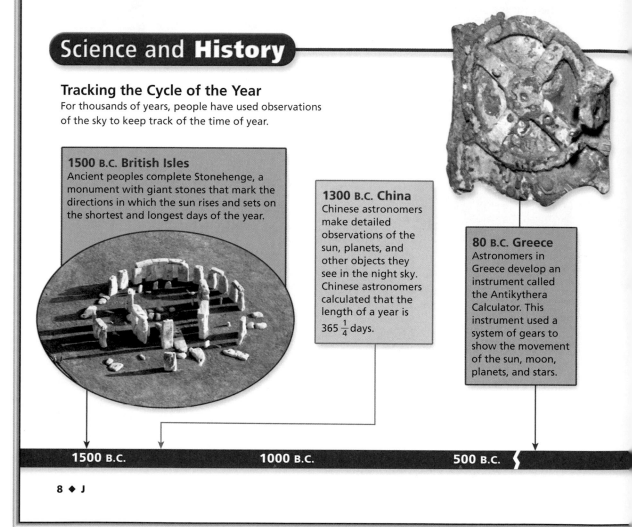

Science and History

Tracking the Cycle of the Year
For thousands of years, people have used observations of the sky to keep track of the time of year.

1500 B.C. British Isles
Ancient peoples complete Stonehenge, a monument with giant stones that mark the directions in which the sun rises and sets on the shortest and longest days of the year.

1300 B.C. China
Chinese astronomers make detailed observations of the sun, planets, and other objects they see in the night sky. Chinese astronomers calculated that the length of a year is $365\frac{1}{4}$ days.

80 B.C. Greece
Astronomers in Greece develop an instrument called the Antikythera Calculator. This instrument used a system of gears to show the movement of the sun, moon, planets, and stars.

1500 B.C.   1000 B.C.   500 B.C.

8 ◆ J

Background

Facts and Figures Stonehenge was built over three main periods. The first period began about 3100 B.C. and included the digging of the circular ditch and a ring of 56 pits. During the second period, about 2100 B.C., huge pillars of rock were erected in concentric circles around the center of the site. The 35-ton heel stone may have been placed during this building period. The placement of this stone was one of the most sophisticated accomplishments of the time. On the morning of the summer solstice, a person standing in the center of the circle can see the sun rising directly over this stone. During the third period, the monument was remodeled, and a circle of 30 upright stones, each weighing up to 50 tons, was erected. The final phase ended around 1500 B.C.

The Romans borrowed the Egyptian calendar of 365 days. But in fact, Earth orbits the sun in about $365\frac{1}{4}$ days. The Romans adjusted the Egyptian calendar by adding one day every four years. You know this fourth year as "leap year." During a leap year, February is given 29 days instead of its usual 28. Using a system of leap years helps to ensure that annual events, such as the beginning of summer, occur on the same date each year.

The Roman calendar was off by a little more than 11 minutes a year. Over the centuries, these minutes added up. By the 1500s, the beginning of spring was about ten days too early. To straighten things out, Pope Gregory XIII dropped ten days from the year 1582. He also made some other minor changes to the Roman system to form the calendar that we use today.

Reading Checkpoint What is a leap year?

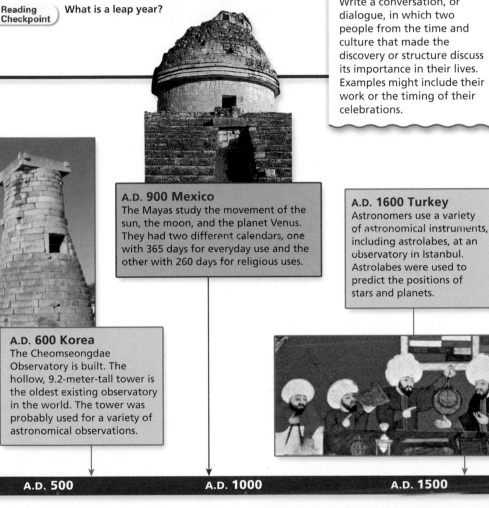

Writing in Science

Writing Dialogue Research one of the accomplishments discussed in the timeline. Write a conversation, or dialogue, in which two people from the time and culture that made the discovery or structure discuss its importance in their lives. Examples might include their work or the timing of their celebrations.

A.D. 600 Korea
The Cheomseongdae Observatory is built. The hollow, 9.2-meter-tall tower is the oldest existing observatory in the world. The tower was probably used for a variety of astronomical observations.

A.D. 900 Mexico
The Mayas study the movement of the sun, the moon, and the planet Venus. They had two different calendars, one with 365 days for everyday use and the other with 260 days for religious uses.

A.D. 1600 Turkey
Astronomers use a variety of astronomical instruments, including astrolabes, at an observatory in Istanbul. Astrolabes were used to predict the positions of stars and planets.

| A.D. 500 | A.D. 1000 | A.D. 1500 |

Science and History

Focus Tell students that anything used to keep track of days, months, and years—as well as the events that occur during various times—can be thought of as a calendar.

Teach Encourage students to discuss how the cultures in the timeline used their astronomical observations. Ask: **How do you think the physical structures shown in the timeline could serve as astronomical observatories?** *(Possible answers: The giant stones at Stonehenge marked sunrise and sunset on the longest day of the year. The Korean and Mayan towers put observers above obstructions on the ground so that repeating patterns in the sky could be more easily observed, measured, and recorded.)*

Writing in Science

Writing Mode Research

Scoring Rubric

4 Exceeds criteria by including a dialogue that is historically correct and exceptionally well written

3 Includes all criteria but does not go beyond requirements

2 Includes a brief dialogue based on weak research

1 Is incomplete and inaccurate

Differentiated Instruction

Gifted and Talented **L3**
Calculating Earth's Movements Tell students that Earth moves at a speed of about 30 km/sec as it travels around the sun. Ask: **How many kilometers does Earth travel in a minute? An hour? A day? A year?** Before they begin their calculations, suggest that students set up the problems on paper to make sure that units cancel out. *(In one minute, 1,800 km; in one hour, 108,000 km; in one day, 2,592,000 km; in one year, about 946.7 million km)* **learning modality: logical/mathematical**

Monitor Progress ____ **L2**

Oral Presentation Have students explain why it was difficult for ancient peoples to develop workable calendars. *(The length of a year and a month are not exact multiples of the length of a day.)*

Answer

Reading Checkpoint A leap year is an adjustment made to the Egyptian calendar by the Romans. During a leap year, which occurs every four years, February is given 29 days instead of its usual 28.

The Seasons on Earth

Teach Key Concepts L2
Angle of Sunlight

Focus Remind students that Earth's poles are colder than areas closer to Earth's equator.

Teach Ask: **Is it warmer directly beneath a heat lamp or somewhat to the side?** *(Directly beneath the lamp)* **Why?** *(The heat comes down at a more direct angle and so is more concentrated in that area.)* Help students understand that Earth's equatorial regions receive sunlight at a more direct angle than Earth's polar regions.

Apply Ask: **Where on Earth could you find tropical plants, such as banana trees?** *(Near the equator)* **Where could you find large continental glaciers?** *(Near the poles)* **learning modality: logical/mathematical**

 **Teaching Resources**
- Transparency J2

Lab zone | Build **Inquiry** L1

Comparing and Contrasting Angles of Sunlight

Materials flashlight, graph paper

Time 15 minutes

Focus Remind students that sunlight hits Earth's surface at different angles.

Teach Have students work in groups to shine a flashlight directly above the paper and trace around the lighted area. Next, have students shine the flashlight at an angle and trace around the lighted area. Ask: **Which area represents sunlight at the equator?** *(The smaller area)*

Apply Ask: **Which receives more energy, the smaller area or the larger area?** *(Both areas receive the same amount.)* **If this were Earth's surface, why would the larger area be colder? Explain in terms of the graph paper squares.** *(Each square in the larger area, the poles, receives less energy than each square in the smaller area, the equator.)*
learning modality: visual

Lab zone | Try This **Activity**

Sun Shadows
The sun's shadow changes predictably through the day.

1. On a sunny day, stand outside in the sun and use a compass to find north.
2. Have your partner place a craft stick about one meter to the north of where you are standing. Repeat for east, south, and west.
3. Insert a meter stick in the ground at the center of the craft sticks. Make sure the stick is straight up.
4. Predict how the sun's shadow will move throughout the day.
5. Record the direction and length of the sun's shadow at noon and at regular intervals during the day.

Predicting How did the actual movement of the sun's shadow compare with your prediction? How do you think the direction and length of the sun's shadow at these same times would change over the next six months?

FIGURE 4
Sunlight Striking Earth's Surface
Near the equator, sunlight strikes Earth's surface more directly and is less spread out than near the poles.
Relating Cause and Effect *Why is it usually colder near the poles than near the equator?*

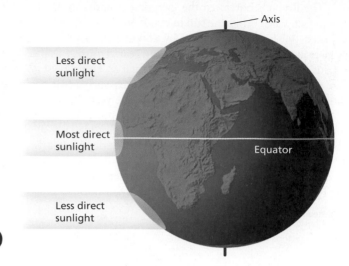

Axis
Less direct sunlight
Most direct sunlight
Equator
Less direct sunlight

The Seasons on Earth

Most places outside the tropics and polar regions have four distinct seasons: winter, spring, summer, and autumn. But there are great differences in temperature from place to place. For instance, it is generally warmer near the equator than near the poles. Why is this so?

How Sunlight Hits Earth Figure 4 shows how sunlight strikes Earth's surface. Notice that sunlight hits Earth's surface most directly near the equator. Near the poles, sunlight arrives at a steep angle. As a result, it is spread out over a greater area. That is why it is warmer near the equator than near the poles.

Earth's Tilted Axis If Earth's axis were straight up and down relative to its orbit, temperatures would remain fairly constant year-round. There would be no seasons. **Earth has seasons because its axis is tilted as it revolves around the sun.**

Notice in Figure 5 that Earth's axis is always tilted at an angle of 23.5° from the vertical. As Earth revolves around the sun, the north end of its axis is tilted away from the sun for part of the year and toward the sun for part of the year.

Summer and winter are caused by Earth's tilt as it revolves around the sun. The change in seasons is not caused by changes in Earth's distance from the sun. In fact, Earth is farthest from the sun when it is summer in the Northern Hemisphere.

✓ **Reading Checkpoint** When is Earth farthest from the sun?

Lab zone | Try This **Activity**

Skills Focus Predicting L2

Materials compass, craft sticks, meter stick

Time 20 min to set up; 10 min for each observation time

Tips Select at least four times during the day to record the shadow's length and position. Times should be at regular intervals.

Expected Outcome Shadows will move around the stick in a clockwise direction. Shadows will be longest in early morning and late afternoon and shortest around noon.

Extend Repeat the activity throughout the school year, selecting times in different seasons so that students can see how the shadow's length varies with the season.

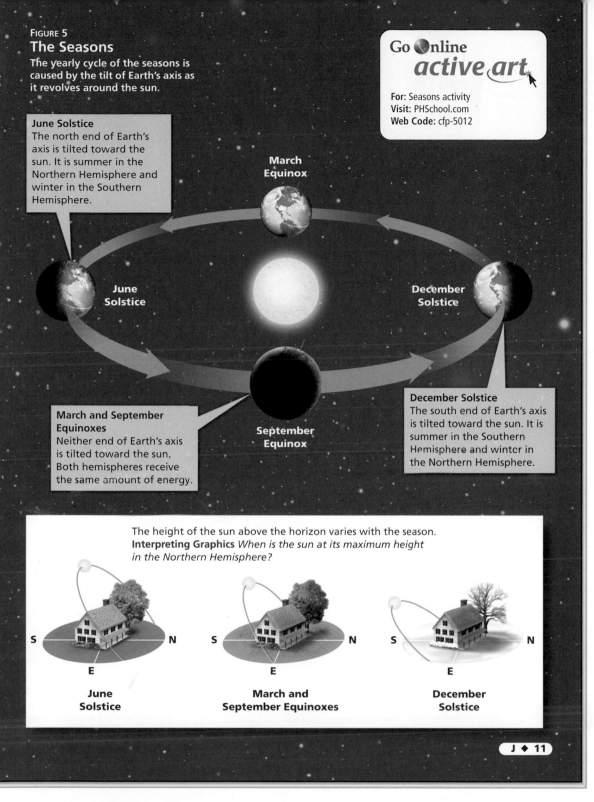

FIGURE 5
The Seasons
The yearly cycle of the seasons is caused by the tilt of Earth's axis as it revolves around the sun.

Go Online
active art

For: Seasons activity
Visit: PHSchool.com
Web Code: cfp-5012

June Solstice
The north end of Earth's axis is tilted toward the sun. It is summer in the Northern Hemisphere and winter in the Southern Hemisphere.

March Equinox

June Solstice

December Solstice

March and September Equinoxes
Neither end of Earth's axis is tilted toward the sun. Both hemispheres receive the same amount of energy.

September Equinox

December Solstice
The south end of Earth's axis is tilted toward the sun. It is summer in the Southern Hemisphere and winter in the Northern Hemisphere.

The height of the sun above the horizon varies with the season.
Interpreting Graphics *When is the sun at its maximum height in the Northern Hemisphere?*

June Solstice	March and September Equinoxes	December Solstice

J ◆ 11

Differentiated Instruction

Special Needs [L1]
Modeling Seasons Place a lamp with a bare bulb on a desk. Tilt a globe so that the Northern Hemisphere is pointed toward the lamp. Ask: **Which season does this represent in the Northern Hemisphere?** *(Summer)* Walk around the lamp in a circle, but keep the tilt of the globe the same relative to the room, not the lamp. Turn the globe so that the United States is facing the sun. As you walk, stop every 90° to represent Earth's position at the equinoxes and the winter solstice. Have students identify each season and describe the conditions in the United States. **learning modality: visual**

Go Online
active art

For: Seasons activity
Visit: PHSchool.com
Web Code: cfp-5012

Students can interact with the art of the seasons online.

Use Visuals: Figure 5 [L2]
The Seasons

Focus Point out that the lines showing Earth's axis are all tilted.

Teach Ask: **Is the angle of the tilt different at different points in Earth's revolution?** *(No)* **What is different?** *(Whether the north end of the axis is pointing toward or away from the sun)* **What is it called when the north end or the south end of the axis is pointed the most directly toward the sun?** *(The solstice)* **What is the position of the axis during an equinox?** *(Neither end of the axis is pointed toward the sun.)*

Apply Direct students' attention to the figure in the lower left. Ask them to list two things that cause it to be summer in the Northern Hemisphere. *(In June, the sun shines more directly on the surface. The sun is above the horizon for a longer period each day.)* Now have students look at the visual in the lower right. Ask them to identify two things that cause it to be winter in the Northern Hemisphere. *(In December, the sun shines less directly on the surface. The sun is above the horizon for a shorter period each day.)* **learning modality: visual**

All in One **Teaching Resources**
• Transparency J3

Monitor Progress [L2]

Drawing Have students draw Earth, showing its tilt in relation to the sun, during a season in the Northern Hemisphere and a different season in the Southern Hemisphere.

Answers
Figure 4 It is colder near the poles because sunlight hits Earth there at a less direct angle and the sun's rays are spread over a larger area.

Figure 5 The sun is at its maximum height in the Northern Hemisphere at the June solstice.

Reading Checkpoint When it is summer in the Northern Hemisphere

Developing and Testing Hypotheses

Materials lamp with bare bulb, modeling clay, plastic foam ball, thin wooden dowel

Time 30 minutes

Focus Challenge small groups to make models to test this hypothesis: *If Earth's axis were not tilted, the length of the days would not change over the course of a year.*

Teach Ask: **How will you model Earth's axis?** *(By placing the dowel through the foam ball)* **How will you ensure that the axis does not tilt?** *(By placing the dowel vertically in the lump of modeling clay)* **How will you model Earth's revolution and rotation?** *(By spinning the ball as it is moved around the lamp)* After groups have set up their models, turn off the lights so that they can demonstrate them. Ask students to observe the pattern of light and shadow on the ball.

Apply Ask: **How do your observations support your hypothesis?** *(As the ball moves around the lamp, the line between light and shadow passes through each pole and does not change. This indicates that the length of days would not change over the year if Earth's axis were not tilted.)* **learning modality: kinesthetic**

Address Misconceptions L1

Earth's Orbit and the Seasons

Focus Drawings of Earth's elliptical orbit are often exaggerated. Students may misinterpret such drawings and think that as Earth comes closer to the sun we have summer and that as Earth swings away from the sun, we have winter.

Teach Explain that Earth's orbit is only slightly elliptical. The distance between Earth and the sun does not change enough to have a large effect on the seasons. Direct students' attention to Figure 5.

Apply Point out the shape of Earth's orbit. Explain that, although it is an ellipse, Earth's orbit is almost a circle. Ask: **Why does the diagram show Earth's orbit as an oval if it's really nearly circular?** *(The diagram is drawn as if you are looking at the ellipse from its side, similar to looking at a dinner plate on edge. If viewed from above, the orbit would more closely resemble a circle.)* **What causes the seasons?** *(The tilt of Earth's axis)* **learning modality: logical/mathematical**

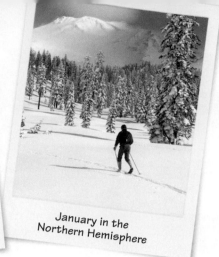

January in the Southern Hemisphere

January in the Northern Hemisphere

FIGURE 6
Solstices and Equinoxes

Summer in the Southern Hemisphere (left) occurs at the same time as winter in the Northern Hemisphere (right). Similarly, when it is spring in the Southern Hemisphere, it is fall in the Northern Hemisphere.
Interpreting Photographs *In which direction was Earth's axis pointing at the time that each of the photographs was taken?*

Earth in June In June, the north end of Earth's axis is tilted toward the sun. In the Northern Hemisphere, the noon sun is high in the sky and there are more hours of daylight than darkness. The combination of direct rays and more hours of sunlight heats the surface more in June than at any other time of the year. It is summer in the Northern Hemisphere.

At the same time south of the equator, the sun's energy is spread over a larger area. The sun is low in the sky and days are shorter than nights. The combination of less direct rays and fewer hours of sunlight heats Earth's surface less than at any other time of the year. It is winter in the Southern Hemisphere.

Earth in December In December, people in the Southern Hemisphere receive the most direct sunlight, so it is summer there. At the same time, the sun's rays in the Northern Hemisphere are more slanted and there are fewer hours of daylight. So it is winter in the Northern Hemisphere.

Solstices The sun reaches its greatest distance north or south of the equator twice each year. Each of these days, when the sun is farthest north or south of the equator, is known as a **solstice** (SOHL stis). The day when the sun is farthest north of the equator is the summer solstice in the Northern Hemisphere. It is also the winter solstice in the Southern Hemisphere. This solstice occurs around June 21 each year. It is the longest day of the year in the Northern Hemisphere and the shortest day of the year in the Southern Hemisphere.

Similarly, around December 21, the sun is farthest south of the equator. This is the winter solstice in the Northern Hemisphere and the summer solstice in the Southern Hemisphere.

October in the Southern Hemisphere

October in the Northern Hemisphere

Figure 6 In January, shortly after a solstice, the south end of Earth's axis is tilted toward the sun. In October, shortly after an equinox, neither end of the axis is pointed toward the sun.

 Reading Checkpoint A day during which the noon sun is directly overhead at the equator and there are equal hours of day and night

Assess

Reviewing Key Concepts

1. a. Rotation and revolution **b.** Rotation
2. a. The tilt of Earth's axis as it revolves around the sun **b.** A solstice occurs when the sun is farthest north or south of the equator. During an equinox, the noon sun is directly over the equator. Solstices mark the beginnings of summer and winter; equinoxes mark the beginnings of fall and spring. **c.** There would be no seasons— temperatures would remain fairly constant year-round at any given location.

Reteach L1

Use Figure 5 to review the yearly cycle of the seasons. Have students describe the tilt of Earth's axis during the December and June solstices and the March and September equinoxes.

Performance Assessment L2

Writing Challenge each student to choose a place on the globe that he or she is not familiar with and write a description of the amount of sunlight received there throughout the year.

All in One Teaching Resources
• Section Summary: *Earth in Space*
• Review and Reinforce: *Earth in Space*
• Enrich: *Earth in Space*

Equinoxes Halfway between the solstices, neither hemisphere is tilted toward or away from the sun. This occurs twice a year, when the noon sun is directly overhead at the equator. Each of these days is known as an **equinox,** which means "equal night." During an equinox, day and night are each about 12 hours long everywhere on Earth. The vernal (spring) equinox occurs around March 21 and marks the beginning of spring in the Northern Hemisphere. The autumnal equinox occurs around September 22. It marks the beginning of fall in the Northern Hemisphere.

Reading Checkpoint What is an equinox?

Section 1 Assessment

Target Reading Skill **Using Prior Knowledge** Review your graphic organizer and revise it based on what you just learned in this section. Use it to help answer Question 2.

Reviewing Key Concepts

1. a. Identifying What are the two major motions of Earth as it travels through space?
   b. Explaining Which motion causes day and night?
2. a. Relating Cause and Effect What causes the seasons?
   b. Comparing and Contrasting What are solstices and equinoxes? How are they related to the seasons?
   c. Predicting How would the seasons be different if Earth were not tilted on its axis?

Writing in Science

Descriptive Paragraph What seasons occur where you live? Write a detailed paragraph describing the changes that take place each season in your region. Explain how seasonal changes in temperature and hours of daylight relate to changes in Earth's position as it moves around the sun.

Lab zone Chapter **Project**

Keep Students on Track Check that students have begun recording their daily observations of the moon. Remind them to draw maps of their observation sites. Help them define coordinate systems and make map keys. Demonstrate how to estimate the moon's altitude by making a fist and holding it at arm's length. One fist is 10° above the horizon, two fists are 20°, and so on.

Writing in Science

Writing Mode Description
Scoring Rubric
4 Exceeds criteria; includes seasonal changes in relation to Earth's position; descriptions are vivid, detailed, and realistic
3 Includes all criteria, but description lacks interest and detail
2 Includes a brief paragraph with some explanations
1 Is inaccurate and incomplete

Reasons for the Seasons

Lab zone Skills Lab

Prepare for Inquiry

Key Concept
The seasons are determined by the tilt of Earth's axis as Earth revolves around the sun.

Skills Objectives
After this lab, students will be able to
- make an Earth/sun model to observe the effect of the tilt of Earth's axis on the seasons
- observe the effect of the angles of light on the amount of energy at different places on the model
- infer the amount of heat received by different parts of the model at different times of the year
- predict the time of year when the model receives different amounts of energy

Prep Time 10 minutes
Class Time 40 minutes

Advance Planning
Make sure that the flashlights are working properly. Have extra batteries on hand. The room must be dim enough for the light from the flashlights to be seen. One acetate sheet can be cut into six grids.

All in One Teaching Resources
- Lab Worksheet: *Reasons for the Seasons*

Reasons for the Seasons

Problem
How does the tilt of Earth's axis affect the light received by Earth as it revolves around the sun?

Skills Focus
making models, observing, inferring, predicting

Materials (per pair of students)
- books
- flashlight
- paper
- pencil
- protractor
- toothpick
- acetate sheet with thick grid lines drawn on it
- plastic foam ball marked with poles and equator

Procedure
1. Make a pile of books about 15 cm high.
2. Tape the acetate sheet to the head of the flashlight. Place the flashlight on the pile of books.
3. Carefully push a pencil into the South Pole of the plastic foam ball, which represents Earth.
4. Use the protractor to measure a 23.5° tilt of the axis of your Earth away from your "flashlight sun," as shown in the top diagram. This position represents winter in the Northern Hemisphere.
5. Hold the pencil so that Earth is steady at this 23.5° angle and about 15 cm from the flashlight head. Turn the flashlight on. Dim the room lights.
6. The squares on the acetate should show up on your model Earth. Move the ball closer if necessary or dim the room lights more. Observe and record the shape of the squares at the equator and at the poles.

7. Carefully stick the toothpick straight into your model Earth about halfway between the equator and the North Pole. Observe and record the length of the shadow.
8. Without changing the tilt, turn the pencil to rotate the model Earth once on its axis. Observe and record how the shadow of the toothpick changes.
9. Tilt your model Earth 23.5° toward the flashlight, as shown in the bottom diagram. This is summer in the Northern Hemisphere. Observe and record the shape of the squares at the equator and at the poles. Observe how the toothpick's shadow changes.
10. Rotate the model Earth and note the shadow pattern.

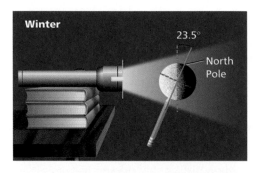

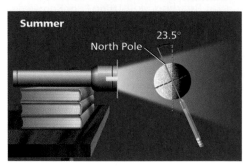

Guide Inquiry

Invitation
Ask: **Why is it warmer in the summer?** *(Many students may hold the common misconception that Earth is closer to the sun.)* Tell students that because Earth's orbit is slightly elliptical, Earth is actually a bit farther from the sun during the Northern Hemisphere summer than it is in the winter. In this activity, they will relate the tilt of Earth's axis to the seasons.

Introduce the Procedure
- Tell students that the ball must be close enough to the flashlight for several grid squares be seen on the ball.
- Review how to use the protractor to measure the angle of Earth's axis.

Analyze and Conclude

1. **Observing** When it is winter in the Northern Hemisphere, which areas on Earth get the most concentrated light? Which areas get the most concentrated light when it is summer in the Northern Hemisphere?

2. **Observing** Compare your observations of how the light hits the area halfway between the equator and the North Pole during winter (Step 6) and during summer (Step 9).

3. **Inferring** If the squares projected on the ball from the acetate become larger, what can you infer about the amount of heat distributed in each square?

4. **Inferring** According to your observations, which areas on Earth are consistently coolest? Which areas are consistently warmest? Why?

5. **Predicting** What time of year will the toothpick's shadow be longest? When will the shadow be shortest?

6. **Drawing Conclusions** How are the amounts of heat and light received in a square related to the angle of the sun's rays?

7. **Communicating** Use your observations of an Earth-sun model to write an explanation of what causes the seasons.

More to Explore

You can measure how directly light from the sun hits Earth's surface by making a shadow stick. You will need a stick or pole about 1 m long. With the help of your teacher, push the stick partway into the ground where it will not be disturbed. Make sure the stick stays vertical. At noon on the first day of every month, measure the length of the stick's shadow. The shorter the shadow, the higher the sun is in the sky and the more directly the sun's rays are hitting Earth. At what time of the year are the shadows longest? Shortest? How do your observations help explain the seasons?

Troubleshooting the Experiment
- Students may have difficulty maintaining the tilt of the ball at 23.5° as they move it. Have the partner measure the angle before recording information on the size and shape of the grid squares.

Expected Outcome
- The grid squares will be smaller and more square in the region of the ball where the light hits directly.
- The grid squares will be larger and more lengthened where the light hits at an angle.

Analyze and Conclude

1. During winter, the area near 23.5° south latitude receives the most concentrated light. In summer, the region near 23.5° north latitude gets the most concentrated light.

2. Light is more concentrated in the middle zone during the summer and more spread out during the winter.

3. The same amount of energy is spread out over a larger area.

4. The poles are consistently coolest because sunlight is most spread out there. The equator is warmest because sunlight is most concentrated there.

5. The shadow will be longest during winter and shortest during summer.

6. As the angle becomes less direct, light and heat become less concentrated and spread out over a larger area. Each square receives a smaller portion of light and heat.

7. During summer in the Northern Hemisphere, the sun's rays hit the Northern Hemisphere most directly. The heating effect is greater, and the Northern Hemisphere is warmed. During winter the rays hit the Northern Hemisphere at a less direct angle, so the heating effect decreases.

Extend Inquiry

More to Explore Over the course of time, the length of the shadow at noon varies. The shadow grows longer and longer until the December solstice, around December 21. Then the shadow grows progressively shorter until the June solstice, on or near June 21. When the shadow is longest, the sun's rays are the most spread out and are the least effective at heating the surface.

Section 2
Integrating Physics
Gravity and Motion

Objectives

After this lesson, students will be able to

J.1.2.1 Identify the factors that determine the strength of the force of gravity between two objects.

J.1.2.2 Describe two factors that keep the moon and Earth in orbit.

Target Reading Skill

Asking Questions Explain that changing a heading into a question helps students anticipate the ideas, facts, and events they are about to read.

Answers

Possible questions and answers:

What is gravity? (*Gravity is the force that attracts all objects toward one another.*) **What is inertia?** (*Inertia is the tendency of an object to resist a change in motion.*)

All in One **Teaching Resources**

• Transparency J4

Preteach

Build Background Knowledge `L1`

Weight

Students have often weighed themselves or compared the weights of various objects. Ask: **What is weight?** (*Possible answer: A value that describes how heavy an object is*) Tell students that weight is related to the force of gravity. In this section, they will learn about gravity and how it relates to Earth's orbit.

Reading Preview

Key Concepts

• What determines the strength of the force of gravity between two objects?

• What two factors combine to keep the moon and Earth in orbit?

Key Terms

• force
• gravity
• law of universal gravitation
• mass
• weight
• inertia
• Newton's first law of motion

Target Reading Skill

Asking Questions Before you read, preview the red headings. In a graphic organizer like the one below, ask a question for each heading. As you read, write answers to your questions.

Gravity

Question	Answer
What is gravity?	Gravity is . . .

Lab zone **Discover Activity**

Can You Remove the Bottom Penny?

1. Place 25 or so pennies in a stack on a table.
2. Write down your prediction of what will happen if you attempt to knock the bottom penny out of the stack.
3. Quickly slide a ruler along the surface of the table and strike the bottom penny. Observe what happens to the stack of pennies.
4. Repeat Step 3 several times, knocking more pennies from the bottom of the stack.

Think It Over
Developing Hypotheses Explain what happened to the stack of pennies as the bottom penny was knocked out of the stack.

Earth revolves around the sun in a nearly circular orbit. The moon orbits Earth in the same way. But what keeps Earth and the moon in orbit? Why don't they just fly off into space?

The first person to answer these questions was the English scientist Isaac Newton. Late in his life, Newton told a story of how watching an apple fall from a tree in 1666 had made him think about the moon's orbit. Newton realized that there must be a force acting between Earth and the moon that kept the moon in orbit. A **force** is a push or a pull. Most everyday forces require objects to be in contact. Newton realized that the force that holds the moon in orbit is different in that it acts over long distances between objects that are not in contact.

Gravity

Newton hypothesized that the force that pulls an apple to the ground also pulls the moon toward Earth, keeping it in orbit. This force, called **gravity,** attracts all objects toward each other. In Newton's day, most scientists thought that forces on Earth were different from those elsewhere in the universe. Although Newton did not discover gravity, he was the first person to realize that gravity occurs everywhere. Newton's **law of universal gravitation** states that every object in the universe attracts every other object.

Lab zone **Discover Activity**

Skills Focus Developing hypotheses `L2`

Materials 25 pennies, thin plastic ruler or thin spatula

Time 10 minutes

Tips It may take students a few attempts before they get a procedure down for knocking out the bottom penny. Make sure that the ruler or spatula is thinner than the height of one penny.

Expected Outcome When done properly, the bottom penny is knocked out of the stack without disturbing the remaining pennies.

Think It Over The law of inertia (objects at rest tend to stay at rest) is demonstrated in this activity. The only penny being acted upon by a horizontal force is the bottom penny. As a result, the remaining pennies tend to remain undisturbed.

The force of gravity is measured in units called newtons, named after Isaac Newton. **The strength of the force of gravity between two objects depends on two factors: the masses of the objects and the distance between them.**

Gravity, Mass, and Weight According to the law of universal gravitation, all of the objects around you, including Earth and even this book, are pulling on you, just as you are pulling on them. Why don't you notice a pull between you and the book? Because the strength of gravity depends in part on the masses of each of the objects. **Mass** is the amount of matter in an object.

Because Earth is so massive, it exerts a much greater force on you than this book does. Similarly, Earth exerts a gravitational force on the moon, large enough to keep the moon in orbit. The moon also exerts a gravitational force on Earth, as you will learn later in this chapter when you study the tides.

The force of gravity on an object is known as its **weight**. Unlike mass, which doesn't change, an object's weight can change depending on its location. For example, on the moon you would weigh about one sixth of your weight on Earth. This is because the moon is much less massive than Earth, so the pull of the moon's gravity on you would be far less than that of Earth's gravity.

Gravity and Distance The strength of gravity is affected by the distance between two objects as well as their masses. The force of gravity decreases rapidly as distance increases. For example, if the distance between two objects were doubled, the force of gravity between them would decrease to one fourth of its original value.

 What is an object's weight?

FIGURE 7
Gravity, Mass, and Distance
The strength of the force of gravity between two objects depends on their masses and the distance between them.
Inferring *How would the force of gravity change if the distance between the objects decreased?*

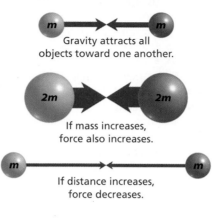
Gravity attracts all objects toward one another.

If mass increases, force also increases.

If distance increases, force decreases.

FIGURE 8
Earth Over the Moon
The force of gravity holds Earth and the moon together.

J ◆ 17

Inertia and Orbital Motion

Teach Key Concepts **L1**

Inertia

Focus Remind students that gravity pulls all objects toward each other.

Teach Ask: **Why does a baseball continue to move after a pitcher lets go of it and stops applying force?** *(The ball has inertia.)* **Why would the ball eventually hit the ground?** *(Gravity pulls it down.)*

Apply Ask students if they have ever seen a magician pull a tablecloth off a table, leaving the dishes that were on top of it in place? Ask: **What role does inertia play in this magic trick?** *(The inertia of the dishes causes them to resist a change in motion—in this case, to resist being moved at all.)* **learning modality: logical/mathematical**

All in One Teaching Resources

• Transparency J6

 **Analyzing Data**

Math Skill Making and Interpreting Graphs

Focus Tell students that to overcome gravity, rockets burn a great deal of fuel when they launch.

Teach Show students that the force of gravity can be located by moving a finger along the *x*-axis until it reaches the appropriate distance, and then upward until it reaches the curve. From there, moving horizontally to the left will take them to the *y*-axis where they will find the force of gravity at that distance.

Answers

1. Force of gravity on the rocket in millions of newtons and distance from planet's center in planetary radii
2. 4 million newtons
3. 1 million newtons
4. It decreases.

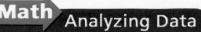 **Analyzing Data**

Gravity Versus Distance

As a rocket leaves a planet's surface, the force of gravity between the rocket and the planet changes. Use the graph at the right to answer the questions below.

1. **Reading Graphs** What two variables are being graphed? In what units is each variable measured?
2. **Reading Graphs** What is the force of gravity on the rocket at the planet's surface?
3. **Reading Graphs** What is the force of gravity on the rocket at a distance of two units (twice the planet's radius from its center)?
4. **Making Generalizations** In general, how does the force of gravity pulling on the rocket change as the distance between it and the planet increases?

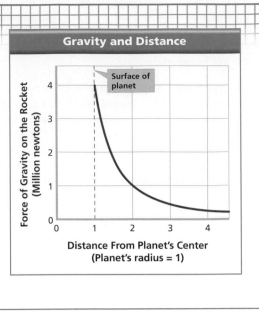

Gravity and Distance

Force of Gravity on the Rocket (Million newtons) vs. *Distance From Planet's Center (Planet's radius = 1)*

Surface of planet

Inertia and Orbital Motion

If the sun and Earth are constantly pulling on one another because of gravity, why doesn't Earth fall into the sun? Similarly, why doesn't the moon crash into Earth? The fact that such collisions have not occurred shows that there must be another factor at work. That factor is called inertia.

Inertia The tendency of an object to resist a change in motion is **inertia.** You feel the effects of inertia every day. When you are riding in a car and it stops suddenly, you keep moving forward. If you didn't have a seat belt on, your inertia could cause you to bump into the car's windshield or the seat in front of you. The more mass an object has, the greater its inertia. An object with greater inertia is more difficult to start or stop.

Isaac Newton stated his ideas about inertia as a scientific law. **Newton's first law of motion** says that an object at rest will stay at rest and an object in motion will stay in motion with a constant speed and direction unless acted on by a force.

✓ Reading Checkpoint What is inertia?

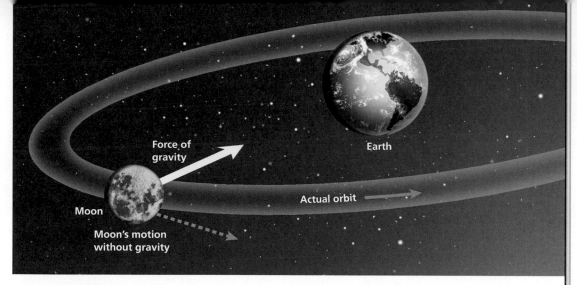

Force of gravity

Earth

Actual orbit

Moon

Moon's motion without gravity

Orbital Motion Why do Earth and the moon remain in their orbits? **Newton concluded that two factors—inertia and gravity—combine to keep Earth in orbit around the sun and the moon in orbit around Earth.**

As shown in Figure 9, Earth's gravity keeps pulling the moon toward it, preventing the moon from moving in a straight line. At the same time, the moon keeps moving ahead because of its inertia. If not for Earth's gravity, inertia would cause the moon to move off through space in a straight line. In the same way, Earth revolves around the sun because the sun's gravity pulls on it while Earth's inertia keeps it moving ahead.

FIGURE 9
Gravity and Inertia
A combination of gravity and inertia keeps the moon in orbit around Earth. If there were no gravity, inertia would cause the moon to travel in a straight line.
Interpreting Diagrams *What would happen to the moon if it were not moving in orbit?*

Section 2 Assessment

Target Reading Skill Asking Questions
Use your graphic organizer about the headings to help answer the questions below.

Reviewing Key Concepts

1. a. **Summarizing** What is the law of universal gravitation?
   b. **Reviewing** What two factors determine the force of gravity between two objects?
   c. **Predicting** Suppose the moon were closer to Earth. How would the force of gravity between Earth and the moon be different?
2. a. **Identifying** What two factors act together to keep Earth in orbit around the sun?

b. **Applying Concepts** Why doesn't Earth simply fall into the sun?
c. **Predicting** How would Earth move if the sun (including its gravity) suddenly disappeared? Explain your answer.

Writing in Science

Cause and Effect Paragraph Suppose you took a trip to the moon. Write a paragraph describing how and why your weight would change. Would your mass change too?

Chapter 1 J ◆ 19

Writing in Science

Writing Mode Exposition
Scoring Rubric
4 Exceeds criteria; includes a detailed explanation of how and why weight would change and tells why mass does not change
3 Meets all criteria but does not go beyond requirements

2 Includes an explanation of weight changes but does not mention mass
1 Is incomplete and inaccurate

Lab zone **Teacher Demo**

Demonstrating Inertia **L1**

Materials quarter; clean, dry coffee mug; 3 × 5 index card
Time 10 minutes

Focus Review Newton's first law of motion by reminding the class that an object at rest will stay at rest until acted upon by a force.

Teach Place an index card over the top of a coffee mug. Place a quarter on top of the card, centering it over the mug. Quickly pull the card out from under the quarter. The quarter will fall into the mug. Ask: **What kept the quarter from moving with the card?** *(Inertia, which made the quarter "remain at rest")* **Why didn't the quarter move with the card it was sitting on?** *(The sideways pulling force was acting on the card, only.)*

Apply Ask how this demonstration is related to orbital motion. *(An object moving in space will resist a change in motion—much as the quarter did—and try to keep moving in a straight line.)* **learning modality: visual**

Monitor Progress **L2**

Answers
Figure 9 Earth's gravity would pull it directly toward Earth.

Reading Checkpoint The tendency of an object to resist a change in motion

Assess

Reviewing Key Concepts

1. **a.** Every object in the universe attracts every other object. **b.** The masses of the objects and the distance between them **c.** It would increase.
2. **a.** Inertia and gravity **b.** Earth's inertia causes it to tend to move in a straight line. **c.** Earth would move in a straight line because no gravitational force would counteract its inertia.

Reteach **L1**

Use the diagrams in this section to summarize how objects stay in orbit.

All in One Teaching Resources
• Section Summary: *Gravity and Motion*
• Review and Reinforce: *Gravity and Motion*
• Enrich: *Gravity and Motion*

Section
3
Phases, Eclipses, and Tides

Objectives

After this lesson, students will be able to

J.1.3.1 Explain the causes of the phases of the moon.

J.1.3.2 Describe solar and lunar eclipses.

J.1.3.3 Identify the causes of tides.

Target Reading Skill

Previewing Visuals Explain that looking at the visuals before students read helps them activate prior knowledge and predict what they are about to read.

Answers

Possible questions and answers:

Why does the moon have phases? *(The changing relative positions of the moon, Earth, and the sun cause the phases of the moon.)* **Do we see different sides of the moon as the phases of the moon appear?** *(No; the same side of the moon always faces Earth.)*

All in One Teaching Resources

• Transparency J7

Preteach

Build Background Knowledge L1

Observing the Moon

Have students describe observations they have made about the moon. Use questions to help prompt their memories. For example, ask: **Have you ever seen the moon low on the horizon? Was it full at the time? Have you ever seen the moon in daytime?** Encourage students to think about their observations as they read this section.

Reading Preview

Key Concepts

• What causes the phases of the moon?

• What are solar and lunar eclipses?

• What causes the tides?

Key Terms

• phases
• eclipse
• solar eclipse
• umbra
• penumbra
• lunar eclipse
• tide
• spring tide
• neap tide

Target Reading Skill

Previewing Visuals Preview Figure 11. Then write two questions about the diagram of the phases of the moon in a graphic organizer like the one below. As you read, answer your questions.

Phases of the Moon

Q. Why does the moon have phases?
A.
Q.

Lab zone Discover Activity

How Does the Moon Move?

1. Place a quarter flat on your desk to represent Earth. Put a penny flat on your desk to represent the moon.

2. One side of the moon always faces Earth. Move the moon through one revolution around Earth, keeping Lincoln's face always looking at Earth. How many times did the penny make one complete rotation?

Think It Over

Inferring From the point of view of someone on Earth, does the moon seem to rotate? Explain your answer.

When people look up at the moon, they often see what looks like a face. Some people call this "the man in the moon." Of course, the moon really has no face. What people are seeing is a pattern of light-colored and dark-colored areas on the moon's surface that just happens to look like a face.

It is interesting to note that this pattern never seems to change. That is, the same side of the moon, the "near side," always faces Earth. The "far side" of the moon always faces away from Earth, so you never see it from Earth. The reason has to do with how the moon moves in space.

Motions of the Moon

Like Earth, the moon moves through space in two ways. The moon revolves around Earth and also rotates on its own axis. It takes the moon about 27.3 days to revolve around Earth.

The moon rotates slowly on its own axis once every 27.3 days. Because the moon also revolves around Earth every 27.3 days, a "day" and a "year" on the moon are the same length. For this reason, the same side of the moon always faces Earth. As the moon revolves around Earth, the relative positions of the moon, Earth, and sun change. **The changing relative positions of the moon, Earth, and sun cause the phases of the moon, eclipses, and tides.**

Lab zone Discover Activity

Skills Focus Inferring

Materials quarters, pennies

Time 10 minutes

Tips Before students try this activity, have them predict how many times the penny will rotate during its revolution around the quarter.

L1 Expected Outcome The penny makes one complete rotation on its axis as it revolves around the quarter.

Think It Over The moon does not appear to rotate when seen from Earth because the same side of the moon is always visible from Earth.

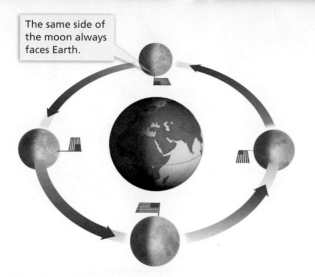

The same side of the moon always faces Earth.

FIGURE 10
The Moon in Motion
The moon rotates on its axis and revolves around Earth in the same amount of time. As a result, the near side of the moon (shown with a flag) always faces Earth.
Interpreting Diagrams *Would Earth ever appear to set below the horizon for someone standing next to the flag on the moon? Explain.*

Phases of the Moon

On a clear night when the moon is full, the bright moonlight can keep you awake. But the moon does not produce the light you see. Instead, it reflects light from the sun. Imagine taking a flashlight into a dark room. If you were to shine the flashlight on a chair, you would see the chair because the light from your flashlight would bounce, or reflect, off the chair. In the same way that the chair wouldn't shine by itself, the moon doesn't give off light by itself. You can see the moon because it reflects the light of the sun.

When you see the moon in the sky, sometimes it appears round. Other times you see only a thin sliver, or crescent. The different shapes of the moon you see from Earth are called **phases.** The moon goes through its whole set of phases each time it makes a complete revolution around Earth.

Phases are caused by changes in the relative positions of the moon, Earth, and the sun. Because the sun lights the moon, half the moon is almost always in sunlight. However, since the moon revolves around Earth, you see the moon from different angles. The half of the moon that faces Earth is not always the half that is sunlit. **The phase of the moon you see depends on how much of the sunlit side of the moon faces Earth.**

Chapter 1   J ◆ 21

Motions of the Moon

Teach Key Concepts   L2
Moon Movements

Focus Review the definitions of rotation and revolution.

Teach Ask: **How long does it take the moon to rotate on its axis?** *(27.3 days)* **How long does it take the moon to revolve around Earth?** *(27.3 days)* **As the moon revolves, what happens to the relative positions of the moon, Earth, and the sun?** *(The angle between them changes.)*

Apply Have students examine Figure 10. Ask: **Which way would the flags be pointing if the moon did not rotate?** *(Only one flag would point toward Earth. The others would point either perpendicular or facing away from Earth.)* **learning modality: visual**

Independent Practice   L2

All in One Teaching Resources
• Guided Reading and Study Worksheet: *Phases, Eclipses, and Tides*

◎ Student Edition on Audio CD

Monitor Progress   L2

Skills Check Have students contrast the revolution of the moon around Earth with the revolution of Earth around the sun and infer why the moon's period of revolution is so much shorter. *(The revolution of Earth around the sun is 365 1/4 days. The circumference of the moon's orbit around Earth is much shorter than that of Earth's orbit around the sun.)*

Answer
Figure 10 No; Earth would not appear to set because that point on the moon's surface is always facing Earth.

J • 21

Phases of the Moon

Teach Key Concepts `L2`

Exploring Phases of the Moon

Focus Have students examine Figure 11.

Teach Tell students that although the same side of the moon always faces Earth, the moon's position in relation to the sun is not fixed. As the moon revolves around Earth, sunlight shines on the near and far sides of the moon at different times. Ask: **Why can you not see the far side of the moon from Earth?** *(The far side always faces away from Earth.)* Prompt students to connect each phase with how the moon looks from Earth. For example, ask: **What do you see in the first quarter?** *(Half of the lighted side of the moon)* **What is happening in the waning gibbous phase?** *(You see more than half of the lighted side of the moon. The amount you can see from Earth decreases each day.)*

Apply Ask: **How can you tell whether the moon is waxing or waning?** *(Observe it over time; a waxing moon gets larger, and a waning moon gets smaller. Also, the right side of the moon is visible during a waxing moon; the left side is visible during a waning moon.)* **learning modality: visual**

All in One **Teaching Resources**

• Transparency J8

 **Lab zone Build Inquiry** `L2`

Predicting Phases of the Moon

Materials newspapers for the current or previous day, current calendar

Time 20 minutes

Focus Remind students that it takes 29.5 days for the moon to complete a cycle.

Teach Have students predict the number of days between the new moon, first quarter, full moon, and third quarter. Students can then use the weather report from the newspaper to compare the data with their predictions.

Apply Ask: **How long does it take for the new moon to reach the first quarter?** *(About one week)* **Why do you think this phase is called a "quarter moon?"** *(One week is about one-quarter of the complete cycle of moon phases.)* **learning modality: logical/ mathematical**

The Moon Seen From Earth

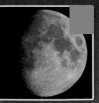

1 New Moon
The sunlit side faces away from Earth.

2 Waxing Cresent
The portion of the moon you can see is waxing, or growing, into a cresent shape.

3 First Quarter
You can see half of the sunlit side of the moon.

4 Waxing Gibbous
The moon continues to wax. The visible shape of the moon is called gibbous.

FIGURE 11
Phases of the Moon

The photos at the top of the page show how the phases of the moon appear when you look up at the moon from Earth's surface. The circular diagram at the right shows how the Earth and moon would appear to an observer in space as the moon revolves around Earth.
Interpreting Diagrams *During what phases are the moon, Earth, and sun aligned in a straight line?*

Go **O**nline
active art
For: Moon Phases and Eclipses activity
Visit: PHSchool.com
Web Code: cfp-5013

View From Space

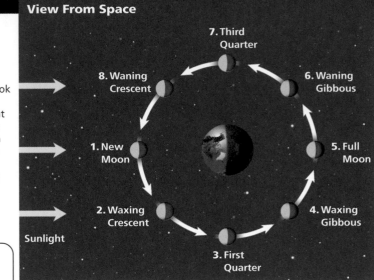

7. Third Quarter

8. Waning Crescent

6. Waning Gibbous

1. New Moon

5. Full Moon

2. Waxing Crescent

4. Waxing Gibbous

3. First Quarter

Sunlight

5 Full Moon
The entire sunlit side faces Earth.

6 Waning Gibbous
The portion of the moon you can see wanes, or shrinks.

7 Third Quarter
You can see half of the moon's lighted side.

8 Waning Cresent
You see a cresent once again.

To understand the phases of the moon, study Figure 11. During the new moon, the side of the moon facing Earth is not lit because the sun is behind the moon. As the moon revolves around Earth, you see more and more of the lighted side of the moon every day, until the side of the moon you see is fully lit. As the moon continues in its orbit, you see less and less of the lighted side. About 29.5 days after the last new moon, the cycle is complete, and a new moon occurs again.

Reading Checkpoint What is a new moon?

Eclipses

As Figure 12 shows, the moon's orbit around Earth is slightly tilted with respect to Earth's orbit around the sun. As a result, in most months the moon revolves around Earth without moving into Earth's shadow or the moon's shadow hitting Earth.

When the moon's shadow hits Earth or Earth's shadow hits the moon, an eclipse occurs. When an object in space comes between the sun and a third object, it casts a shadow on that object, causing an **eclipse** (ih KLIPS) to take place. There are two types of eclipses: solar eclipses and lunar eclipses. (The words *solar* and *lunar* come from the Latin words for "sun" and "moon.")

FIGURE 12
The Moon's Orbit
The moon's orbit is tilted about 5 degrees relative to Earth's orbit around the sun.

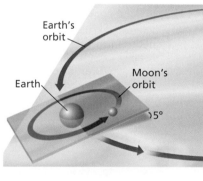

Earth's orbit

Earth

Moon's orbit

5°

Chapter 1 J ◆ 23

Eclipses

Teach Key Concepts **L2**
Causes and Effects of Eclipses

Focus Remind students about the moving shadow cast by an isolated cloud.

Teach Ask: **What causes an eclipse?** *(When an object in space moves between the sun and a third object, it casts a shadow on the third object.)* **Describe some events that might occur when the moon blocks out the sun.** *(Possible answer: Day becomes as dark as night, the air cools, and the sky becomes an eerie color.)*

Apply Ask students to describe what has to happen to the relative positions of the sun, the moon, and Earth for an eclipse to occur. *(They all have to line up perfectly so that the moon blocks the sun from Earth or Earth blocks the sun from the moon.)* **learning modality: verbal**

Help Students Read
Visualizing Instruct students to close their eyes and form mental pictures as you slowly read aloud *Eclipses.* Then tell students to read the passage by themselves and recreate the mental images they formed earlier. Explain that visualizing the text as they read will be particularly useful throughout the next two pages, which discuss the positions of the moon, Earth, and the sun during solar and lunar eclipses.

Monitor Progress **L2**

Drawing Have students sketch the position of the moon relative to Earth and the sun at the time of new moon, first-quarter moon, full moon, and third-quarter moon and write brief explanations for how these phases occur. Students can save their drawings in their portfolios.

Answers
Figure 11 A new moon and a full moon

Reading Checkpoint The phase in which the side of the moon facing Earth is not lit because the sun is behind the moon

---

⌐ Differentiated Instruction ⌐

English Learners/Beginning **L1**
Vocabulary: Prior Knowledge The term *phase* is used in many different ways in science. Give examples of how *phase* is used in science, such as phases of the moon, phases of matter, and color phases in a species of animal or plant. Give the appropriate definition for each example. **learning modality: verbal**

English Learners/Intermediate **L2**
Vocabulary: Prior Knowledge Have students brainstorm at least three different ways that the term *phase* is used in science. Use one of the meanings in a sentence, such as "The moon undergoes a cycle of phases." Have students write sentences incorporating other scientific meanings of the term *phase.* **learning modality: verbal**

Use Visuals: Figure 13 L1

Solar Eclipses

Focus Tell students that the words *umbra* and *penumbra* are derived from Latin words meaning "shadow" and "almost shadow."

Teach Ask: **What causes a solar eclipse?** (*The moon passes directly between the sun and Earth.*) **Which side of the moon receives the light of the sun during a solar eclipse?** (*The far side*) **Would people in the moon's penumbra experience a total or a partial eclipse?** (*Partial*)

Apply Ask students to infer whether a solar eclipse can be viewed from a large area of Earth. (*No; the sun's rays are blocked over only a small area.*) **Why does a solar eclipse last only a few minutes?** (*Because Earth rotates*) **learning modality: visual**

All in One Teaching Resources
• Transparency J9

Use Visuals: Figure 14 L2

Lunar Eclipses

Focus Show students photographs of a full moon. Have them compare these images with the photograph of the moon during a total lunar eclipse.

Teach Ask: **Why do lunar eclipses occur only during a full moon?** (*Earth must come between the sun and moon during a lunar eclipse; this happens only during the full-moon phase.*) **Why does the moon appear reddish during a lunar eclipse?** (*Some sunlight is bent as it passes through Earth's atmosphere and then strikes the moon.*)

Apply Have students infer why lunar eclipses last much longer than solar eclipses. (*Earth is much larger than the moon. Its shadow is also larger. As a result, the moon may take several hours to pass completely through Earth's shadow. In contrast, during a solar eclipse, the moon's small shadow sweeps across a point on Earth's surface in a matter of minutes.*) **learning modality: visual**

All in One Teaching Resources
• Transparency J10

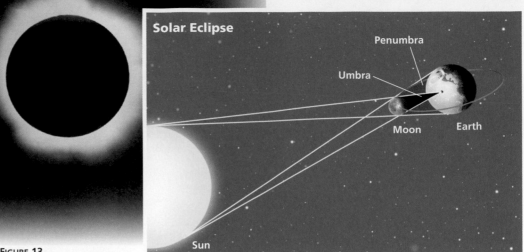

FIGURE 13
The outer layer of the sun's atmosphere, the solar corona, is visible surrounding the dark disk of the moon during a solar eclipse. During a solar eclipse, the moon blocks light from the sun, preventing sunlight from reaching parts of Earth's surface.

When Do Solar Eclipses Occur? During a new moon, the moon lies between Earth and the sun. But most months, as you have seen, the moon travels a little above or below the sun in the sky. **A solar eclipse occurs when the moon passes directly between Earth and the sun, blocking sunlight from Earth.** The moon's shadow then hits Earth, as shown in Figure 13. So a **solar eclipse** occurs when a new moon blocks your view of the sun.

Total Solar Eclipses The very darkest part of the moon's shadow, the **umbra** (UM bruh), is cone-shaped. From any point in the umbra, light from the sun is completely blocked by the moon. The moon's umbra happens to be long enough so that the point of the cone can just reach a small part of Earth's surface. Only the people within the umbra experience a total solar eclipse. During the short period of a total solar eclipse, the sky grows as dark as night, even in the middle of a clear day. The air gets cool and the sky becomes an eerie color. You can see the stars and the solar corona, which is the faint outer atmosphere of the sun.

Partial Solar Eclipses In Figure 13, you can see that the moon casts another part of its shadow that is less dark than the umbra. This larger part of the shadow is called the **penumbra** (peh NUM bruh). In the penumbra, part of the sun is visible from Earth. During a solar eclipse, people in the penumbra see only a partial eclipse. Since an extremely bright part of the sun still remains visible, it is not safe to look directly at the sun during a partial solar eclipse (just as you wouldn't look directly at the sun during a normal day).

Lab zone Skills Activity

Making Models

Here is how you can draw a scale model of a solar eclipse. The moon's diameter is about one fourth Earth's diameter. The distance from Earth to the moon is about 30 times Earth's diameter. Make a scale drawing of the moon, Earth, and the distance between them. (*Hint:* Draw Earth 1 cm in diameter in one corner of the paper.) From the edges of the moon, draw and shade in a triangle just touching Earth to show the moon's umbra.

24 ◆ J

Lab zone Skills Activity

Skills Focus Making models

Materials paper, metric rulers, calculators

Time 15 minutes

Tips Guide students to find the other distances in terms of Earth's diameter.

Expected Outcome With Earth as 1 cm in diameter, the moon will be 2.5 mm in

L2

diameter, 30 cm away in the opposite corner of the page.

Extend Challenge students to find the distance from Earth to the sun and then estimate where they would place the sun in their scale drawings. (*At about 11,725 cm, or 117 m*) **learning modality: logical/mathematical**

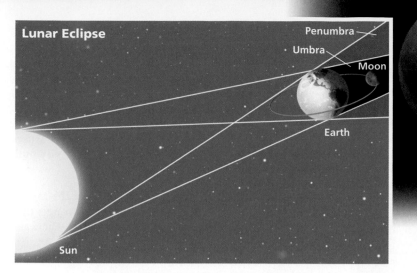

Lunar Eclipse

Penumbra
Umbra
Moon
Earth
Sun

When Do Lunar Eclipses Occur? During most months, the moon moves near Earth's shadow but not quite into it. A **lunar eclipse** occurs at a full moon when Earth is directly between the moon and the sun. You can see a lunar eclipse in Figure 14. **During a lunar eclipse, Earth blocks sunlight from reaching the moon.** The moon is then in Earth's shadow and looks dim from Earth. Lunar eclipses occur only when there is a full moon because the moon is closest to Earth's shadow at that time.

Total Lunar Eclipses Like the moon's shadow in a solar eclipse, Earth's shadow has an umbra and a penumbra. When the moon is in Earth's umbra, you see a total lunar eclipse. You can see the edge of Earth's shadow on the moon before and after a total lunar eclipse.

Unlike a total solar eclipse, a total lunar eclipse can be seen anywhere on Earth that the moon is visible. So you are more likely to see a total lunar eclipse than a total solar eclipse.

Partial Lunar Eclipses For most lunar eclipses, Earth, the moon, and the sun are not quite in line, and only a partial lunar eclipse results. A partial lunar eclipse occurs when the moon passes partly into the umbra of Earth's shadow. The edge of the umbra appears blurry, and you can watch it pass across the moon for two or three hours.

Reading Checkpoint During which phase of the moon can lunar eclipses occur?

FIGURE 14
During a lunar eclipse, Earth blocks sunlight from reaching the moon's surface. The photo of the moon above was taken during a total lunar eclipse. The moon's reddish tint occurs because Earth's atmosphere bends some sunlight toward the moon.
Interpreting Diagrams *What is the difference between the umbra and the penumbra?*

Go Online
active art

For: Moon Phases and Eclipses activity
Visit: PHSchool.com
Web Code: cfp-5013

Chapter 1   J ◆ 25

Go Online
active art

For: Moon Phases and Eclipses
Visit: PHSchool.com
Web Code: cfp-5013

Students can interact with moon phases and eclipses online.

Lab zone   Build Inquiry   L2

Comparing and Contrasting Solar and Lunar Eclipses

Materials pen, paper
Time 15 minutes

Focus Tell students that *comparing* means "explaining how things or events are similar" and that *contrasting* means "explaining how things or events are different."

Teach Organize students into small groups. Tell them to make tables that compare and contrast the umbra and penumbra of the moon during a total and partial solar eclipse with the umbra and penumbra of Earth during a total and partial lunar eclipse. Groups should first decide what headings to use for their tables—that is, which aspects of the umbra and penumbra to compare and contrast. Suggested headings might include: "Portion of the surface covered by the umbra," "Phase of the moon when the eclipse occurs," and "Portion of Earth from which eclipse is visible." Have students present their tables to the class.

Apply Tell students to suppose they are standing on the near side of the moon. The moon moves between Earth and the sun. Would they see an eclipse? If so, where? (*The shadow of the moon would fall on Earth; they would see a partial "Earth eclipse."*) **learning modality: verbal**

Differentiated Instruction

Special Needs   L1
Modeling Eclipses Give students three different-sized balls. Tell them that the largest ball represents the sun, the second-largest ball represents Earth, and the smallest ball represents the moon. Have students arrange the balls in proper order to model the positions of the sun, the moon, and Earth during a solar eclipse and a lunar eclipse. You might also try using the natural light from a window as the sun. (*During a solar eclipse, the balls should be arranged in the following order: sun, moon, Earth. During a lunar eclipse the balls should be arranged in the following order: sun, Earth, moon.*)

Monitor Progress   L2

Drawing Have students sketch the positions of the sun, the moon, and Earth during a solar eclipse and a lunar eclipse.

Answers
Figure 14 During a lunar eclipse, the umbra is the darkest part of Earth's shadow. The penumbra is the larger, less dark part of Earth's shadow.

Reading Checkpoint Full moon

Tides

Teach Key Concepts L2

What Causes Tides

Focus Tell students to look at points A and C in Figure 16.

Teach Explain that the moon's gravity is pulling Earth's water at A, and a high tide forms. Ask: **What happens at C?** *(The moon pulls more strongly on the solid part of Earth than on the water at C. Earth is pulled toward the moon and water flows toward point C, causing a high tide there.)* **What happens at B and D?** *(Water is flowing away toward A and C, so low tides form at B and D.)*

Apply Ask: **Why might it be helpful to know when high and low tides occur?** *(Possible answer: People who fish need to know the tide cycle because it affects when they fish and what they catch.)* **learning modality: visual**

All in One **Teaching Resources**
• Transparency J11

Lab zone **Teacher Demo** L1

Modeling the Moon's Pull of Gravity

Materials round balloon

Time 10 minutes

Focus Tell students that you are going to demonstrate the moon's pull of gravity on Earth.

Teach Partially blow up the balloon and knot the stem. Hold the balloon securely by the knotted end and the opposite end. Pull on the knotted end. Ask: **What represents the moon in this model?** *(The hand pulling the knotted end)*

Apply Have students draw diagrams showing the shape of the balloon as it is being pulled and indicating where tides would occur if the balloon were Earth. **learning modality: visual**

Help Students Read

Outline Instruct students to outline the passage *Tides*, writing the subheads and leaving room between each one. As students read, they can list details under each subhead.

High Tide

Low Tide

FIGURE 15
High and Low Tides
In some locations, such as along this beach in Australia, there can be dramatic differences between the height of high and low tides.

Tides

Have you ever built a sand castle on an ocean beach? Was it washed away by rising water? This is an example of **tides,** the rise and fall of ocean water that occurs every 12.5 hours or so. The water rises for about six hours, then falls for about six hours, in a regular cycle.

The force of gravity pulls the moon and Earth (including the water on Earth's surface) toward each other. **Tides are caused mainly by differences in how much the moon's gravity pulls on different parts of Earth.**

The Tide Cycle Look at Figure 16. The force of the moon's gravity at point A, which is closer to the moon, is stronger than the force of the moon's gravity on Earth as a whole. The water flows toward point A, and a high tide forms.

The force of the moon's gravity at point C, which is on the far side of Earth from the moon, is weaker than the force of the moon's gravity on Earth as a whole. Earth is pulled toward the moon more strongly than the water at point C, so the water is "left behind." Water flows toward point C, and a high tide occurs there too. Between points A and C, water flows away from points B and D, causing low tides.

At any one time there are two places with high tides and two places with low tides on Earth. As Earth rotates, one high tide stays on the side of Earth facing the moon. The second high tide stays on the opposite side of Earth. Each location on Earth sweeps through those two high tides and two low tides every 25 hours or so.

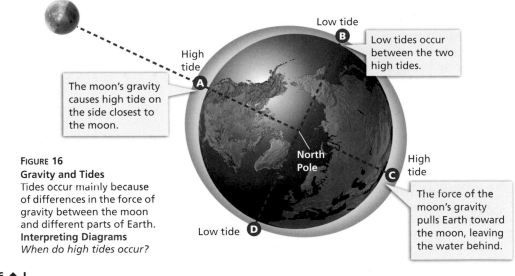

Moon

Low tide
B
Low tides occur between the two high tides.

High tide

The moon's gravity causes high tide on the side closest to the moon.

A

North Pole

High tide
C

The force of the moon's gravity pulls Earth toward the moon, leaving the water behind.

Low tide
D

FIGURE 16
Gravity and Tides
Tides occur mainly because of differences in the force of gravity between the moon and different parts of Earth.
Interpreting Diagrams
When do high tides occur?

Spring Tides The sun's gravity also pulls on Earth's waters. As shown in the top diagram of Figure 17, the sun, moon, and Earth are nearly in a line during a new moon. The gravity of the sun and the moon pull in the same direction. Their combined forces produce a tide with the greatest difference between consecutive low and high tides, called a **spring tide**.

At full moon, the moon and the sun are on opposite sides of Earth. Since there are high tides on both sides of Earth, a spring tide is also produced. It doesn't matter in which order the sun, Earth, and moon line up. Spring tides occur twice a month, at new moon and at full moon.

Neap Tides During the moon's first-quarter and third-quarter phases, the line between Earth and the sun is at right angles to the line between Earth and the moon. The sun's pull is at right angles to the moon's pull. This arrangement produces a **neap tide**, a tide with the least difference between consecutive low and high tides. Neap tides occur twice a month.

✓ **Reading Checkpoint** What is a neap tide?

FIGURE 17
Spring and Neap Tides
When Earth, the sun, and the moon are in a straight line (top), a spring tide occurs. When the moon is at a right angle to the sun (bottom), a neap tide occurs.

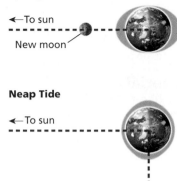

Spring Tide

←To sun

New moon

Neap Tide

←To sun

First-quarter moon

Section 3 Assessment

🎯 **Target Reading Skill Previewing Visuals** Refer to your questions and answers about Figure 11 to help you answer Question 1 below.

Reviewing Key Concepts

1. a. **Explaining** What causes the moon to shine?
   b. **Relating Cause and Effect** Why does the moon appear to change shape during the course of a month?
   c. **Interpreting Diagrams** Use Figure 11 to explain why you can't see the moon at the time of a new moon.
2. a. **Explaining** What is an eclipse?
   b. **Comparing and Contrasting** How is a solar eclipse different from a lunar eclipse?
   c. **Relating Cause and Effect** Why isn't there a solar eclipse and a lunar eclipse each month?
3. a. **Summarizing** What causes the tides?
   b. **Explaining** Explain why most coastal regions have two high tides and two low tides each day.
   c. **Comparing and Contrasting** Compare the size of high and low tides in a spring tide and a neap tide. What causes the difference?

Lab zone At-Home Activity

Tracking the Tides Use a daily newspaper or the Internet to track the height of high and low tides at a location of your choice for at least two weeks. Make a graph of your data, with the date as the *x*-axis and tide height as the *y*-axis. Also find the dates of the new moon and full moon and add them to your graph. Show your completed graph to a relative and explain what the graph shows.

A "Moonth" of Phases

Prepare for Inquiry

Key Concept
The phases of the moon are caused by the moon's position relative to Earth and the sun.

Skills Objectives
After this lab, students will be able to
- make a model of the Earth-moon-sun system to explore the phases of the moon
- observe and record the phases of the model system

Prep Time 15 minutes
Class Time 40 minutes

Advance Planning
Collect lamps (one for each pair of students), extra bulbs (150-watt bulbs work best), and plastic foam balls (one per student pair).

Safety
Remind students to be careful while moving around the lamps and extension cords. Tell them not to look directly into the lights. Review the safety guidelines in Appendix A.

All in One Teaching Resources
- Lab Worksheet: A "Moonth" of Phases

Guide Inquiry

Invitation
Have students think about the variations of the moon's appearance in the night sky. Ask volunteers to describe variations they have seen. (*Possible answer: The moon may appear round. Sometimes, it cannot be seen at all, or only part of it may be visible.*)

Introduce the Procedure
- Review the photograph to make sure that students understand how to position themselves.
- Suggest that students make sketches of their predictions, showing what they will see at each turn.

A "Moonth" of Phases

Problem
What causes the phases of the moon?

Skills Focus
making models, observing, drawing conclusions

Materials
- floor lamp with 150-watt bulb
- pencils
- plastic foam balls

Procedure

1. Place a lamp in the center of the room. Remove the lampshade.
2. Close the doors and shades to darken the room, and switch on the lamp.
3. Carefully stick the point of a pencil into the plastic foam ball so that the pencil can be used as a "handle."
4. Draw 8 circles on a sheet of paper. Number them 1–8.
5. Have your partner hold the plastic foam ball at arm's length in front and slightly above his or her head so that the ball is between him or her and the lamp. **CAUTION:** *Do not look directly at the bulb.*
6. The ball should be about 1 to 1.5 m away from the lamp. Adjust the distance between the ball and the lamp so that the light shines brightly on the ball.

7. Stand directly behind your partner and observe what part of the ball facing you is lit by the lamp. If light is visible on the ball, draw the shape of the lighted part of the ball in the first circle.
8. Have your partner turn 45° to the left while keeping the ball in front and at arm's length.
9. Repeat Step 7. Be sure you are standing directly behind your partner.
10. Repeat Steps 8 and 9 six more times until your partner is facing the lamp again. See the photograph for the 8 positions.
11. Change places and repeat Steps 4–10.

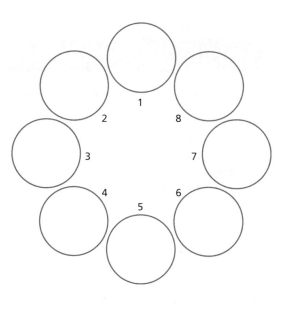

Troubleshooting the Experiment
- When students model the full moon, make sure that they hold the ball slightly above their heads so that the ball is not in their shadow.
- Make sure that the student who is drawing stands directly behind the student with the ball so that they have the same view.

Expected Outcome
Students will identify the eight phases of the moon.

Analyze and Conclude

1. **Making Models** In your model, what represents Earth? The sun? The moon?

2. **Observing** Refer back to your 8 circles. How much of the lighted part of the ball did you see when facing the lamp?

3. **Classifying** Label your drawings with the names of the phases of the moon. Which drawing represents a full moon? A new moon? Which represents a waxing crescent? A waning crescent?

45°

4. **Observing** How much of the lighted part of the ball did you see after each turn?

5. **Drawing Conclusions** Whether you could see it or not, how much of the ball's surface was always lit by the lamp? Was the darkness of the new moon caused by an eclipse? Explain your answer.

6. **Communicating** Write a brief analysis of this lab. How well did making a model help you understand the phases of the moon? What are some disadvantages of using models? What is another way to make a model to represent the various phases of the moon?

More to Explore

Design a model to show a lunar eclipse and a solar eclipse. What objects would you use for Earth, the sun, and the moon? Use the model to demonstrate why there isn't an eclipse every full moon and new moon.

Analyze and Conclude

1. The student holding the ball represents Earth. The lamp represents the sun. The plastic foam ball represents the moon.

2. None

3. 1: new moon, 2: waxing crescent, 3: first quarter, 4: waxing gibbous, 5: full moon, 6: waning gibbous, 7: third quarter, 8: waning crescent

4. For the first four turns, about 25% more of the lighted part of the ball was visible with each turn. Then the lighted part of the ball was completely visible (full moon). For the next four turns, about 25% less of the lighted part was visible with each turn until the dark side of the moon (new moon) faced the observer again.

5. One-half of the ball was always lit. The darkness of the new moon was not caused by an eclipse; when the moon is between Earth and the sun, an observer on Earth sees the moon's unlit side.

6. Possible answer: The model allows you to observe the cycle of phases in a short amount of time. The disadvantage of a model is that it does not always show the true size, shape, or color of the real item. Another model could use a ball painted black on one hemisphere and white on the other. The white half would represent the sunlit side of the moon. A student could walk around the ball to view the different phases.

Extend Inquiry

More to Explore A solar eclipse occurs when the moon (plastic foam ball) is directly between the sun (lamp) and Earth (partner holding the ball). In this position, the new moon casts a total eclipse (shadow) on one part of Earth and a partial eclipse on another part. A lunar eclipse appears during a full moon when the moon (plastic foam ball) passes through the shadow of Earth (partner holding the ball). The moon's orbit is tilted slightly with respect to Earth's orbit around the sun.

Objectives

After this lesson, students will be able to
J.1.4.1 Describe features found on the moon's surface.
J.1.4.2 Identify some characteristics of the moon.
J.1.4.3 Explain how the moon formed.

Target Reading Skill ↻

Identifying Main Ideas Explain that identifying main ideas and details helps students sort the facts from the information into groups. Each group can have a main topic, subtopics, and details.

Answers

Possible answers:
Detail: Dark, flat areas called maria, which formed from huge lava flows
Detail: Large, round pits called craters, which were caused by the impact of meteoroids
Detail: Highlands, or mountains, which cover much of the moon's surface

All in One Teaching Resources

• Transparency J12

Preteach

Build Background Knowledge · L2

Impact Craters

Hold up a rock. Tell students to suppose that the rock is as large as a building and is traveling through space. Ask them to picture the rock falling through Earth's atmosphere and landing in an open desert. Ask: **What do you think would happen?** *(Possible answer: The rock would leave a large depression in the desert sand or explode on impact.)*

Reading Preview

Key Concepts
• What features are found on the moon's surface?
• What are some characteristics of the moon?
• How did the moon form?

Key Terms
• telescope • maria
• craters • meteoroids

↻ Target Reading Skill

Identifying Main Ideas As you read "The Moon's Surface," write the main idea—the biggest or most important idea—in a graphic organizer like the one below. Then write three supporting details that further explain the main idea.

Main Idea

The moon's surface has a variety of features, such as . . .

Detail	Detail	Detail

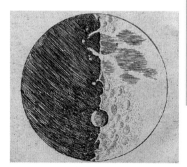

Lab zone Discover Activity

Why Do Craters Look Different From Each Other?

The moon's surface has pits in it, called craters.

1. Put on your goggles. Fill a large plastic basin to a depth of 2 cm with sand.
2. Drop marbles of different masses from about 20 cm high. Take the marbles out and view the craters they created.
3. Predict what will happen if you drop marbles from a higher point. Smooth out the sand. Now drop marbles of different masses from about 50 cm high.
4. Take the marbles out and view the craters they left.

Think It Over
Developing Hypotheses In which step do you think the marbles were moving faster when they hit the sand? If objects hitting the moon caused craters, how did the speeds of the objects affect the sizes of the craters? How did the masses of the objects affect the sizes of the craters?

For thousands of years, people could see shapes on the surface of the moon, but didn't know what caused them. The ancient Greeks thought that the moon was perfectly smooth. It was not until about 400 years ago that scientists could study the moon more closely.

In 1609, the Italian scientist Galileo Galilei heard about a **telescope,** a device built to observe distant objects by making them appear closer. Galileo soon made his own telescope by putting two lenses in a wooden tube. The lenses focused the light coming through the tube, making distant objects seem closer. When Galileo pointed his telescope at the moon, he was able to see much more detail than anyone had ever seen before. What Galileo saw astounded him. Instead of the perfect sphere imagined by the Greeks, he saw that the moon has an irregular surface with a variety of remarkable features.

◄ Galileo used a telescope to help make this drawing of the moon.

Lab zone Discover Activity

Skills Focus Developing hypotheses · L2
Materials plastic basin or mixing bowl about 25 cm across, sand, 3 marbles of different masses, meter stick
Time 20 minutes
Tips After Step 2, have students measure the depth and diameter of the craters.

Expected Outcome The size of the craters will increase with mass and with height.

Think It Over The marbles are moving faster in Step 3. The more massive the impacting object or the faster it hits, the larger the resulting crater will be.

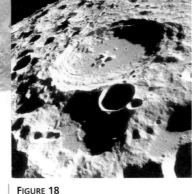

The dark, flat areas on the moon's surface are called maria.

The light-colored features that cover much of the moon's surface are highlands.

The Moon's Surface

Recent photos of the moon show much more detail than Galileo could see with his telescope. **Features on the moon's surface include maria, craters, and highlands.**

Maria The moon's surface has dark, flat areas, which Galileo called **maria** (MAH ree uh), the Latin word for "seas." Galileo incorrectly thought that the maria were oceans. The maria are actually hardened rock formed from huge lava flows that occurred between 3 and 4 billion years ago.

Craters Galileo saw that the moon's surface is marked by large round pits called **craters.** Some craters are hundreds of kilometers across. For a long time, many scientists mistakenly thought that these craters had been made by volcanoes. Scientists now know that these craters were caused by the impacts of **meteoroids,** chunks of rock or dust from space.

The maria have few craters compared to surrounding areas. This means that most of the moon's craters formed from impacts early in its history, before the maria formed. On Earth, such ancient craters have disappeared. They were worn away over time by water, wind, and other forces. But since the moon has no liquid water or atmosphere, its surface has changed little for billions of years.

Highlands Galileo correctly inferred that some of the light-colored features he saw on the moon's surface were highlands, or mountains. The peaks of the lunar highlands and the rims of the craters cast dark shadows, which Galileo could see. The rugged lunar highlands cover much of the moon's surface.

 **Reading Checkpoint** What are maria?

FIGURE 18
The Moon's Surface
The moon's surface is covered by craters, maria, and highlands. Craters on the moon formed from the impact of meteoroids. Most large craters are named after famous scientists or philosophers.
Observing *What are the light regions in the top photograph called?*

Go **O**nline
SCi**LINKS** NSTA

For: Links on Earth's moon
Visit: www.SciLinks.org
Web Code: scn-0614

Chapter 1 J ◆ 31

Characteristics of the Moon

Teach Key Concepts L2
Moon Properties

Focus Remind students that Earth has an atmosphere, a comfortable temperature range, and water in three states—liquid, gas, and solid.

Teach Ask: **How does the moon's diameter compare to Earth's?** (*The moon is about one-fourth Earth's diameter.*) **Why do temperatures on the moon vary so much?** (*The moon has no atmosphere.*) **In which state of matter would you likely find water on the moon?** (*Solid*)

Apply Have students relate the characteristics of the moon to the challenge of building a viable moon colony. **learning modality: verbal**

The Origin of the Moon

Teach Key Concepts L2
How the Moon Formed

Focus Have students examine Figure 21.

Teach Have students use the diagram to summarize the collision-ring theory.

Apply Ask: **What evidence do you think might be used to support a theory that the moon was formed from material from Earth's outer layers?** (*The moon's average density is similar to the density of Earth's outer layers.*) **learning modality: verbal**

All in One **Teaching Resources**

• Transparency J13

FIGURE 19
The Moon's Size
The diameter of the moon is a little less than the distance across the contiguous United States.
Calculating *What is the ratio of the moon's diameter to the distance between Earth and the moon?*

FIGURE 20
The Moon's Surface
This photo of a large boulder field and hills on the moon's surface was taken by one of the crew members of *Apollo 17*.

Characteristics of the Moon

Would you want to take a vacation on the moon? At an average distance of about 384,000 kilometers (about 30 times Earth's diameter), the moon is Earth's closest neighbor in space. Despite its proximity, the moon is very different from Earth. **The moon is dry and airless. Compared to Earth, the moon is small and has large variations in its surface temperature.** If you visited the moon, you would need to wear a bulky space suit to provide air to breathe, protect against sunburn, and to keep you at a comfortable temperature.

Size and Density The moon is 3,476 kilometers in diameter, a little less than the distance across the United States. This is about one-fourth Earth's diameter. However, the moon has only one-eightieth as much mass as Earth. Though Earth has a very dense core, its outer layers are less dense. The moon's average density is similar to the density of Earth's outer layers.

Temperature and Atmosphere On the moon's surface, temperatures range from a torrid 130°C in direct sunlight to a frigid 2180°C at night. Temperatures on the moon vary so much because it has no atmosphere. The moon's surface gravity is so weak that gases can easily escape into space.

Water The moon has no liquid water. However, there is evidence that there may be large patches of ice near the moon's poles. Some areas are shielded from sunlight by crater walls. Temperatures in these regions are so low that ice there would remain frozen. If a colony were built on the moon in the future, any such water would be very valuable. It would be very expensive to transport large amounts of water to the moon from Earth.

✓ **Reading Checkpoint** Where on the moon is there evidence of the existence of ice?

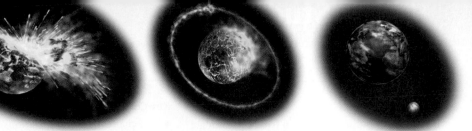

The Origin of the Moon

People have long wondered how the moon formed. Scientists have suggested many possible theories. For example, was the moon formed elsewhere in the solar system and captured by Earth's gravity as it came near? Was the moon formed near Earth at the same time that Earth formed? Scientists have found reasons to reject these ideas.

The theory of the moon's origin that seems to best fit the evidence is called the collision-ring theory. It is illustrated in Figure 21. About 4.5 billion years ago, when Earth was very young, the solar system was full of rocky debris. Some of this debris was the size of small planets. **Scientists theorize that a planet-sized object collided with Earth to form the moon.** Material from the object and Earth's outer layers was ejected into orbit around Earth, where it formed a ring. Gravity caused this material to combine to form the moon.

Reading Checkpoint What theory best explains the moon's origin?

FIGURE 21
Formation of the Moon
According to the collision-ring theory, the moon formed early in Earth's history when a planet-sized object struck Earth. The resulting debris formed the moon.

Discovery CHANNEL SCHOOL

Earth, Moon, and Sun
Video Preview
▶ Video Field Trip
Video Assessment

Section 4 Assessment

Target Reading Skill Identifying Main Ideas
Use your graphic organizer to help you answer Question 1 below.

Reviewing Key Concepts
1. a. **Identifying** Name three major features of the moon's surface.
   b. **Explaining** How did the moon's craters form?
   c. **Relating Cause and Effect** Why is the moon's surface much more heavily cratered than Earth's surface?
2. a. **Describing** Describe the range of temperatures on the moon.
   b. **Comparing and Contrasting** Compare Earth and the moon in terms of size and surface gravity.

c. **Relating Cause and Effect** What is the relationship between the moon's surface gravity, lack of an atmosphere, and temperature range?
3. a. **Describing** What was the solar system like when the moon formed?
   b. **Sequencing** Explain the various stages in the formation of the moon.

Lab zone **At-Home Activity**

Moonwatching With an adult, observe the moon a few days after the first-quarter phase. Make a sketch of the features you see. Label the maria, craters, and highlands.

Chapter 1 J ◆ 33

Lab zone **At-Home Activity**

Moonwatching If weather ⬛L1 conditions or light pollution prevent viewing the moon in the night sky, suggest that students visit NASA Web sites with a family member to view photographs of the moon.

Lab zone **Chapter Project**

Keep Students on Track Check that students are looking for patterns in their data. Encourage them to compare changes noticeable in one evening and changes over the course of the project. Provide moon maps and charts, and suggest that they look for surface features with binoculars. The elevated walls of craters are most visible during the crescent and quarter phases.

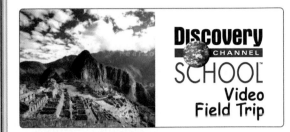

Discovery CHANNEL SCHOOL
Video Field Trip

Earth, Moon, and Sun

Show the Video Field Trip to let students consider the various theories about the origin of Earth's moon. Discussion question: **What is the most widely accepted theory of the moon's origin?** (*The collision-ring, or impact, theory*)

Assess

Reviewing Key Concepts

1. **a.** Craters, maria, and highlands
b. Meteoroid impacts **c.** Water, wind, and other forces wore away craters on Earth. There is no wind or liquid water on the moon.
2. **a.** 130°C to −180°C **b.** The moon is one-fourth the diameter of Earth. The moon's surface gravity is much weaker than Earth's. **c.** The moon's weak surface gravity allows gases to escape into space, so the moon has no atmosphere, resulting in widely varying surface temperatures.
3. **a.** It was full of rocky debris. **b.** A planet-sized object collided with Earth. Material was ejected into orbit around Earth and formed a ring. Gravity caused this material to combine into the moon.

Reteach ⬛L1
Have students compare and contrast the properties of the moon and Earth.

J ● 33

Study Guide

Interactive Textbook
- Complete student edition
- Section and chapter self-assessments
- Assessment reports for teachers

Help Students Read

Building Vocabulary

Word-Part Analysis Remind students that they can use what they know about word parts to figure out the meanings of words. Use the words *rotation* and *revolution* as examples. Tell students that *-ion* means "the act of" or "the result of an act." Explain that *rota* comes from a Latin word meaning "wheel" and that *revolvere* comes from another Latin word meaning "to turn over" or "to roll back."

Vocabulary Knowledge Rating Chart

Have students make a four-column chart with the headings Term, Can Define/Use It, Heard/Seen It, and Don't Know. Have them put vocabulary terms in the first column and then rate their knowledge of each term by putting a checkmark in one of the other columns. Have students create another chart after they have completed the chapter review.

Connecting Concepts

Concept Maps Help students develop one way to show how the information in this chapter is related. The movements and relative positions of Earth, the moon, and the sun cause Earth to experience day and night, years, seasons, moon phases, eclipses, and tides. Have students brainstorm to identify the key concepts, key terms, details, and examples, and then write each one on a sticky note and attach it at random on chart paper or on the board.

Tell students that this concept map will be organized in hierarchical order and to begin at the top with the key concepts. Ask students these questions to guide them to categorize the information on the sticky notes: **How does Earth move? What phenomena are caused by the movement of Earth, the moon, and the sun? What are features on the moon?**

① Earth in Space

Key Concepts
- Earth moves through space in two major ways: rotation and revolution.
- Earth has seasons because its axis is tilted as it revolves around the sun.

Key Terms

astronomy	axis
rotation	revolution
orbit	calendar
solstice	equinox

② Gravity and Motion

Key Concepts
- The strength of the force of gravity between two objects depends on two factors: the masses of the objects and the distance between them.
- Newton concluded that two factors—inertia and gravity—combine to keep Earth in orbit around the sun and the moon in orbit around Earth.

Key Terms
force
gravity
law of universal gravitation
mass
weight
inertia
Newton's first law of motion

③ Phases, Eclipses, and Tides

Key Concepts
- The changing relative positions of the moon, Earth, and sun cause the phases of the moon, eclipses, and tides.
- The phase of the moon you see depends on how much of the sunlit side of the moon faces Earth.
- When the moon's shadow hits Earth or Earth's shadow hits the moon, an eclipse occurs.
- A solar eclipse occurs when the moon passes directly between Earth and the sun, blocking sunlight from Earth.
- During a lunar eclipse, Earth blocks sunlight from reaching the moon.
- Tides are caused mainly by differences in how much the moon's gravity pulls on different parts of Earth.

Key Terms

phases	eclipse
solar eclipse	umbra
penumbra	lunar eclipse
tide	spring tide
neap tide	

④ Earth's Moon

Key Concepts
- Features on the moon's surface include maria, craters, and highlands.
- The moon is dry and airless. Compared to Earth, the moon is small and has large variations in its surface temperature.
- Scientists theorize that a planet-sized object collided with Earth to form the moon.

Key Terms
telescope
maria
craters
meteoroids

Prompt students by using connecting words or phrases, such as "are caused by" and "formed when," to indicate the basis for the organization of the map. The phrases should form a sentence between or among a set of concepts.

Answer Accept logical presentations by students.

All in One Teaching Resources
- Key Terms Review: *Earth, Moon, and Sun*

Organizing Information

Concept Mapping Copy the concept map about how Earth moves in space onto a separate sheet of paper. Then complete it and add a title. (For more on Concept Mapping, see the Skills Handbook.)

Reviewing Key Terms

Choose the letter of the best answer.

1. The movement of Earth around the sun once a year is called Earth's
   a. inertia.   b. rotation.
   c. revolution.   d. axis.

2. A day when the sun reaches its greatest distance north or south of the equator is called a(an)
   a. umbra.
   b. penumbra.
   c. equinox.
   d. solstice.

3. The tendency of an object to resist a change in motion is called
   a. gravity.
   b. inertia.
   c. force.
   d. the law of universal gravitation.

4. When Earth's shadow falls on the moon, the shadow causes a
   a. new moon.
   b. solar eclipse.
   c. full moon.
   d. lunar eclipse.

5. The craters on the moon were caused by
   a. tides.   b. volcanoes.
   c. meteoroids.   d. maria.

If the statement is true, write *true*. If it is false, change the underlined word or words to make the statement true.

6. Earth's spinning on its axis is called <u>rotation</u>.

7. The force that attracts all objects toward each other is called <u>inertia</u>.

8. The tilt of Earth's axis as Earth revolves around the sun causes <u>eclipses</u>.

9. The amount of matter in an object is its <u>weight</u>.

10. The greatest difference between low and high tides occurs during a <u>neap</u> tide.

Writing in Science

News Report Imagine that you are a reporter asked to write a story about the origin of the moon. Write an article explaining how the moon formed.

Earth, Moon, and Sun
Video Preview
Video Field Trip
▶ Video Assessment

Chapter 1   J ◆ 35

Organizing Information
a. rotates
b. around the sun
c. night and day

Reviewing Key Terms
1. c   2. d   3. b   4. d   5. c
6. true
7. gravity
8. seasons
9. mass
10. spring

Writing in Science

Writing Skill Description
Scoring Rubric
4 Exceeds criteria by including a vivid, detailed description of how the moon formed
3 Meets all criteria, but description is uninteresting
2 Includes only a brief description
1 Is incomplete and inaccurate

Discovery CHANNEL SCHOOL
Video Assessment

Earth, Moon, and Sun

Show the Video Assessment to review chapter content and as a prompt for the writing assignment. Discussion question: **Currently, what is the most probable or likely theory that explains the origin of Earth's moon?** (*Early in its history, Earth was struck by a planet-sized object. This produced a ring of debris around Earth that eventually coalesced to form the moon.*)

 **Teaching Resources**
• Transparency J14
• Chapter Test
• Performance Assessment Teacher Notes
• Performance Assessment Teacher Worksheet
• Performance Assessment Scoring Rubric

💿 **ExamView® Computer Test Bank CD-ROM**

Checking Concepts

11. Earth takes 24 hours to rotate once; each 24-hour cycle is called a day. Earth takes about 365 days, or one year, to complete one orbit around the sun.

12. The force of gravity between them would decrease.

13. An object at rest will not move, and an object in motion will keep moving at the same speed and in the same direction, unless acted on by a net force.

14. Phases are caused by changes in the relative positions of the moon, Earth, and the sun.

15. A total lunar eclipse can be seen any place on Earth where the moon is visible. During a total solar eclipse, the moon's umbra reaches only a small part of Earth's surface, and only people within the umbra can see the total eclipse.

16. Closest to the moon, the moon's gravitational pull on water at Earth's surface is stronger than its pull on Earth as a whole, and water flows toward that point. Farthest from the moon, the moon pulls more strongly on Earth as a whole than on water at Earth's surface, creating a high tide at that point as well.

17. Spring tide; the sun, moon, and Earth are aligned in a straight line.

18. By using a telescope, Galileo was able to determine that the moon was not the perfect sphere envisioned by the Greeks. Rather, it had an irregular surface with a variety of features such as craters, maria, and highlands.

19. The moon does not have an atmosphere; atmospheric gases help trap heat from the sun and moderate temperature variations.

20. Scientists theorize that a planet-sized object collided with Earth. Material from the collision was ejected into orbit around Earth, where it formed a ring. Gravity caused this material to eventually combine into the moon.

Checking Concepts

11. Explain how the length of the day and year are related to Earth's movement through space.

12. Suppose you moved two objects farther apart. How would this affect the force of gravity between those objects?

13. Explain Newton's first law of motion in your own words.

14. Why does the moon have phases?

15. Why do more people see a total lunar eclipse than a total solar eclipse?

16. Why is there a high tide on the side of Earth closest to the moon? On the side of Earth farthest from the moon?

17. Does the diagram below show a spring tide or a neap tide? How do you know?

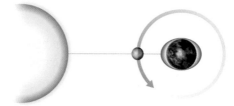

18. How did the invention of the telescope contribute to our knowledge of the moon's surface?

19. Why do temperatures vary so much on the moon?

20. Explain how scientists think the moon originated.

Thinking Critically

21. Inferring Mars's axis is tilted at about the same angle as Earth's axis. Do you think Mars has seasons? Explain your answer.

22. Comparing and Contrasting How are mass and weight different?

23. Calculating Suppose a person weighs 450 newtons (about 100 pounds) on Earth. How much would she weigh on the moon?

24. Applying Concepts At about what time does the full moon rise? Is it visible in the eastern sky or the western sky?

25. Posing Questions Suppose you were assigned to design a spacesuit for astronauts to wear on the moon. What characteristics of the moon would be important to consider in your design?

Applying Skills

Use the illustration below to answer Questions 26–28.

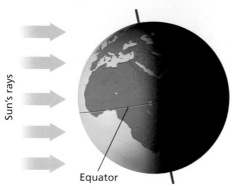

Sun's rays

Equator

26. Interpreting Diagrams On which hemisphere are the sun's rays falling most directly?

27. Inferring In the Northern Hemisphere, is it the summer solstice, winter solstice, or one of the equinoxes? How do you know?

28. Predicting Six months after this illustration, Earth will have revolved halfway around the sun. Draw a diagram that shows which end of Earth's axis will be tilted toward the sun.

Lab zone Chapter **Project**

Performance Assessment Present your observation log, map, and drawings of the moon. Some ways to graph your data include time of moonrise for each date; how often you saw the moon in each direction; or how often you saw the moon at a specific time. Display your graphs. Discuss any patterns that you discovered.

Lab zone Chapter **Project**

Performance Assessment Emphasize these patterns: 1) In the course of a day, the moon's position changes from the eastern sky, through the southern sky, to the western sky; 2) Moonrise gets progressively later throughout the cycle; 3) The moon will be seen mostly in the southern half of the sky; 4) The lit portion of the moon starts on the right side and waxes until full; as it wanes, the right side progressively becomes dark; the moon's location in the sky at sunset is more toward the east each day.

Encourage students to write about the easiest and hardest parts of the project. What would they do differently if they observed the moon for another month? What surprised them about their observations?

Standardized Test Prep

Choose the letter of the best answer.

1. You observe a thin crescent moon in the western sky during the early evening. About two weeks later, a full moon is visible in the eastern sky during the early evening. Which conclusion is best supported by these observations?

  A The moon revolves around Earth.

  B The moon rotates on its axis.

  C Earth revolves around the sun.

  D Earth's axis is tilted relative to the moon.

2. Only one side of the moon is visible from Earth because

  F the moon does not rotate on its axis.

  G the moon does not revolve around Earth.

  H the moon rotates faster than it revolves.

  J the moon revolves once and rotates once in the same period of time.

3. What type of eclipse occurs when Earth's umbra covers the moon?

  A a partial solar eclipse

  B a total solar eclipse

  C a partial lunar eclipse

  D a total lunar eclipse

4. The force of gravity depends on

  F mass and weight.

  G speed and distance.

  H mass and distance.

  J weight and speed.

The diagram below shows the relative positions of the sun, moon, and Earth. The numbers indicate specific locations of the moon in its orbit. Use the diagram to answer Questions 5 and 6.

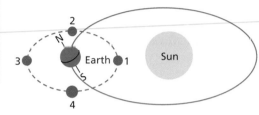

5. Which of the following can occur when the moon is at location 1?

  A only a lunar eclipse

  B only a solar eclipse

  C both a solar and a lunar eclipse

  D neither a solar nor a lunar eclipse

6. When the moon is at location 2, at most coastal locations there would be

  F only one high tide each day.

  G only one low tide each day.

  H two high tides and two low tides each day, with the most difference between high and low tide.

  J two high tides and two low tides each day, with the least difference between high and low tide.

Constructed Response

7. The sun rises on the east coast of the United States before it rises on the west coast of the United States. Explain why this happens.

Thinking Critically

21. Yes; Mars has seasons because its north and south pole are pointed toward or away from the sun at different times during its revolution.

22. Mass is the amount of matter in an object. Weight is the force of gravity on an object.

23. The person would weigh one-sixth of her weight on Earth, or about 75 newtons (17 pounds).

24. The full moon rises at sunset because it has to be opposite the sun in the sky for its face to be fully lighted. It therefore rises in the east as the sun sets in the west.

25. Possible answer: You would have to consider the moon's lack of atmosphere, its varying surface temperatures, and its terrain.

Applying Skills

26. They are falling most directly on the Northern Hemisphere.

27. It is the summer solstice because the north end of Earth's axis is pointed toward the sun.

28. Students' sketches should show the south end of Earth's axis tilted toward the sun.

Standardized Test Prep

1. A **2.** D **3.** D **4.** C **5.** B **6.** D

7. Sample answer: Earth rotates from west to east, so the sun appears to rise in the east before it rises in the west. Naturally, the east coast is east of the west coast. As Earth rotates, the sun will rise on the east coast before it rises on the west coast.

Chapter at a Glance

Chapter at a Glance

PRENTICE HALL
TeacherEXPRESS™
Plan • Teach • Assess

 Chapter Project *Space Exploration Vehicle*

Technology

Local Standards

All in One Teaching Resources
- Chapter Project Teacher Notes, pp. 102–103
- Chapter Project Student Overview, pp. 104–105
- Chapter Project Student Worksheets, pp. 106–107
- Chapter Project Scoring Rubric, p. 108

DISCOVERY CHANNEL SCHOOL
Video Preview

 Section 1

3 periods
1 1/2 blocks

The Science of Rockets
J.2.1.1 Explain how rockets were developed.
J.2.1.2 Demonstrate how a rocket works.
J.2.1.3 Identify the main advantage of a multistage rocket.

Go Online
active art

 Section 2

1 period
1/2 block

The Space Program
J.2.2.1 Describe the space race.
J.2.2.2 Discuss the Apollo program.

Go Online
PHSchool.com

 Section 3

1 period
1/2 block

Exploring Space Today
J.2.3.1 Distinguish between the roles of space shuttles and those of space stations.
J.2.3.2 Identify features that space probes have in common.

DISCOVERY CHANNEL SCHOOL
Video Field Trip

Section 4

3 periods
1 1/2 blocks

Using Space Science on Earth
J.2.4.1 Explain how the conditions in space are different from those on Earth.
J.2.4.2 Identify the benefits that space technology has provided for modern society.
J.2.4.3 Describe some uses of satellites orbiting Earth.

Go Online
SciLINKS
NSTA

Review and Assessment

Test Preparation

All in One Teaching Resources
- Key Terms Review, p. 139
- Transparency J21
- Performance Assessment Teacher Notes, p. 148
- Performance Assessment Scoring Rubric, p. 149
- Performance Assessment Student Worksheet, p. 150
- Chapter Test, pp. 151–154

Go Online
PHSchool.com

DISCOVERY CHANNEL SCHOOL
Video Assessment

Test Preparation
Blackline Masters

Lab zone: Chapter Activities Planner

For more activities

LAB ZONE
Easy Planner
CD-ROM

Student Edition	Inquiry	Time	Materials	Skills	Resources
Chapter Project, p.39	Open-Ended	Ongoing (3 to 4 weeks)	**All in One Teaching Resources** See p. 102	Observing, making models	**Lab zone Easy Planner**
Section 1					
Discover Activity, p. 40	Guided	10 minutes	Safety goggles, balloon	Inferring	**Lab zone Easy Planner**
Try This Activity, p. 42	Directed	20 minutes	Plastic or paper cup, paper, tape, film canister with a lid that snaps on inside the canister, water, fizzing antacid tablet, safety goggles	Observing	**Lab zone Easy Planner**
Technology Lab, pp. 46–47	Guided	45 minutes	Water rocket launcher, tire pump, round balloon, scissors, tap water, inclinometer, 50 paper clips in plastic bag, empty 2-liter soda bottle, poster board, modeling clay, hot glue gun or tape	Observing, inferring	**Lab zone Easy Planner Lab Activity Video** Technology Lab: *Design and Build a Water Rocket*, pp. 116–117
Section 2					
Discover Activity, p. 48	Guided	15 minutes	Moon map	Inferring	**Lab zone Easy Planner**
Skills Activity, p. 50	Directed	10 minutes	Calculator	Calculating	**Lab zone Easy Planner**
Section 3					
Discover Activity, p. 53	Guided	15 minutes	Pen and paper	Drawing conclusions	**Lab zone Easy Planner**
Section 4					
Discover Activity, p. 58	Guided	15 minutes	Cordless drill, drill with electric cord, space pen, regular pen	Drawing conclusions	**Lab zone Easy Planner**
Consumer Lab, p. 63	Directed	30 minutes	1 cloth blanket piece, 1 foil blanket piece, 4 thermometers, 3 identical small test tubes, 3 identical large test tubes, 1 beaker (600 mL), ice, cellophane tape or rubber bands, cotton balls, hot water, tap water	Graphing, interpreting data	**Lab zone Easy Planner Lab Activity Video** **All in One Teaching Resources** Consumer Lab: *Space Spinoffs*, pp. 137–138

Section 1 The Science of Rockets

3 periods, 1–1/2 blocks

ABILITY LEVELS
L1 Basic to Average
L2 For All Students
L3 Average to Advanced

Objectives

J.2.1.1 Explain how rockets were developed.

J.2.1.2 Demonstrate how a rocket works.

J.2.1.3 Identify the main advantage of a multistage rocket.

Key Terms

• rocket • thrust • velocity • orbital velocity • escape velocity

Local Standards

Preteach

Build Background Knowledge

Ask students to describe what happens when a rocket is launched, on the basis of what they have seen in news specials or movies.

Lab zone Discover Activity *What Force Moves a Balloon?* **L1**

Targeted Print and Technology Resources

All in One Teaching Resources

L2 Reading Strategy Transparency J15: *Using Prior Knowledge*

○ **Presentation-Pro CD-ROM**

Instruct

A History of Rockets Discuss the development of rockets and create a timeline.

How Do Rockets Work? Examine a diagram of a rocket and describe action and reaction forces.

Multistage Rockets Use a sequenced diagram to analyze the stages in a multistage rocket launch.

Lab zone Technology Lab *Design and Build a Water Rocket* **L2**

Targeted Print and Technology Resources

All in One Teaching Resources

L2 Guided Reading, pp. 111–113

L2 Transparencies J16, J17

L2 Technology Lab: *Design and Build a Water Rocket,* pp. 116–117

Lab Activity Video/DVD
Technology Lab: *Design and Build a Water Rocket,*
PHSchool.com Web Code: cfp-5021

○ **Student Edition on Audio CD**

Assess

Section Assessment Questions

To answer the questions, have students use the questions and answers they prepared when they were using prior knowledge.

Reteach

Have students sketch and identify the forces acting on the balloon in the Discover activity.

Targeted Print and Technology Resources

All in One Teaching Resources

• Section Summary, p. 110

L1 Review and Reinforce, p. 114

L3 Enrich, p. 115

Section 2 The Space Program

🕐 *1 period, 1/2 block*

ABILITY LEVELS
L1 Basic to Average
L2 For All Students
L3 Average to Advanced

Objectives

J.2.2.1 Describe the space race.
J.2.2.2 Discuss the Apollo program.

Key Terms

• satellite

Local Standards

Preteach

Build Background Knowledge

Ask students to tell what they know about moon missions.

Lab zone **Discover Activity** *Where on the Moon Did Astronauts* **L1**
Land?

Targeted Print and Technology Resources

All in One Teaching Resources

L2 Reading Strategy Transparency
J18: Asking Questions

🔘 **Presentation-Pro CD-ROM**

Instruct

The Race for Space Examine how the competition between the United States and the former Soviet Union drove the space race.

Missions to the Moon Consider how the moon has been explored and discuss moon landings by humans.

Targeted Print and Technology Resources

All in One Teaching Resources

L2 Guided Reading, pp. 120–122

PHSchool.com Web Code: cfd-5022

🔘 **Student Edition on Audio CD**

Assess

Section Assessment Questions

⊙ To answer the questions, have students use their graphic organizers with their own questions and answers.

Reteach

Have students develop a timeline of events in this section.

Targeted Print and Technology Resources

All in One Teaching Resources

• Section Summary, p. 119
L1 Review and Reinforce, p. 123
L3 Enrich, p. 124

Section 3 **Exploring Space Today**

🕐 *1 period, 1/2 block*

ABILITY LEVELS
L1 Basic to Average
L2 For All Students
L3 Average to Advanced

Objectives

J.2.3.1 Distinguish between the roles of space shuttles and those of space stations.

J.2.3.2 Identify features that space probes have in common.

Key Terms

• space shuttle • space station • space probe • rover

Local Standards

Preteach

Build Background Knowledge

Challenge students to think of technologies that they use that depend on satellites.

Lab zone **Discover Activity** *What Do You Need to Survive in Space?* **L1**

Targeted Print and Technology Resources

All in One **Teaching Resources**

L2 Reading Strategy Transparency J19: Outlining Visuals

⊙ **Presentation-Pro CD-ROM**

Instruct

Working in Space Identify the functions of space shuttles, and compare and contrast them with those of space stations.

Space Probes Examine illustrations of space probes, and identify the missions of each of these probes.

Targeted Print and Technology Resources

All in One **Teaching Resources**

L2 Guided Reading, pp. 127–128

www.SciLinks.org Web Code: scn-0623

⊙ **Student Edition on Audio CD**

Assess

Section Assessment Questions

↻ To answer the questions, have students use their outlines.

Reteach

Have students provide details to compare and contrast space shuttles, space stations, and space probes.

Targeted Print and Technology Resources

All in One **Teaching Resources**

• Section Summary, p. 126

L1 Review and Reinforce, p. 129

L3 Enrich, p. 130

Section 4 Using Space Science on Earth

ABILITY LEVELS
L1 Basic to Average
L2 For All Students
L3 Average to Advanced

3 periods, 1 1/2 blocks

Objectives

J.2.4.1 Explain how the conditions in space are different from those on Earth.
J.2.4.2 Identify the benefits that space technology has provided for modern society.
J.2.4.3 Describe some uses of satellites orbiting Earth.

Local Standards

Key Terms

• vacuum • microgravity • space spinoff • geosynchronous orbit
• remote sensing

Preteach

Build Background Knowledge

Have students compare their descriptions of using a remote-controlled toy with the use of remote sensing in satellites.

Lab zone Discover Activity *Which Tool Would Be More Useful in Space?* **L1**

Targeted Print and Technology Resources

All in One Teaching Resources
L2 Reading Strategy Transparency J20: Identifying Main Ideas

Presentation-Pro CD-ROM

Instruct

The Challenges of Space Identify conditions in space that are different from those on Earth.

Space Spinoffs Examine those materials developed for the space program that have applications for use on Earth.

Satellites Discuss the types of data collected by satellites.

Lab zone Consumer Lab *Space Spinoffs* **L2**

Targeted Print and Technology Resources

All in One Teaching Resources
L2 Guided Reading, pp. 133–134
L2 Consumer Lab: *Space Spinoffs,* pp. 137–138
Lab Activity Video/DVD
Consumer Lab: *Space Spinoffs*
www.SciLinks.org Web Code: scn-0624

Student Edition on Audio CD

Assess

Section Assessment Questions

Have students use their main ideas and details to answer the questions.

Reteach

Have students review conditions in space that have led to the development of spinoffs.

Targeted Print and Technology Resources

All in One Teaching Resources
• Section Summary, p. 132
L1 Review and Reinforce, p. 135
L3 Enrich, p. 136

Chapter 2 Content Refresher

Go Online

NSTA-PDLINKS

For: Professional development support
Visit: NSTA.org
Web Code: scf-0620

Professional Development

Section 1 The Science of Rockets

Atlas Rockets Since the late 1950s, NASA has used *Atlas* rockets to launch probes into space and satellites into orbit around Earth. Recent versions of the rockets are approximately 58 meters high. They are usually made up of three stages. The first stage, simply called *Atlas,* uses both solid-fuel boosters and liquid-fuel engines to launch the payload into space. The second stage, known as *Centaur,* uses liquid-fuel engines to maneuver into proper orbit. The third stage is the payload—the satellite or spacecraft carried by the rocket. The payload is released from the *Centaur,* which falls back to Earth and burns up on reentry into the atmosphere.

Atlas rockets have been regularly upgraded over time. They were used to launch the *Surveyor* missions to the moon and the early *Pioneer* missions. More recently, they have been used to launch satellites into space for both governmental and commercial enterprises.

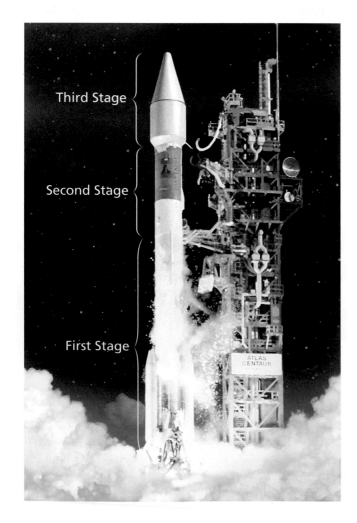

Third Stage

Second Stage

First Stage

ATLAS CENTAUR

Section 2 The Space Program

History of NASA The National Aeronautics and Space Administration (NASA) was begun in 1958. Its mission was to explore space. In 1958, that meant human space flight. As a result, NASA immediately embarked on Project Mercury to see whether humans could survive in space. The project involved sending an astronaut into Earth's orbit on board a small craft. The success of the program led to Project Gemini, which involved using spacecraft built for a crew of two astronauts. During Project Gemini, NASA learned about living and working in space, as well as how to maneuver spacecraft in orbit. This last lesson became important later in the space program when spacecraft had to dock, or join up with, each other. Project Gemini was quickly followed by Project Apollo, which put astronauts on the surface of the Moon in 1969. Although the last Apollo mission was in 1972, NASA began human space missions again in 1981 with the birth of the Space Shuttle program.

Apollo 13 *Apollo 13* was launched on April 11, 1970. At first it seemed that this might be the smoothest flight of the entire program. Two days into the flight, however, an oxygen tank blew up. Like all Apollo projects, *Apollo 13* had a three-passenger Command Module (CM) and a two-passenger Lunar Module (LM). The CM's supply of electricity, light, and water was lost.

Mission Control on Earth and the crew decided to use the LM to pilot the crippled CM around the moon and back to Earth. The astronauts had enough oxygen, but they had to conserve water, power, and food. They also had to find a way to remove carbon dioxide from the spacecraft, which they were finally able to do by using materials on board. On April 17, after surviving frigid temperatures and losing a total of almost 15 kg through dehydration, the crew landed safely in the Pacific Ocean near Samoa.

Going Back to the Moon The end of Project Apollo did not spell the end of lunar exploration. Since 1972, three NASA spacecraft have visited the moon. All have been uncrewed. In 1990 and 1992, on its way to Jupiter, the *Galileo* probe photographed the lunar north pole and sent back new information about the surface of the moon. Both passes by the moon were part of planetary flybys that gave *Galileo* a gravitational boost to continue on toward Jupiter. In 1994, *Clementine* was sent to map the lunar surface. In 1998, *Lunar Prospector* was put into a low polar orbit around the moon to look for possible polar ice deposits and to measure the moon's magnetic and gravity fields.

Section 3 Exploring Space Today

Floating Robots A new type of technology planned for the International Space Station (ISS) includes a small robot called a "personal satellite assistant." Under microgravity conditions, the spherical robot floats next to an astronaut, using small internal fans to change course or move in various directions.

Powered by solar cells, the personal satellite assistant is equipped with sensors that can monitor temperature, pressure, and air quality. This, in turn, will alert astronauts to any potential problems in the space station environment. Its small size allows the robot to easily monitor the most remote parts of the station, and it is programmed to conduct regularly scheduled maintenance checks on its own.

In addition to a camera and light, the personal satellite assistant has a "videophone" that will allow astronauts to communicate with one another, regardless of where they are in the station. The videophone is also linked to Mission Control on Earth.

> ⚑ **Address Misconceptions**
>
> *Students may think that the ISS is far from Earth. However, the ISS orbits Earth at an average altitude of 354 kilometers.* For a strategy for overcoming this misconception, see **Address Misconceptions** in *Exploring Space Today.*

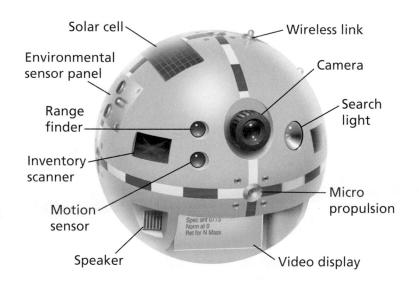

- Solar cell
- Wireless link
- Environmental sensor panel
- Camera
- Range finder
- Search light
- Inventory scanner
- Motion sensor
- Micro propulsion
- Speaker
- Video display

Section 4 Using Space Science on Earth

Benefits of Space Science According to NASA, less than 1 percent of the U.S. budget is spent on the space program. NASA officials estimate that for every dollar invested in its ventures, the U.S. economy receives a $7 return in the form of job creation, economic growth, and taxes.

NASA stresses its contribution to the country's economic welfare for good reason—many people argue against funding the space program. These people believe that the money would be better spent elsewhere, such as for education or for medical research.

To counter these arguments, NASA includes a detailed justification of space exploration on the program's Web site. In the document, NASA points out that the basic knowledge about the universe gained through space exploration gives us a better understanding of Earth. Space exploration has allowed applications in satellite communications. Many technological breakthroughs have resulted from the space program. The space program supports many jobs, and so it is good for the economy. The exploration of space serves as an inspiration to humans to explore the unknown and push back boundaries.

Help Students Read

Thinking Aloud
Verbalizing Thought Processes While Reading

Strategy Model cognitive and metacognitive processes that students can use to build meaning, self-correct, and monitor their own comprehension. Choose part of a section and preview it. As you do, imagine that you are reading these paragraphs for the first time, just as your students will be doing. Make a copy of the section, and on it write comments and questions that you can use as "thinking-aloud" models.

Example

1. Read several paragraphs aloud and have your students follow along silently. Have them listen to how you pause to check your own comprehension and to determine meaning at trouble spots. You might model some of the following strategies aloud as you read:
- Make a prediction, then revise or verify it.
- Describe mental pictures as they form.
- Connect new information with prior knowledge or related ideas; share an analogy.
- Verbalize confusing points and work out steps to clarify their meaning; adjust your reading pace, if necessary.

2. Select a logical stopping point. Then, have students read the next paragraph silently and apply similar strategies internally. Afterward, ask students to tell which strategies they used. Repeat this step several times.

Interactive Textbook
- Complete student edition
- Video and audio
- Simulations and activities
- Section and chapter activities

Chapter 2

Exploring Space

An astronaut working on the International Space Station in orbit around Earth ▶

Chapter Preview

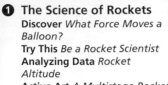
Interactive Textbook

 Chapter **Project** L3

Objectives

This project will help students understand the difficulties involved in using remotely controlled technology to explore space. After this Chapter Project, students will be able to
- observe and identify many of the geological features found on the planets and moons of the solar system
- problem-solve ways to build a vehicle that can move around the landscape of a planet or moon
- design, build, and test a model of the vehicle
- communicate the features of the model to the class

Skills Focus

observing, problem solving, making models, communicating

Project Time Line 3 to 4 weeks

All in One Teaching Resources
- Chapter Project Teacher Notes
- Chapter Project Worksheet 1
- Chapter Project Worksheet 2
- Chapter Project Scoring Rubric

Developing a Plan

Encourage small groups to each select a different planet or moon with a solid surface for its project. Students should get approval from you before they build or test their vehicles. Before students test their vehicles, have them determine the criteria they will use to evaluate the models.

Possible Materials

Students will need construction and design tools such as rulers, scissors, and glue. Prototypes can be built out of simple materials such as cardboard, foam board, and craft sticks. Wooden dowels may be helpful for wheel axles. Have students attach a long string to each vehicle so that it can be pulled across a test course. If you are testing the vehicles in the classroom, a test course can be made by placing obstacles such as books, boxes, or rugs on the floor.

 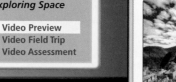

Exploring Space

Show the Video Preview to present an overview of the chapter content. Discussion question: **How does underwater training help prepare astronauts for their space flight?** (*Weighted underwater, the astronauts are able to simulate the feeling of being in an environment of microgravity.*)

Lab zone™ Chapter **Project**

Design and Build a Space Exploration Vehicle

How do scientists study the other planets in our solar system? One way is to send a remotely operated vehicle to explore the surface, as was done by two Mars rovers in 2004. Such a vehicle must be designed to meet specific requirements, such as communicating with scientists on Earth and being able to operate in a variety of environments.

Your Goal To design, build, and test a vehicle for exploring the surface of a planet

You will

● identify the geological features that are found on the planets and moons of the solar system

● select a planet or moon, and brainstorm ways to build a vehicle that can move around its surface

● design and sketch a model of the vehicle

● build and test a model vehicle, and present your vehicle to the class

● follow the safety guidelines in Appendix A

Plan It! Begin by identifying the different types of planetary surfaces found in the solar system. Next, brainstorm how a vehicle could move over some of these surfaces. You may want to think about how all-terrain vehicles on Earth are designed. Consider how you would build a model of the vehicle, and what materials you will need. Then build and test your vehicle.

Chapter 2 J ♦ 39

Possible Shortcuts

Give the class a list of geological features found on a particular planet or moon. Have all students design their vehicles to negotiate the terrain on that planet or moon. Allow students to work in groups when building and testing the vehicles.

Launching the Project

Display photographs of all-terrain vehicles (ATVs) on Earth. Ask: **What features do these vehicles have in common?** (*Possible answer: Wide tires, powerful engines, independent suspension systems*) Stress that ATVs can move over rough landscapes on Earth that are similar to those found on certain planets and moons.

Performance Assessment

The Chapter Project Scoring Rubric will help you evaluate how well students complete the Chapter Project. Share the rubric with students at the beginning of the project so that they will know what is expected. Students will be assessed on

● how thoroughly they researched their chosen planet or moon

● how well they designed the model vehicle

● how well the vehicle performed

● how thorough, organized, and complete the presentation is

Objectives

After this lesson, students will be able to
J.2.1.1 Explain how rockets were developed.
J.2.1.2 Demonstrate how a rocket works.
J.2.1.3 Identify the main advantage of a multistage rocket.

Target Reading Skill

Using Prior Knowledge Explain that using prior knowledge helps students connect what they already know to what they are about to read.

Answers

Possible answers include the following:

What You Know
1. Rockets were used to help transport astronauts to the moon.
2. Rockets burn fuel.
3. Rockets must move at high speeds to escape the force of gravity.

What You Learned
1. The first rockets were made in China in the 1100s.
2. Burning fuel creates thrust—the reaction force that propels a rocket forward.
3. The escape velocity a rocket needs to leave Earth's gravitational pull is about 40,200 kilometers per hour.

All in One Teaching Resources
• Transparency J15

Preteach

Build Background Knowledge   **L2**

Spacecraft Launches
Many students will have watched rockets being launched in news specials, documentaries, or movies. Invite students to describe what happens when a rocket is launched. Ask them to consider the motion of the rocket in their responses. (*Possible answer: Engines are fired, large clouds of gas come from the rocket boosters, and then the rocket or space shuttle pulls away from Earth.*)

The Science of Rockets

Reading Preview

Key Concepts
• How were rockets developed?
• How does a rocket work?
• What is the main advantage of a multistage rocket?

Key Terms
• rocket • thrust • velocity
• orbital velocity • escape velocity

Target Reading Skill
Using Prior Knowledge Before you read, write what you know about rockets in a graphic organizer like the one below. As you read, write what you learn.

What You Know
1. Rockets were used to help transport astronauts to the moon.
2.

What You Learned
1.
2.

FIGURE 1
Jules Verne's Spacecraft
Jules Verne imagined that a spacecraft and crew were shot to the moon by a cannon.

Lab zone Discover Activity

What Force Moves a Balloon?

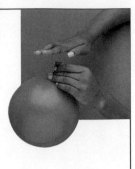

1. Put on your goggles. Blow up a balloon and hold its neck closed with your fingers.
2. Point the far end of the balloon in a direction where there are no people. Put your free hand behind the balloon's neck, so you will be able to feel the force of the air from the balloon on your hand. Let go of the balloon. Observe what happens.
3. Repeat Steps 1 and 2 without your free hand behind the neck of the balloon.

Think It Over
Inferring What happened when you let go of the balloon? Which direction did the balloon move in comparison to the direction the air moved out of the balloon? What force do you think caused the balloon to move in that direction? Did the position of your free hand affect the balloon's movement?

People have dreamed of traveling through space for centuries. Although the moons and planets of our solar system are much closer than the stars, they are still very far away. How could someone travel such great distances through space?

In the 1860s, the science fiction writer Jules Verne envisioned a spacecraft shot to the moon out of a huge cannon. When people finally did travel to the moon, though, they used rockets rather than cannons. Although Verne was wrong about how humans would reach the moon, he did anticipate many aspects of the space program. By the late 1900s, rocket-powered spacecraft were able to travel to the moon and to many other places in the solar system.

Lab zone Discover Activity

Skills Focus inferring

Materials safety goggles, balloon

Time 10 minutes

Tips Remind students to blow up the balloons to the same size each time so that they can compare their results.

L1 **Expected Outcome** The balloon will move across the room in both trials.

Think It Over Air rushed out of the balloon. The balloon moved in the direction opposite that of the rushing air. Action-reaction forces made the balloon move. The position of the free hand did not affect the balloon's movement.

A History of Rockets

You've probably seen rockets at fireworks displays. As the rockets moved skyward, you may have noticed a fiery gas rushing out of the back. A **rocket** is a device that expels gas in one direction to move in the opposite direction. **Rocket technology originated in China hundreds of years ago and gradually spread to other parts of the world.** Rockets were developed for military use as well as for fireworks.

Origins of Rockets The first rockets were made in China in the 1100s. These early rockets were very simple—they were arrows coated with a flammable powder that were lighted and shot with bows. By about 1200, the Chinese were using gunpowder inside their rockets.

The British greatly improved rocketry in the early 1800s. British ships used rockets against American troops in the War of 1812. The *Star-Spangled Banner* contains the words "the rockets' red glare, the bombs bursting in air." These words describe a British rocket attack on Fort McHenry in Baltimore, Maryland.

Development of Modern Rockets Modern rockets were first developed in the early 1900s. They owe much of their development to a few scientists. One was the Russian physicist Konstantin Tsiolkovsky. In the early 1900s, Tsiolkovsky described in scientific terms how rockets work and proposed designs for advanced rockets. The American physicist Robert Goddard also designed rockets. Beginning around 1915, Goddard went a step further and built rockets to test his designs.

Rocket design made major advances during World War II. Military rockets were used to carry explosives. The Germans used a rocket called the V2 to destroy both military and civilian targets. The V2 was a large rocket that could travel about 300 kilometers. The designer of the V2, Wernher von Braun, came to the United States after the war was over. Von Braun used his experience to direct the development of many rockets used in the United States space program.

Reading Checkpoint Name three scientists who contributed to the development of modern rockets.

FIGURE 2
Chinese Rockets
According to a Chinese legend, around 1500 an official named Wan-Hoo tried to fly to the moon by tying a number of rockets to his chair. The rockets exploded with a tremendous roar. Once the smoke cleared, there was no trace of Wan-Hoo or his chair.

Instruct

A History of Rockets

Teach Key Concepts · L2

Rocket Timeline

Focus Remind students that modern technology often builds or improves on earlier inventions.

Teach Ask: **Who developed the first rockets?** (*The Chinese*) **When were modern rockets first developed?** (*In the early 1900s*) **What have rockets been used for?** (*Military functions, such as carrying explosives; civilian uses, such as launching spacecraft and fireworks*)

Apply Have each student make a timeline that shows the history of the development of rockets. The timeline should begin in the 1100s and continue into the 1970s. Have students add captions to the timeline. An example of a caption might be *British troops use rockets against American troops in the War of 1812.* **learning modality: logical/mathematical**

Independent Practice · L2

All in One Teaching Resources

• Guided Reading and Study Worksheet: *The Science of Rockets*

⊙ Student Edition on Audio CD

Differentiated Instruction

English Learners/Beginning · L1 Comprehension: Ask Questions Write and provide students with a simplified version of the text on this page. Ask simple questions that can be answered directly from the rewritten text. If necessary, point out the answers in the rewritten text. Read the answers aloud with students. **learning modality: verbal**

English Learners/Intermediate · L2 Comprehension: Ask Questions Give students copies of the rewritten text from this page. Have them develop their own questions, including any concepts that are unclear to them. Then ask additional questions to check for understanding. For example, you might ask: **How did World War II contribute to the development of rockets?** **learning modality: verbal**

Monitor Progress · L1

Writing Have each student write a paragraph explaining this statement: In a sense, the development of spacecraft began with the launching of simple rockets in the 1100s.

Answer

Reading Checkpoint Konstantin Tsiolkovsky, Robert Goddard, and Wernher von Braun

How Do Rockets Work?

Teach Key Concepts   **L3**
Action/Reaction Forces

Focus Have students examine Figure 3.

Teach Ask: **What action force is shown in the diagram?** *(The force of gas coming from the back of the rocket engine)* **What reaction force is shown?** *(The force making the rocket move in the opposite direction)*

Apply Tell students that the English scientist Isaac Newton developed the law of action and reaction, also known as Newton's third law of motion. Have students brainstorm other examples of this law. They should classify the forces as action or reaction. *(Possible answer: A person jumping down on a trampoline is an example of an action force. The force exerted by the trampoline that sends the person upward is an example of a reaction force.)* **learning modality: visual**

All in One Teaching Resources

- Transparency J16

Help Students Read

Vocabulary Knowledge Rating Chart

Have students construct a chart with four columns labeled *Term, Can Define or Use It, Have Heard or Seen It,* and *Don't Know* to rate their knowledge of each term. Ask students to share what they know about *orbital velocity* and other terms from this section. Help students establish a purpose for reading by having them use the terms to predict the text content. After students have read the section, have them re-rate themselves.

Lab zone Try This Activity

Be a Rocket Scientist
You can build a rocket.

1. Use a plastic or paper cup as the rocket body. Cut out a paper nose cone. Tape it to the bottom of the cup.
2. Obtain an empty film canister with a lid that snaps on inside the canister. Go outside to do Steps 3–5.
3. Fill the canister about one-quarter full with water.
4. Put on your goggles. Now add half of a fizzing antacid tablet to the film canister and quickly snap on the lid.
5. Place the canister on the ground with the lid down. Place your rocket over the canister and stand back.

Observing
What action happened inside the film canister? What was the reaction of the rocket?

How Do Rockets Work?

A rocket can be as small as your finger or as large as a skyscraper. An essential feature of any rocket, though, is that it expels gas in one direction. **A rocket moves forward when gases shooting out the back of the rocket push it in the opposite direction.**

A rocket works in much the same way as a balloon that is propelled through the air by releasing gas. In most rockets, fuel is burned to make hot gas. The gas pushes outward in every direction, but it can leave the rocket only through openings at the back. The movement of gas out of these openings moves the rocket forward. Figure 3 shows how rockets move.

Action and Reaction Forces The movement of a rocket demonstrates a basic law of physics: For every force, or action, there is an equal and opposite force, or reaction. The force of the air moving out of a balloon is an action force. An equal force—the reaction force—pushes the balloon forward.

The reaction force that propels a rocket forward is called **thrust.** The amount of thrust depends on several factors, including the mass and speed of the gases propelled out of the rocket. The greater the thrust, the greater a rocket's velocity. **Velocity** is speed in a given direction.

Orbital and Escape Velocity In order to lift off the ground, a rocket must have more upward thrust than the downward force of gravity. Once a rocket is off the ground, it must reach a certain velocity in order to go into orbit. **Orbital velocity** is the velocity a rocket must achieve to establish an orbit around Earth. If the rocket moves slower than orbital velocity, Earth's gravity will cause it to fall back to the surface.

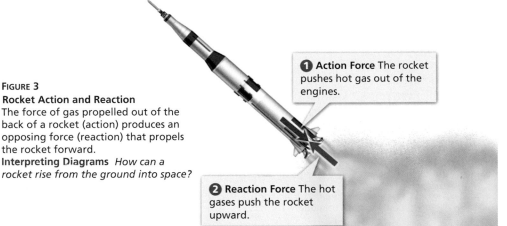

FIGURE 3
Rocket Action and Reaction
The force of gas propelled out of the back of a rocket (action) produces an opposing force (reaction) that propels the rocket forward.
Interpreting Diagrams *How can a rocket rise from the ground into space?*

1 Action Force The rocket pushes hot gas out of the engines.

2 Reaction Force The hot gases push the rocket upward.

42 ◆ J

Lab zone Try This Activity

Skills Focus observing   **L2**

Materials plastic or paper cup, paper, tape, film canister with a lid that snaps on inside the canister, water, fizzing antacid tablet, safety goggles

Time 20 minutes

Tips CAUTION: *Do not allow students to place sharp objects on the rocket.*

Expected Outcome The rocket will lift off and shoot 2 to 5 meters into the air. Gas pressure builds up inside the canister as a result of the reaction of the antacid and water. Pressure continues to build until the lid of the canister blows off and the rocket is launched.

Extend Challenge students to design and launch rockets powered by two, three, or more film canisters. **learning modality: kinesthetic**

Rocket Altitude

A rocket's altitude is how high it is above the ground. Use the graph at the right to answer the following questions about how a model rocket's altitude changes over time.

1. **Reading Graphs** What two variables are being graphed? In what unit is each measured?

2. **Reading Graphs** What was the rocket's altitude after 2 seconds? After 4 seconds?

3. **Reading Graphs** At what time did the rocket reach its greatest altitude?

4. **Inferring** Why do you think the rocket continued to rise after it ran out of fuel?

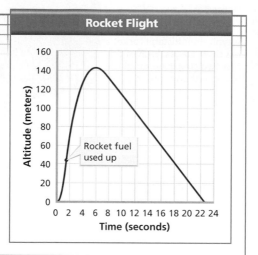

Rocket Flight

Rocket fuel used up

If the rocket has an even greater velocity, it can fly off into space. **Escape velocity** is the velocity a rocket must reach to fly beyond a planet's gravitational pull. The escape velocity a rocket needs to leave Earth is about 40,200 kilometers per hour. That's more than 11 kilometers every second!

Rocket Fuels Rockets create thrust by ejecting gas. Three types of fuel are used to power modern spacecraft: solid fuel, liquid fuel, and electrically charged particles of gas (ions). Solid-fuel and liquid-fuel rockets carry oxygen that allows the fuel to burn.

In a solid-fuel rocket, oxygen is mixed with the fuel, which is a dry explosive chemical. A fireworks rocket is a good example of a solid-fuel rocket. For such a simple rocket, a match can be used to ignite the fuel. Large solid-fuel rockets have a device called an igniter that can be triggered from a distance. Once a solid-fuel rocket is ignited, it burns until all the fuel is gone.

In a liquid-fuel rocket, both the oxygen and the fuel are in liquid form. They are stored in separate compartments. When the rocket fires, the fuel and oxygen are pumped into the same chamber and ignited. An advantage of liquid-fuel rockets is that the burning of fuel can be controlled by regulating how much liquid fuel and oxygen are mixed together.

Ion rockets do not burn chemical fuels. Rather, they expel gas ions out of their engines at very high speeds. Ion rockets generally create less thrust than solid-fuel or liquid-fuel rockets. But they are very fuel efficient.

Reading Checkpoint What are the three types of rocket fuel?

FIGURE 4
Rocket Velocity
This artist's view shows a NASA rocket rising into space.

J ◆ 43

Math Skill Making and interpreting graphs

Focus Remind students that line graphs often show how something changes over time. This graph shows how the rocket's altitude changes.

Teach Have students examine the line graph. Ask: **What do the numbers on the x-axis represent?** (*Time in seconds*)

Answers

1. Altitude and time, meters and seconds
2. About 65 meters; about 128 meters
3. 6 seconds
4. The rocket's inertia caused it to continue to rise after its fuel ran out. Eventually friction caused the rocket to slow down and gravity caused the rocket to fall.

Lab zone **Build Inquiry** L2

Drawing Conclusions About Rocket Propulsion Technologies

Materials reference materials

Time 30 minutes

Focus Remind students that early rockets were powered by gunpowder.

Teach Organize students into small groups to research developments in rocket propulsion. Then have students chart their findings chronologically. Brief descriptions should accompany each development. Encourage students to include emerging and possible future propulsion technologies, such as ion drive, antimatter, and fusion.

Apply Have each student write a paragraph summarizing how fuel technologies have changed. **learning modality: verbal**

Monitor Progress _____ L2

Skills Check Have students sequence and illustrate the steps in a rocket launch. Students may place their sequences in their portfolios.

Portfolio

Answers
Figure 3 To lift a rocket from the ground, the power of the upward thrust must be greater than the downward force of gravity. Most rockets create thrust by burning fuels. The rocket moves forward as gases shoot out the back.

Reading Checkpoint Solid fuel, liquid fuel, and gas ions

Differentiated Instruction

Gifted and Talented L3
Researching Ion Propulsion Have each student research ion propulsion and prepare a presentation for the class. Give students these questions to answer: **What is ion propulsion? How is it similar to and different from chemical fuels? How is it used?** (*Ion propulsion is a technology that involves ionizing [giving an electrical charge to] the gas xenon to propel a craft. At high speeds, the ions are emitted as exhaust and push the spacecraft in the opposite direction. Ion propulsion can push a spacecraft up to ten times as fast as chemical propulsion, but ion propulsion cannot be used for rapid acceleration because its thrust is too gentle.*)
learning modality: verbal

Multistage Rockets

Teach Key Concepts　L1

Rocket Stages

Focus Remind students that the fuel used in rockets has weight.

Teach Direct students to Figure 5. Ask: **Which stage is the heaviest?** (*The first stage*) **Why does the second stage ignite only after the first stage has fallen away?** (*The fuel used in the second stage is intended to move less weight than the fuel for the first stage does, so the empty fuel container must fall away first.*)

Apply Ask: **Why is a multistage rocket more efficient than a single-stage rocket?** (*Because the weight of the rocket is gradually reduced as empty fuel containers are cast off*)
learning modality: visual

 **Teaching Resources**

• Transparency J17

 **Teacher Demo**　L3

Modeling Multistage Rockets

Materials safety goggles, 2 long balloons, nylon fishing line, 2 plastic drinking straws, plastic foam cup, masking tape, scissors

Time 15 minutes

Focus Remind students that as each stage of a rocket uses up its fuel, it drops off.

Teach Thread the straws onto the fishing line. Tie the line securely across the room. Cut the top ring from a foam cup. Inflate one balloon about three quarters of the way. Hold the neck tight, but do not tie it. Ask a volunteer to help you place the neck of the balloon through the plastic foam ring and hold it tightly closed. Inflate the second balloon so that the round end extends a short way through the ring. After some practice, you will be able to inflate the second balloon so that it presses the neck of the first balloon against the ring and holds it shut. Hold the neck of the second balloon firmly, and tape each balloon to one of the straws on the line. When you release the balloon, the escaping air will propel the balloons down the line. When the first balloon runs out of air, it will release the other.

Apply Ask: **How many stages were part of this rocket model?** (*Two*) **Which balloon was the first stage?** (*The one that first ran out of air*) **learning modality: visual**

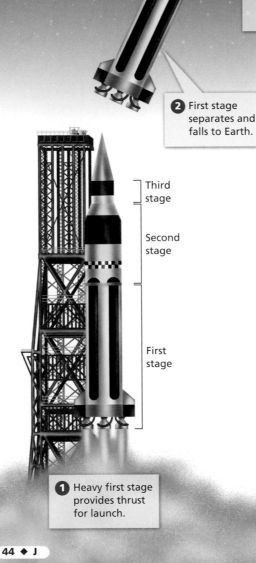

FIGURE 5
A Multistage Rocket
A typical multistage rocket has three stages. Each of the first two stages burns all its fuel and then drops off. The next stage then takes over.
Interpreting Diagrams
Which part of the rocket reaches the rocket's final destination?

4 Second stage separates and falls to Earth.

3 Second stage ignites and continues with third stage.

2 First stage separates and falls to Earth.

Third stage

Second stage

First stage

1 Heavy first stage provides thrust for launch.

44 ◆ J

Multistage Rockets

A rocket can carry only so much fuel. As the fuel in a rocket burns, its fuel chambers begin to empty. Even though much of the rocket is empty, the whole rocket must still be pushed upward by the remaining fuel. But what if the empty part of the rocket could be thrown off? Then the remaining fuel wouldn't have to push a partially empty rocket. This is the idea behind multistage rockets.

Konstantin Tsiolokovsky proposed the idea of multistage rockets in 1903. **The main advantage of a multistage rocket is that the total weight of the rocket is greatly reduced as the rocket rises.**

In a multistage rocket, smaller rockets, or stages, are placed one on top of the other and then fired in succession. Figure 5 shows how a multistage rocket works. As each stage of the rocket uses up its fuel, the empty fuel container falls away. The next stage then ignites and continues powering the rocket toward its destination. At the end, there is just a single stage left, the very top of the rocket.

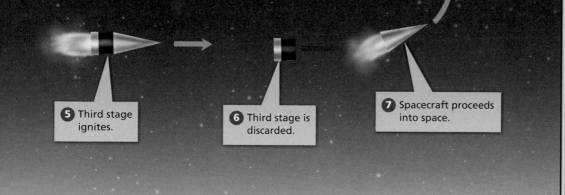

5 Third stage ignites.

6 Third stage is discarded.

7 Spacecraft proceeds into space.

Go Online
active art

For: Multistage Rocket activity
Visit: PHSchool.com
Web Code: cfp-5021

In the 1960s, the development of powerful multistage rockets such as the Saturn V made it possible to send spacecraft to the moon and the solar system beyond. The mighty Saturn V rocket stood 111 meters tall—higher than the length of a football field. It was by far the most powerful rocket ever built. Today, multistage rockets are used to launch a wide variety of satellites and space probes.

Reading Checkpoint What is a multistage rocket?

Section **1** Assessment

Target Reading Skill **Using Prior Knowledge** Review your graphic organizer and revise it based on what you just learned in the section.

Reviewing Key Concepts

1. a. Defining What is a rocket?
  b. Reviewing Where and when were rockets first developed?
  c. Summarizing For what purposes were rockets initially developed?
2. a. Explaining What is thrust?
  b. Explaining How do rockets create thrust?
  c. Interpreting Diagrams Use Figure 3 to explain how a rocket moves forward.
3. a. Describing Describe how a multistage rocket works.

  b. Comparing and Contrasting What is the main advantage of a multistage rocket compared to a single-stage rocket?
  c. Relating Cause and Effect Why can the third stage of a multistage rocket go faster than the first stage of the rocket, even though it has less fuel?

Writing in Science

Interview Suppose you were able to interview one of the scientists who helped to develop modern rockets. Choose one of the scientists identified in the section and write a series of questions that you would like to ask this person. Then use what you've learned to construct likely answers to these questions.

Chapter 2 J ◆ 45

Go Online
active art

For: Rocket activity
Visit: PHSchool.com
Web Code: cfp-5021

Students can interact with the art of a rocket online.

Monitor Progress _____ **L1**

Answers
Figure 5 The very top of the rocket

Reading Checkpoint A rocket in which smaller rockets, or stages, are placed one on top of the other and then fired in succession

Assess

Reviewing Key Concepts

1. a. A device that expels gas in one direction to allow movement in the opposite direction **b.** In China in the 1100s **c.** For military use and fireworks
2. a. The reaction force that propels a rocket forward **b.** Most rockets create thrust by burning fuel. **c.** Burning fuels makes hot gas that pushes outward in every direction. The gas can escape only through openings at the back of the rocket and shoots out through these openings. This action force results in an equal reaction force that pushes the rocket forward.
3. a. A set of rocket sections are placed one on top of the other and then fired in succession. As each stage uses up its fuel, the empty fuel container falls away. The next stage then ignites and continues powering the rocket toward its destination. **b.** In a multistage rocket, the total weight of the rocket is greatly reduced as the rocket rises. **c.** It carries less weight and already has been accelerated by the earlier stages.

Reteach **L1**

Refer students to the Discover activity at the beginning of this section. Have each of them sketch a diagram that uses arrows to show the forces that act on the balloon as it is released.

All in One Teaching Resources

• Section Summary: *The Science of Rockets*
• Review and Reinforce: *The Science of Rockets*
• Enrich: *The Science of Rockets*

Lab zone Chapter **Project**

Keep Students on Track Check that students have completed their research on the geological features of planets and moons, and each student or group has selected a particular planet or moon for the project. Set aside some time for groups of students to brainstorm how a vehicle could move over the terrain found on a particular planet or moon.

Writing in Science

Writing Mode: Description
Scoring Rubric
4 Exceeds criteria by using interesting questions with correct answers, written as an informative and lively interview
3 Meets all criteria, but interview lacks interest
2 Includes questions and answers, but includes inaccurate information
1 Is incomplete, inaccurate, and uninspired

Design and Build a Water Rocket

Prepare for Inquiry

Key Concept
By designing a water rocket, students will experience the three-step design process: research and investigate, design and build, and evaluate and redesign.

Skills Objectives
After this lab, students will be able to
- Design an experiment
- Evaluate results against specified criteria
- Troubleshoot problems that occur during the design and build stage

Prep Time 30 min (2 hours if a rocket launcher needs to be built)

Class Time 45 min

Advance Preparation
Obtain all of the materials a day or two before beginning the activity. Ask students to bring empty soda bottles from home. Be sure to do the activity yourself first to help you explain the procedure. A launcher can be built according to directions on the NASA Web site: http://quest.arc.nasa.gov/space/teacher/rockets/act10.html. Launchers can also be purchased from supply houses.

Safety ⚠ 🔬
A preferred launch device is one that can be operated remotely. The operator should stand 3–4 meters from the launch point. Observers should stand 8–10 meters away from the launch point. The launch range should be clear of all people approximately 30 meters on each side of the intended flight path in case the rocket goes off course. The rocket should be pumped to a pressure of no more than 50 pounds per square inch. Review the safety guidelines in Appendix A.

All in One Teaching Resources
- Lab Worksheet: *Design and Build a Water Rocket*

Guide Inquiry

Invitation
Ask students to give examples of jet propulsion. Make sure that they understand the principles behind the method used for determining the maximum altitude reached

---

Lab zone Technology Lab
· Tech & Design ·

Design and Build a Water Rocket

Problem
Can you design and build a rocket propelled by water and compressed air?

Design Skills
observing, evaluating the design, redesigning

Materials
- large round balloon   • tap water
- graduated cylinder   • modeling clay
- 50 paper clips in a plastic bag
- empty 2-liter soda bottle   • poster board
- scissors   • hot glue gun or tape
- bucket, 5 gallon   • stopwatch
- rocket launcher and tire pump (one per class)

Procedure 🌀 🗄 ✂ ⚠

PART 1   Research and Investigate

1. Copy the data table onto a separate sheet of paper.

Data Table	
Volume of Water (mL)	Motion of Balloon
No water	

2. In an outdoor area approved by your teacher, blow up a large round balloon. Hold the balloon so the opening is pointing down. Release the balloon and observe what occurs. ***CAUTION:*** *If you are allergic to latex, do not handle the balloon.*

3. Measure 50 mL of water with a graduated cylinder. Pour the water into the balloon. Blow it up to about the same size as the balloon in Step 2. Hold the opening down and release the balloon. Observe what happens.

---

4. Repeat Step 3 twice, varying the amount of water each time. Record your observations in the data table.

PART 2   Design and Build

5. You and a partner will design and build a water rocket using the materials provided or approved by your teacher. Your rocket must
   - be made from an empty 2-liter soda bottle
   - have fins and a removable nosecone
   - carry a load of 50 paper clips
   - use air only or a mixture of air and water as a propulsion system
   - be launched on the class rocket launcher
   - remain in the air for at least 5 seconds

6. Begin by thinking about how your rocket will work and how you would like it to look. Sketch your design and make a list of materials that you will need.

7. Rockets often have a set of fins to stabilize them in flight. Consider the best shape for fins, and decide how many fins your rocket needs. Use poster board to make your fins.

8. Decide how to safely and securely carry a load of 50 paper clips in your rocket.

9. Based on what you learned in Part 1, decide how much, if any, water to pour into your rocket.

10. After you obtain your teacher's approval, build your rocket.

◀ Rocket launcher

---

by the rocket. Review action and reaction forces by asking: **What basic law of physics is illustrated by the movement of a rocket?** *(For every force, or action, there is an equal and opposite force, or reaction.)* **What is the name of the reaction force that propels a rocket forward?** *(Thrust)*

Introduce the Procedure
In Part 1, students are asked to blow up balloons, release them, and observe their "flight." The flight of each balloon will be very erratic because there are no wings and the balloon changes shape as it loses air. However, make sure that students note a marked difference in the "acceleration rate" between the balloon with just air in it and those trials that have both air and water in the balloon.

PART 3 Evaluate and Redesign

11. Test your rocket by launching it on the rocket launcher provided by your teacher.
CAUTION: *Make sure that the rocket is launched vertically in a safe, open area that is at least 30 m across. All observers should wear goggles and stay at least 8–10 m away from the rocket launcher. The rocket should be pumped to a pressure of no more than 50 pounds per square inch.*

12. Use a stopwatch to determine your rocket's flight time (how long it stays in the air.)

13. Record in a data table the results of your own launch and your classmates' launches.

14. Compare your design and results with those of your classmates.

Analyze and Conclude

1. **Observing** What did you observe about the motion of the balloon as more and more water was added?

2. **Drawing Conclusions** What purpose did adding water to the balloon serve?

3. **Designing a Solution** How did your results in Part 1 affect your decision about how much water, if any, to add to your rocket?

4. **Evaluating the Design** Did your rocket meet all the criteria listed in Step 5? Explain.

5. **Evaluating the Design** How did your rocket design compare to the rockets built by your classmates? Which rocket had the greatest flight time? What design features resulted in the most successful launches?

6. **Redesigning** Based on your launch results and your response to Question 5, explain how you could improve your rocket. How do you think these changes would help your rocket's performance?

7. **Evaluating the Impact on Society** Explain how an understanding of rocket propulsion has made space travel possible.

Communicate

Write a paragraph that describes how you designed and built your rocket. Explain how it worked. Include a labeled sketch of your design.

Go Online
PHSchool.com

For: Data sharing
Visit: PHSchool.com
Web Code: cfd-5021

J ◆ 47

Extend Inquiry

Communicate Paragraphs will vary but should include a brief description of the procedure used by students in designing and building their rocket. They should also demonstrate an understanding of rocket propulsion; that is, a force in one direction creates an equal force in the opposite direction.

Go Online
PHSchool.com

For: More on Data Sharing
Visit: PHSchool.com
Web Code: cfd-5021

Students can share data from their experiment online.

Troubleshooting the Experiment

Be sure to designate a safe area for Part 1 of the experiment because when the water comes out of the balloon, it will make a mess. Going outside or spreading newspapers on the floor might help cleanup. Do not attempt the rocket flights when it is too windy outside. The wind will alter the course of the rockets.

Expected Outcome

The more water added to the rocket, the higher and faster it will fly, up to a point. If there is sufficient time for students to conduct multiple launches, they will be able to determine the minimum amount of water to add to achieve the maximum altitude.

Analyze and Conclude

1. Answers should reflect an understanding that when water was added, the extra mass being expelled by the balloon made the balloon go higher.

2. The water provided extra mass that when expelled from the balloon, provided force to propel the balloon.

3. Students should note that the addition of water to the balloon caused it to fly higher when released. This observation should cause them to add a significant amount of water to their rocket in Part 2. However, if too much water is added, the force required to lift the rocket may offset the additional propulsion provided by the water.

4. Answers will vary but should demonstrate an understanding of meeting the design criteria.

5. Answers should describe several different design features incorporated into various rockets and note which design features appear to have contributed to the most successful launches.

6. Answers will vary but possible improvements may include adjusting the amount of water, modifying the shape or number of fins, or using different materials.

7. Answers will vary but should include an understanding of how rocket propulsion has enabled space travel.

Objectives

After this lesson, students will be able to
J.2.2.1 Describe the space race.
J.2.2.2 Discuss the Apollo program.

Target Reading Skill 🎯

Asking Questions Explain that changing a heading into a question helps students anticipate ideas, facts, and events that they will read about.

Answers

Possible answers include the following:
What was the "space race"? *The rivalry in the exploration of space between the United States and the former Soviet Union* **Which country placed a person in orbit first?** *The Soviet Union* **When did people first walk on the moon?** *In 1969*

All in One Teaching Resources

• Transparency J18

Preteach

Build Background Knowledge L1

Moon Missions

Some students may have watched documentaries on moon missions or movies based on actual moon missions. Ask students to share what they know about these missions. As a class, brainstorm questions that scientists hope to answer by having spacecraft and astronauts explore our solar system. *(Possible answers: Is there life elsewhere in the solar system? How did the planets form?)*

Reading Preview

Key Concepts
• What was the space race?
• What were the major events in human exploration of the moon?

Key Term
• satellite

🎯 Target Reading Skill

Asking Questions Before you read, preview the red headings. In a graphic organizer like the one below, ask a question for each heading. As you read, write answers to your questions.

The Space Program

Question	Answer
What was the "space race"?	The "space race" was . . .

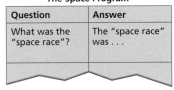

Lab zone — Discover **Activity**

Where on the Moon Did Astronauts Land?

1. Use a large map of the moon to find these locations: Sea of Tranquility, Ocean of Storms, Fra Mauro, Apennine Mountains, Descartes Highlands, and Valley of Taurus-Littrow.
2. American astronauts landed on and explored each of the locations you found. Using what you know about the moon and what you can see on the map, describe what you think astronauts saw at each place.

Think It Over
Inferring Did the names of the moon locations seem to fit with what you could see? Do you think the astronauts had to use boats to explore the Sea of Tranquility and the Ocean of Storms?

Sometimes competition results in great achievements. Maybe you've been motivated to try harder in a foot race when someone passed you by. Perhaps watching a friend accomplish a feat made you determined to do it, too. Competition resulted in one of the greatest achievements in history: In 1969 the first human set foot on the moon. This competition, though, was not between friends, but between the two most powerful nations in the world, the United States and the Soviet Union. Their rivalry in the exploration of space was called the "space race."

The Race for Space

The space race began in the 1950s. At that time, the Soviet Union was the greatest rival to the United States in politics and military power. The tensions between the two countries were so high that they were said to be in a "cold war." These tensions increased when the Soviets launched a satellite into space. **The space race began in 1957 when the Soviets launched the satellite *Sputnik I* into orbit. The United States responded by speeding up its own space program.**

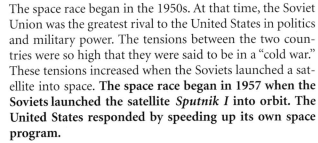

◄ The first living creature sent into space was a dog named Laika. She orbited Earth aboard the Soviet spacecraft *Sputnik II* in November 1957.

Lab zone — Discover **Activity**

Skills Focus inferring

Materials moon map

Time 15 minutes

Tips Team students with visual impairments with partners who can easily describe features on the moon's surface.

Expected Outcome Students will describe various mountains, plateaus, and lowlands on the moon.

L1

Think It Over The names of the moon locations are sometimes descriptive of actual locations on the map, but they are not necessarily accurate. For example, a "sea" on the moon may be a smooth area, but it is not an ocean. Astronauts did not need boats to explore the Sea of Tranquility and the Ocean of Storms.

FIGURE 6
John Glenn
Friendship 7 lifted off from Cape Canaveral, Florida, in February 1962. It carried astronaut John Glenn, the first American to orbit Earth. The closeup photo shows Glenn climbing into the *Friendship 7* space capsule.
Observing *Where on the rocket was the space capsule located?*

The First Artificial Satellites A **satellite** is an object that revolves around another object in space. The moon is a natural satellite of Earth. A spacecraft orbiting Earth is an artificial satellite. *Sputnik I* was the first artificial satellite. This success by the Soviets caused great alarm in the United States.

The United States responded in early 1958 by launching its own satellite, *Explorer 1*, into orbit. Over the next few years, both the United States and the Soviet Union placed many more satellites into orbit around Earth.

Later in 1958, the United States established a government agency in charge of its space program, called the National Aeronautics and Space Administration (NASA). NASA brought together the talents of many scientists and engineers who worked together to solve the many difficult technical problems of space flight.

Humans in Space In 1961 the space race heated up even more when the Soviets launched the first human into space. Yuri Gagarin flew one orbit around Earth aboard *Vostok 1*. Less than a month later, astronaut Alan Shepard became the first American in space. His tiny spacecraft, called *Freedom 7*, was part of the U.S. Mercury space program. Other Soviet cosmonauts and American astronauts soon followed into space.

The first American to orbit Earth was John Glenn, who was launched into space in 1962 aboard *Friendship 7*. The spacecraft he traveled in was called a space capsule because it was like a small cap on the end of the rocket. The tiny capsule orbited Earth three times before returning to the surface.

✓ Reading Checkpoint Who was the first American in space?

Instruct

The Race for Space

Teach Key Concepts   L1
Space Race

Focus Remind students that in the 1950s, the United States and the Soviet Union were the two most powerful countries in the world.

Teach Explain that when the Soviet Union launched a satellite, U.S. leaders interpreted the launch as a sign that the Soviets were ahead in math and science and possessed technology that could make the Soviet Union more powerful than the United States. Ask: **What was the response of the United States to the launching of *Sputnik I*?** (*The United States established a government agency to take charge of its space program and launched its first satellite in 1958.*) **What caused the space race to become even more competitive after the United States launched a satellite?** (*The Soviets launched the first human into space.*) **How did the United States respond?** (*The U.S. launched a person into space less than a month later.*)

Apply Tell students that the Soviets' launch of *Sputnik I* spurred the United States to make educational reforms. The United States began to place more emphasis on science, including science education in the elementary schools.
learning modality: verbal

Independent Practice   L2

All in One Teaching Resources
• Guided Reading and Study Worksheet: *The Space Program*

⊙ **Student Edition on Audio CD**

Monitor Progress ───── L1

Writing Ask each student to write a brief paragraph that describes the role of competition in the development of the U.S. space program.

Answers
Figure 6 At the top

✓ Reading Checkpoint Alan Shepard

Missions to the Moon

Teach Key Concepts   L2
The Apollo Program

Focus Point out that landing a person on the moon was a goal that grew out of the space race between the United States and the Soviet Union.

Teach Ask: **What was the Apollo program?** *(The American effort to land astronauts on the moon.)* **How did astronauts explore the moon's surface?** *(The first astronauts walked on the surface, collecting rock samples. Later astronauts used lunar buggies.)* **Why has exploration of the moon lagged over the past few decades?** *(The cost was high compared with the benefits.)* **What recent interest does the United States have in the moon?** *(To establish a base from which missions can be launched.)*

Apply Tell students that when Neil Armstrong stepped onto the moon, he left "a" out of his quote. He meant to say "...one small step for [a] man..." Ask students what they think he meant. *(Accept all reasonable answers.)* **learning modality: verbal**

Lab zone   Build Inquiry   L2

Applying the Concept of Moon Exploration

Materials none

Time 20 minutes

Focus Ask a student volunteer to read aloud the quote by President John F. Kennedy.

Teach Organize students into small groups. Tell them to suppose that they are NASA scientists during the early 1960s. Have students brainstorm factors to consider when landing a human on the moon. Encourage students to consider survival requirements and technical factors involved in landing safely on the moon and returning to Earth. Ask students to list items necessary for survival and share the lists with the class.

Apply Ask: **How did the properties of the moon help you decide what would be necessary for survival?** *(Possible answer: The lack of oxygen and water means that supplies of those items would have to last through the entire trip.)* **learning modality: logical/mathematical**

Lab zone   Skills Activity

Calculating

If you went to the moon, your weight would be about one sixth of your weight on Earth. Recall that in SI, weight is measured in newtons (1 lb ≈ 4.5 N). To find the approximate weight of an object on the moon, divide its weight on Earth by six.

An astronaut weighs 667 N on Earth. She wears a spacesuit and equipment that weigh 636 N on Earth. What is the astronaut's total weight on the moon?

FIGURE 7
Apollo 11
On July 20, 1969, *Apollo 11* astronaut Neil Armstrong became the first person to walk on the moon. He took this photograph of Buzz Aldrin. The inset photo shows Armstrong's footprint on the lunar soil.

Missions to the Moon

"I believe that this nation should commit itself to achieving the goal, before the decade is out, of landing a man on the moon and returning him safely to Earth." With these words from a May 1961 speech, President John F. Kennedy launched an enormous program of space exploration and scientific research. **The American effort to land astronauts on the moon was named the Apollo program.**

Exploring the Moon Between 1964 and 1972, the United States and the Soviet Union sent many unpiloted spacecraft to explore the moon. When a U.S. spacecraft called *Surveyor* landed on the moon, it didn't sink into the surface. This proved that the moon had a solid surface. Next, scientists searched for a suitable place to land humans on the moon.

The Moon Landings In July 1969, three American astronauts circled the moon aboard *Apollo 11.* Once in orbit, Neil Armstrong and Buzz Aldrin entered a tiny spacecraft called *Eagle*. On July 20, the *Eagle* descended toward a flat area on the moon's surface called the Sea of Tranquility. When Armstrong radioed that the *Eagle* had landed, cheers rang out at the NASA Space Center in Houston. A few hours later, Armstrong and Aldrin left the *Eagle* to explore the moon. When Armstrong first set foot on the surface, he said, "That's one small step for man, one giant leap for mankind." Armstrong meant to say, "That's one small step for *a* man," meaning himself, but in his excitement he never said the "a."

Lab zone   Skills Activity

Skills Focus calculating

Materials calculator

Time 10 minutes

Tips Point out that the activity asks for the astronaut's total weight, which would include the spacesuit and equipment.

Expected Outcome 667 N + 636 N = 1303 N; 1303 N ÷ 6 = 217 N

   L3

Extend Tell students that density is found by dividing mass by volume. Ask students to hypothesize how the density of an object would be affected on the moon. *(Density would not change because mass and volume remain the same.)* Have students explain the reasoning behind their hypotheses. **learning modality: logical/mathematical**

On the Moon's Surface Everything that the *Apollo 11* astronauts found was new and exciting. For about two hours, Armstrong and Aldrin explored the moon's surface, collecting samples to take back to Earth. They also planted an American flag.

Over the next three years, five more Apollo missions landed on the moon. In these later missions, astronauts were able to stay on the moon for days instead of hours. As shown in Figure 8, some astronauts even used a lunar rover, or buggy, to explore larger areas of the moon.

Moon Rocks and Moonquakes The astronauts collected nearly 400 kilograms of lunar samples, commonly called "moon rocks." When scientist analyzed these samples, they learned a great deal about the moon. For instance, they learned that the minerals that make up moon rocks are the same minerals that are found on Earth. However, in some moon rocks these minerals combine to form kinds of rocks that are not found on Earth. Scientists were also able to calculate the ages of the moon rocks. With that information, they could better estimate when different parts of the moon's surface formed.

One way that Apollo astronauts explored the structure of the moon was to purposely crash equipment onto the moon's surface. Instruments they left behind measured the "moonquake" waves that resulted. Using data collected from these artificial moonquakes, scientists determined that the moon may have a small core of molten rock at its center.

 **Reading Checkpoint** What did scientists learn from analyzing moon rocks?

FIGURE 8
Lunar Buggy
Astronauts on the later Apollo missions had a lunar buggy.
Inferring How could a lunar buggy help the astronauts to explore the earth's surface?

Go Online
PHSchool.com

For: More on lunar exploration
Visit: PHSchool.com
Web Code: cfd-5022

Go Online
PHSchool.com

For: More on lunar exploration
Visit: PHSchool.com
Web Code: cfd-5022

Students can review lunar exploration in an online interactivity.

Use Visuals: Figure 8 L2
Lunar Buggies

Focus Remind students that the first astronauts on the moon did not have lunar buggies.

Teach Ask: **What can you tell about the moon's surface from this picture?** (*It is bumpy and rocky and has craters.*) **Why does the lunar buggy need large, soft wheels?** (*To go over rocks and through small craters*)

Apply Ask: **What advantage do lunar rovers have over astronauts' being on foot?** (*Larger areas can be explored. Also, astronauts can collect more samples to carry in the rover.*)
learning modality: visual

Help Students Read
Summarizing Summarizing the information presented in the text will help students focus on main ideas and remember what they have read. Have students read the passages about missions to the moon and summarize them by restating the main ideas in their own words.

Monitor Progress ———— L2

Oral Presentation Tell students to imagine that they are the first astronauts to step onto the surface of the moon or Mars. Ask students to write a short statement or poem that they will recite as they make that first step.

Answers
Figure 8 It allowed them to explore a larger area.

Reading Checkpoint They learned about the moon's mineral composition. They were also able to estimate when different parts of the moon's surface formed.

Differentiated Instruction

Gifted and Talented L3
Communicating the First Moon Landing Acquire a recording or videotape of the first moon landing, available at local libraries, or direct students to the Internet. Many multimedia encyclopedias also contain audio or video recordings of this event. Have students listen to or watch the recording. Then ask them to take on the role of newscasters creating a broadcast of the event to present to the class. Students can present live broadcasts or record them on audio- or videotape. **learning modality: verbal**

Monitor Progress _____ L2

Answer

Figure 9 A lunar base would provide a proving ground for new technologies that could be used on Mars. Also, from a lunar base, missions could be launched to carry people to Mars.

Assess

Reviewing Key Concepts

1. a. The rivalry in the exploration of space between the United States and the Soviet Union **b.** The launching of *Sputnik I* into orbit **c.** Competition played a great role, causing the United States and the Soviet Union to try harder and achieve great results. **2. a.** The U.S. effort to land astronauts on the moon **b.** *Sputnik I*, NASA formed, Yuri Gagarin orbits Earth, first American in space, John Glenn orbits Earth, first humans on the moon **c.** Yes. The program was successful because humans landed on the moon in 1969.

Reteach   L1

Have students work in pairs to develop a timeline of events in this section. Remind partners to write one or two important details for each event.

Performance Assessment   L2

Drawing Have students work in groups to design and sketch a lunar base station. Drawings should include features necessary to support a team of scientists, such as a water recycling and treatment system. Have students write brief captions explaining the function of each feature of their designs.

All in One Teaching Resources

- Section Summary: *The Space Program*
- Review and Reinforce: *The Space Program*
- Enrich: *The Space Program*

FIGURE 9
Lunar Base
A possible future base on the moon is shown in this painting.
Predicting *How might a lunar base be useful for the future human exploration of Mars?*

New Missions to the Moon The Apollo missions were a tremendous achievement. They yielded fascinating information and memorable images. Yet, the cost of those missions was high, and there were few immediate benefits beyond the knowledge gained about the moon. NASA moved on to other projects. For decades, the moon was largely ignored.

Recently, however, interest in the moon has revived. In 2003, the European Space Agency launched an unpiloted spacecraft to orbit the moon. Its main purpose was to collect data for a detailed map of the moon. Private businesses have funded similar research spacecraft.

Soon, humans may walk again on the moon. In 2004, the United States announced a plan to establish a permanent colony of people on the moon. From such a base, missions could be launched to carry people to Mars.

Section 2 Assessment

 **Target Reading Skills** **Asking Questions** Use the answers to the questions you wrote about the headings to help you answer the questions below.

Reviewing Key Concepts

1. a. **Summarizing** What was the "space race"?
   b. **Identifying** What event began the space race?
   c. **Relating Cause and Effect** What role did competition play in the space race? Who were the competitors?
2. a. **Identifying** What was the Apollo program?
   b. **Sequencing** Place these events in the correct sequence: first humans on the moon, *Sputnik I*, first American in space, John Glenn orbits Earth, NASA formed, Yuri Gagarin orbits Earth.
   c. **Drawing Conclusions** Was the Apollo program successful in meeting President Kennedy's challenge?

Lab zone At-Home Activity

Landmarks in Space Flight
Interview someone who remembers the early space programs. Prepare your questions in advance, such as: What did you think when you heard that *Sputnik* was in orbit? How did you feel when the first Americans went into space? Did you watch any of the space flights on TV? You may want to record your interview and then write it out later.

Lab zone At-Home Activity

Landmarks in Space Flight   L2
Students may be able to interview parents, grandparents, or other relatives or guardians about the first moon landing. Encourage students to prepare a list of *who, what, when, where, why,* and *how* questions before the interview. Provide examples of interviews from newspapers and magazines for students to use as style guides.

Section 3 — Exploring Space Today

Reading Preview

Key Concepts
- What are the roles of space shuttles and space stations?
- What features do space probes have in common?

Key Terms
- space shuttle
- space station
- space probe
- rover

Target Reading Skill
Outlining As you read, make an outline about exploring space. Use the red headings for the main topics and the blue headings for the subtopics.

Exploring Space Today
I. Working in space
A. Space shuttles
B.
II. Space probes
A.

Lab zone — Discover Activity

What Do You Need to Survive in Space?

1. Make a list of everything that would be essential to your well-being if you were placed in a spacecraft in orbit around Earth.
2. Cross out everything on the list that you wouldn't be able to find while in orbit.
3. For each of the items you crossed out, suggest a way you could provide yourself with that essential item while in space.

Think It Over
Drawing Conclusions Is there anything necessary to your well-being that you wouldn't have to take with you into space? How hard would it be to provide everything you need for a journey into space?

Can you imagine living in space? When you're in orbit, you feel weightless, so there is no up or down. Astronaut Janet Kavandi knows how it feels. She spent eleven days aboard the Russian space station *Mir*. As she floated inside the central cabin, she could look into modules that extended outward in every direction.

"It was very amusing to look into one module and see people standing on the wall, working on an experiment. In the adjacent module, someone might be jogging on a treadmill on the ceiling. Beneath your feet, you might see someone having a meal. Above your head, you'd hear the thumping of a body coming toward you, and you'd have to move aside to let him pass."

◄ Janet Kavandi aboard the space shuttle

J ◆ 53

Lab zone — Discover Activity

Skills Focus drawing conclusions

Materials pen and paper

Time 15 minutes

Tips Point out that the same items essential to survival on Earth—clean air, clean water, food, and shelter—are essential to survival in space.

L1 **Think It Over** No. Everything you would need, such as air, water, and food, could not be found in space. It probably would be difficult to bring all of these items into space. Food, for example, would have to be stored and preserved. You would need to design an air-circulation system and a way to store, purify, and reuse water.

Section 3 — Exploring Space Today

Objectives
After this lesson, students will be able to
J.2.3.1 Distinguish between the roles of space shuttles and those of space stations.
J.2.3.2 Identify features that space probes have in common.

Target Reading Skill

Outlining Explain that using an outline format helps students organize information by main topic, subtopic, and details.

Answers

Exploring Space Today
- I. Working in Space
  - A. Space Shuttles
  - B. Space Stations
- II. Space Probes
  - A. How Do Probes Work?
  - B. Exploring With Space Probes

All in One Teaching Resources
- Transparency J19

Preteach

Build Background Knowledge **L1**
Everyday Satellite Technology
Challenge students to think of technologies that they use that depend on satellites. *(Possible answers: Using a GPS system, watching an international television event such as the Olympics, or listening to a weather report)*. Tell students that these types of technology often depend on satellites in orbit around Earth. These satellites are capable of transmitting signals around the world.

Working in Space

Teach Key Concepts   L2

Spacecraft for Living and Working

Focus Remind students that early spacecraft could be used for only one mission.

Teach Ask: **What functions do space shuttles serve?** (*They take satellites into orbit, deliver astronauts to repair damaged satellites, and carry astronauts and equipment to and from space stations.*) **How do space shuttles differ from space stations?** (*Shuttles transport astronauts and equipment. Stations allow people to live and work in space for long periods.*) **How are these spacecraft alike?** (*Both provide areas where astronauts can wear regular clothes and breathe without oxygen tanks.*)

Apply Refer students to Figure 10. Ask: **How are space shuttles similar to and different from the rockets we have studied?** (*Space shuttles use fuel containers that fall away after the fuel is emptied; unlike most rockets, space shuttles are reusable.*) **learning modality: verbal**

Independent Practice   L2

All in One **Teaching Resources**

- Guided Reading and Study Worksheet: *Exploring Space Today*

⊙ **Student Edition on Audio CD**

▶ Address Misconceptions   L2

Distance of the ISS From Earth

Focus Students may think that the ISS is far from Earth.

Teach Tell students that the ISS orbits Earth at an average altitude of 354 kilometers (220 miles) and at an inclination of 51.6 degrees to the equator. Use a string or paper ruler to measure a distance on the surface of a globe approximately 350 km from your location. Mark the string or ruler, and hold it perpendicular to the globe to show the altitude at which the ISS is orbiting.

Apply Ask: **What is one advantage of a low-Earth orbit?** (*Possible answer: The shuttles traveling between the ISS and Earth have less distance to cover.*) **learning modality: visual**

FIGURE 10
The Space Shuttle
The Space Shuttle *Discovery* is launched into space by liquid–fuel powered engines as well as by a pair of reusable solid-fuel booster rockets.
Inferring What is one advantage of a reusable space vehicle?

External fuel tank

Solid fuel rocket booster

Shuttle orbiter

54 ◆ J

Working in Space

After the great success of the moon landings, the question for space exploration was, "What comes next?" Scientists and public officials decided that one goal should be to build space shuttles and space stations where astronauts can live and work.

Space Shuttles Before 1983, spacecraft could be used only once. In contrast, a space shuttle is like an airplane—it can fly, land, and then fly again. A **space shuttle** is a spacecraft that can carry a crew into space, return to Earth, and then be reused for the same purpose. A shuttle includes large rockets that launch it into orbit and then fall away. At the end of a mission, a shuttle returns to Earth by landing like an airplane. **NASA has used space shuttles to perform many important tasks. These include taking satellites into orbit, repairing damaged satellites, and carrying astronauts and equipment to and from space stations.**

During a shuttle mission, astronauts live in a pressurized crew cabin at the front of the shuttle. There, they can wear regular clothes and breathe without an oxygen tank. Behind the crew cabin is a large, open area called the payload bay. The payload bay is like the trailer end of a large truck that carries supplies to stores and factories. A shuttle payload bay might carry a satellite to be released into orbit or a scientific laboratory in which astronauts can perform experiments.

NASA has built six shuttles. Tragically, two—*Challenger* and *Columbia*—were destroyed during flights. After the *Columbia* disaster in 2003, there was much debate about whether to continue the shuttle program. One reason to keep flying space shuttles is to deliver astronauts and supplies to the International Space Station. NASA currently plans to retire the shuttle by 2010 and replace it with a new reusable spacecraft.

FIGURE 11
International Space Station
The International Space Station is a cooperative project involving 16 countries, including the United States, Russia, Japan, and Canada. This is an artist's view of how the station will look when completed.

Space Stations A **space station** is a large artificial satellite on which people can live and work for long periods. **A space station provides a place where long-term observations and experiments can be carried out in space.** In the 1970s and 1980s, both the United States and the Soviet Union placed space stations in orbit. The Soviet space station *Mir* stayed in orbit for 15 years before it fell to Earth in 2001. Astronauts from many countries, including Janet Kavandi and other Americans, spent time aboard *Mir*.

In the 1980s, the United States and 15 other countries began planning the construction of the International Space Station. The first module, or section, of the station was placed into orbit in 1998. Since then, many other modules have been added. On board, astronauts and scientists from many countries are already carrying out experiments in various fields of science. They are also learning more about how humans adapt to space. Figure 11 shows how the space station will look when completed. It will be longer than a football field, and the living space will be about as large as the inside of the largest passenger jet.

The International Space Station has large batteries to guarantee that it always has power. Its main source of power, though, is its eight large arrays of solar panels. Together, the solar panels contain more than 250,000 solar cells, each capable of converting sunlight into electricity. At full power, the solar panels produce enough electricity to power about 55 houses on Earth.

Reading Checkpoint What is a space station?

DISCOVERY CHANNEL SCHOOL

Exploring Space

Video Preview
▶ Video Field Trip
Video Assessment

DISCOVERY CHANNEL SCHOOL Video Field Trip

Exploring Space
Show the Video Field Trip to let students experience exploring space and understand how discoveries are made by astronauts and with space probes. Discussion question: **What exciting finding did robots discover on Mars in 2004?** (*Evidence that liquid water once existed on Mars*)

Lab zone Build **Inquiry** L2

Communicating Knowledge About the International Space Station (ISS)

Materials poster board, markers, information from the NASA Web site

Time 30 minutes

Focus Ask students to suppose that they are scientists from different countries, working together on the ISS.

Teach Organize students into four groups, and assign each group to research and summarize one of the following: design of the space station and how it works; experiments conducted on the ISS; how people live and work on the ISS; and transportation to and from the ISS. Groups can present their findings to the class.

Apply Ask students to summarize how the information learned from living and working on the ISS benefits society as a whole. (*Possible answer: Developing more efficient ways of recycling water*) **learning modality: visual**

Monitor Progress ⬛ L2

Skills Check Ask students to contrast the relationship between the United States and the Soviet Union in regard to the space program in the 1950s and today.

Answers
Figure 10 It is probably less expensive than using new rockets for each mission. It can also be landed like an airplane.

Reading Checkpoint A large artificial satellite on which people can live and work for long periods

Differentiated Instruction

Special Needs L1
Investigating Solar Power Take apart a solar-powered calculator, and show students the wiring inside. Point out that solar cells gather and use energy from the sun. The solar panels of the space station are basically much larger versions of these solar cells. **learning modality: kinesthetic**

Less Proficient Readers L1
Rewriting Headings Suggest that students rewrite the main headings and subheadings in this section as *how, why,* or *what* questions before they read each passage. Encourage students to answer the questions on the basis of what they already know and to revise their answers as they read. **learning modality: verbal**

Space Probes

Teach Key Concepts L2
Data from Space Probes

Focus Have students examine Figure 12.

Teach Ask: **What did scientists learn from the *Lunar Prospector*?** *(Evidence of ice on the moon's surface and identification of minerals)* **What is the mission of the Mars rovers *Opportunity* and *Spirit*?** *(To explore Mars' surface and search for evidence that liquid water existed there in the distant past)*

Apply Tell students that probes launched during the 1970s moved faster through space than later probes. Have students infer why NASA slowed down its probes. *(A fast-moving space probe is difficult to stop—it speeds past its destination, giving it little time to gather data. A slow-moving spacecraft is more easily controlled and can be made to swing around a planet, allowing plenty of time to gather data.)* **learning modality: logical/mathematical**

Space Probes Versus Crewed Mission L1

Materials diagram of the solar system
Time 10 minutes

Focus Tell students that both probes and crewed missions have advantages and disadvantages.

Teach Point out Earth and the moon on the diagram. Then point out Mars. Ask: **Which trip would involve the longest traveling time: a trip to Mars or a trip to the moon?** *(Mars)* Tell students that a trip to Mars would take several months but a trip to the moon would take only a few days. Ask: **How would such a long journey affect people in space?** *(Answers will vary but should suggest that it would be difficult for the crew.)*

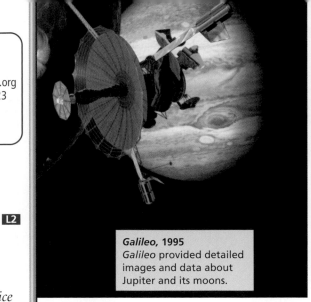

Galileo, 1995
Galileo provided detailed images and data about Jupiter and its moons.

Lunar Prospector, 1998
Lunar Prospector found evidence of water ice and identified other minerals on the moon's surface.

FIGURE 12
Space Probes
These are artist's views of the *Galileo, Lunar Prospector, Mars Exploration Rover,* and *Cassini* space probes.
Comparing and Contrasting *What advantage does a rover have compared to a probe that remains in orbit?*

Space Probes

Since space exploration began in the 1950s, only 24 people have traveled as far as the moon—and no one has traveled farther. Yet, during this period space scientists have gathered great amounts of information about other parts of the solar system. This data was collected by space probes. A **space probe** is a spacecraft that carries scientific instruments that can collect data, but has no human crew.

How Do Probes Work? Each space probe is designed for a specific mission. Some probes are designed to land on a certain planet. Other probes are designed to fly by and collect data about more than one planet. Thus, each probe is unique. Still, all probes have some features in common. **Each space probe has a power system to produce electricity, a communication system to send and receive signals, and scientific instruments to collect data and perform experiments.**

The scientific instruments that a probe contains depend on the probe's mission. Some probes are equipped to photograph and analyze the atmosphere of a planet. Other probes are equipped to land on a planet and analyze the materials on its surface. Some probes have small robots called **rovers** that move around on the surface. A rover typically has instruments that collect and analyze soil and rock samples.

Apply Ask: **What are some advantages of having space probes go to Mars instead?** *(Possible answers: If the mission fails, no lives would be lost. Costs would be lower.)* Ask: **What advantages would a crewed mission have?** *(Possible answer: People could move around easily and their would be more flexibility to explore and investigate.)* **learning modality: visual**

Mars Exploration Rovers, 2004
Two rovers, *Opportunity* and *Spirit,* explored Mars's surface and found evidence of ancient water.

Cassini, 2004
Cassini is exploring Saturn's moons. It will launch a smaller probe, *Huygens,* to explore Titan, Saturn's largest moon.

Exploring With Space Probes To date, probes have visited or passed near to all the planets except Pluto. They have also explored many moons, asteroids, and comets. The information gathered by probes has given scientists tremendous new insights about the environments on the different planets. These probes have helped to solve many of the mysteries of the solar system.

✔ **Reading Checkpoint** What is a rover?

Section 3 Assessment

🎯 **Target Reading Skill Outlining** Use the information in your outline about exploring space to answer the questions below.

Reviewing Key Concepts

1. **a. Describing** What is the space shuttle? What is its main advantage?
   b. Defining What is a space station?
   c. Comparing and Contrasting What are the roles of space shuttles and space stations in the space program?
2. **a. Summarizing** What is a space probe?
   b. Listing List three features that are common to all space probes.
   c. Making Judgments What do you think are some advantages and disadvantages of a space probe compared to a piloted spacecraft?

Writing in Science

News Report As a newspaper reporter, you are covering the launch of a new space probe. Write a brief news story, including details on the probe's mission and how the probe works. What planet will it explore? What question will it try to answer?

Chapter 2 J ◆ 57

Lab zone Chapter **Project**

Keep Students on Track Check that students are completing their designs and sketches of the model vehicles. Approve all designs before students begin building their models.

Writing in Science

Writing Mode: Description
Scoring Rubric
4 Exceeds criteria by including full details about the probe's mission and how it works, written in the style of an informative news article
3 Meets criteria, but is uninteresting
2 Includes only brief details
1 Includes inaccurate and incomplete information

Monitor Progress _____ L2

Answers
Figure 12 A rover can move around on a planet's surface and obtain a closeup view. It can also collect and analyze materials such as soil and rock.

✔ **Reading Checkpoint** A small robot that can move around on the surface of a planet or moon

Assess

Reviewing Key Concepts

1. a. A spacecraft that can carry crew members into space and return them to Earth; it can perform this task repeatedly. **b.** A large artificial satellite on which people can live and work for long periods **c.** Space shuttles take satellites into orbit, deliver crew to repair damaged satellites, and carry astronauts and equipment to and from space stations. Space stations permit long-term experiments and observations to occur in space.
2. a. An uncrewed spacecraft with various scientific instruments that can collect data, including visual images **b.** A power system that produces electricity, a communication system to send and receive signals, and scientific instruments to collect data and perform experiments **c.** Possible answers: Advantages: Lower cost because items essential for human survival need not be carried on uncrewed space probes, no risk to astronauts; Disadvantages: Less flexibility, no one is present to repair problems that the space probe might encounter.

Reteach L1

Draw a chart on the board with three columns: *Shuttles, Stations,* and *Probes.* Have students provide details to compare and contrast these spacecraft as you list them.

Performance Assessment L2

Drawing Have each student create a poster showing how a space station is launched into orbit and used for practical applications on Earth.

All in One Teaching Resources
• Section Summary: *Exploring Space Today*
• Review and Reinforce: *Exploring Space Today*
• Enrich: *Exploring Space Today*

Section 4
· Tech & Design ·
Using Space Science on Earth

Objectives

After this lesson, students will be able to

J.2.4.1 Explain how the conditions in space are different from those on Earth.

J.2.4.2 Identify the benefits that space technology has provided for modern society.

J.2.4.3 Describe some uses of satellites orbiting Earth.

Target Reading Skill

Identifying Main Ideas Explain that identifying main ideas and details helps students sort facts into groups. Each group can have a main topic, subtopics, and details.

Answers

Possible answers include the following:

Detail: Medical science—technology of the space program has led to lasers that can clean clogged arteries.

Detail: Materials—fire-resistant material developed for spacesuits is used in fireproof clothing.

Detail: Consumer products—cordless power tools were first developed for astronauts.

All in One Teaching Resources

• Transparency J20

Preteach

Build Background Knowledge L2

Remote Sensing

Ask students whether they have ever used a remote-controlled toy, such as a model airplane or car. Have them describe how they controlled the toy's movements. *(By using a control box to make the toy move)* Point out that they did not need to touch the toy directly to make it work. Satellites receive signals in a similar way. Tell students that they will learn more about satellites in this section.

Reading Preview

Key Concepts

• How are the conditions in space different from those on Earth?

• How has space technology benefited modern society?

• What are some uses of satellites orbiting Earth?

Key Terms

• vacuum • microgravity
• space spinoff
• remote sensing
• geosynchronous orbit

Target Reading Skill

Identifying Main Ideas As you read the Space Spinoffs section, write the main idea in a graphic organizer like the one below. Then write three supporting details that give examples of the main idea.

Main Idea

The space program has produced many spinoffs in areas such as . . .

Detail	Detail	Detail

Lab zone Discover **Activity**

Which Tool Would Be More Useful in Space?

1. Observe your teacher using two types of drills.
2. Pick up each drill and examine how it works.
3. Repeat Step 2 for a space pen and a regular pen.

Think It Over

Drawing Conclusions What is the main difference between the two drills? The pens? Which drill would be more useful to have while constructing the International Space Station? Why? How would a space pen be useful in space?

You've probably used a joystick to play a video game. A joystick is a great way to control images on a screen. It's easy to use because it is designed to fit the hand just right. Joystick controllers have many uses besides video games. They're so well engineered that people with disabilities can use them to operate a wheelchair.

The joystick was invented for controlling airplanes. It was later improved by NASA for the space program. Apollo astronauts used a joystick to operate a lunar rover on the moon. From the surface of the moon to video games on Earth—it's not such a stretch. Many materials and devices have made a similar transition from use in space to everyday use by people on Earth.

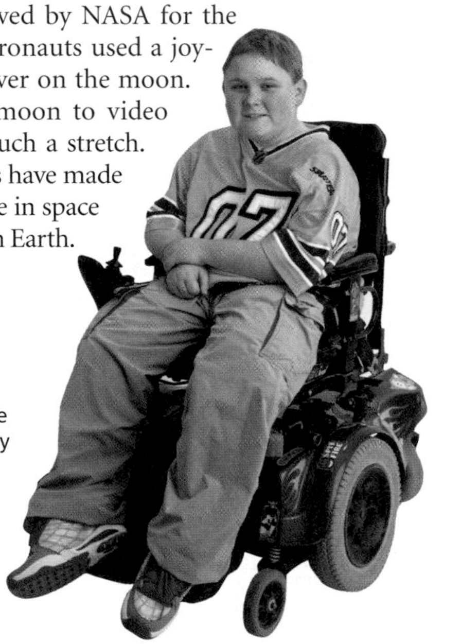

FIGURE 13
Joystick Controls
The joysticks used for some wheelchairs were originally improved for the space program.

Lab zone Discover **Activity**

Skills Focus drawing conclusions L1

Materials cordless drill, drill with electric cord, space pen, regular pen

Time 15 minutes

Tips If you cannot obtain the items, use photographs from catalogs that describe the features of the items.

CAUTION: *Do not allow students to plug in or turn on the drills.*

Expected Outcome Students will find that certain items are better suited for work in space.

Think It Over The cordless drill would be more useful on the International Space Station because it can operate without being plugged into an electrical system. Weightless astronauts can use the space pen while floating in any position.

The Challenges of Space

Astronauts who travel into space face conditions that are very different from those on Earth. **Conditions in space that differ from those on Earth include near vacuum, extreme temperatures, and microgravity.** Many types of engineers and scientists have worked together to respond to the challenges of space.

Vacuum Space is nearly a vacuum. A **vacuum** is a place that is empty of all matter. Except for a few stray atoms and molecules, most of space is empty. Since there is no air in space, there is no oxygen for astronauts to breathe. To protect astronauts, spacecraft must be airtight.

Because there is no air, there is nothing to hold the sun's heat. In direct sunlight, the surface of a spacecraft heats up to high temperatures. But in shadow, temperatures fall to very low levels. Spacecraft must be well insulated to protect astronauts against the extreme temperatures outside.

Microgravity Astronauts in orbit experience a feeling of weightlessness, or **microgravity**. Their mass is the same as it was on Earth, but on a scale their weight would register as zero. Although they are in microgravity, they are still under the influence of Earth's gravity. In fact, Earth's gravity is holding them in orbit. Astronauts in orbit feel weightless because they are falling through space with their spacecraft. They don't fall to Earth because their inertia keeps them moving forward.

Space engineers must create systems and devices that are capable of working in microgravity. For example, drink containers must be designed so that their contents do not simply float off. Long periods in microgravity can cause health problems. Scientists are trying to discover how to reduce the effects of microgravity on people.

FIGURE 14
Microgravity
This astronaut appears to be floating in space, but he is actually falling through space at the same rate as the nearby spacecraft.
Inferring *Why doesn't the astronaut fall directly down toward Earth?*

Reading Checkpoint What is microgravity?

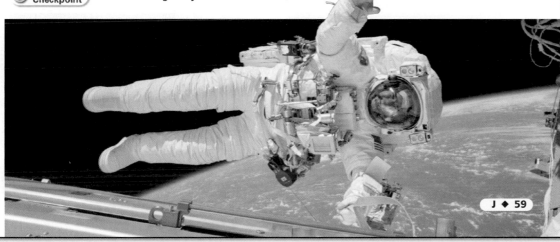

J ◆ 59

Differentiated Instruction

English Learners/Beginning L1
Vocabulary: Word Analysis Have students look up the word *astronaut* and write down the meanings of its prefix and word part. (*Astro-* means "star," and naut *means* "sailor.") **learning modality: verbal**

English Learners/Intermediate L2
Vocabulary: Word Analysis Have students look up the prefix *micro-* in the dictionary and the definition of *gravity*. Ask them to write a definition of microgravity in their own words and then contrast the meanings of the terms *microgravity* and *gravity*. **learning modality: verbal**

The Challenges of Space

Teach Key Concepts L2
Conditions in Space

Focus Remind students that space has different gravity conditions and no air.

Teach Ask: **What is a vacuum?** (*A place that is empty of all matter*) **Why are there temperature extremes in space?** (*There is virtually no matter, so there is nothing to hold the sun's heat. When sunlight strikes an object in space, the object heats up. When sunlight is blocked, temperatures fall.*) **Is it correct to say that no gravity acts on astronauts orbiting Earth?** (*No. Gravity acts on the astronauts, but the astronaut and the spacecraft are falling through space together and falling around Earth, rather than toward it, because of their inertia.*)

Apply Ask: **What features do you think spacesuits must have to protect astronauts from the extreme temperatures of space?** (*Possible answer: Insulation to protect against both cold and heat and a cooling/ventilation system to protect against heat*) **learning modality: logical/mathematical**

Independent Practice L2

All in One Teaching Resources

• Guided Reading and Study Worksheet: *Using Space Science on Earth*

⊙ **Student Edition on Audio CD**

Monitor Progress ———— L2

Writing Have each student write a brief paragraph that summarizes how conditions in space differ from those on Earth.

Answer
Figure 14 Inertia keeps the astronaut moving forward so that he stays in orbit with the spacecraft.

Reading Checkpoint The condition in which people and objects in orbit experience weightlessness because they are falling together through space with the spacecraft

Space Spinoffs

Teach Key Concepts L2
Benefits of Space Science

Focus Remind students that the space program has provided many benefits beyond space exploration.

Teach Ask: **Why are spacecraft and spacesuits airtight and well insulated?** *(To protect astronauts against the near vacuum and extreme temperatures of space)* **How has the technology used to protect spacecraft and spacesuits been applied on Earth?** *(Insulating materials are used in homes, cars, trucks, and firefighters' clothes.)* **What types of space spinoffs are used in medicine?** *(Lasers, pacemakers, and computer-aided imaging techniques)* **What are some spinoffs that benefit consumers?** *(Joystick controllers, cordless power tools, and bar codes)*

Apply Ask: **Why do you think so many of the devices developed by the space program are miniaturized and lightweight?** *(Spacecraft travel faster and use less fuel when they carry less mass. Also, smaller devices take up less room.)* **learning modality: logical/ mathematical**

Help Students Read
Thinking Aloud Refer to the Content Refresher for guidance in thinking aloud. Set the example for this strategy by verbalizing your own thought processes while reading aloud from this section. Encourage student volunteers to read a passage while quietly verbalizing their thought processes. Then have a class discussion about the advantages students found in staying focused on a logical thought process when reading in this manner.

FIGURE 15
Spinoffs From the Space Program
Many technologies that were developed for the space program have proved useful on Earth as well. A few of these technologies are shown here.
Applying Concepts *What advantage is there to fog-free vision in space? On Earth?*

▲ Miniature parts developed for space have been adapted for use on Earth. Artificial limbs have been made with controls as small as coins.

Space Spinoffs

The scientists and engineers who have worked on the space program have developed thousands of new materials and devices for use in space. Many of these items have proved useful on Earth, as well. An item that has uses on Earth but was originally developed for use in space is called a **space spinoff**. Often such spinoffs are modified somewhat for use on Earth.

The space program has developed thousands of products that affect many aspects of modern society, including consumer products, new materials, medical devices, and communications satellites. Figure 15 shows a few familiar examples.

Consumer Products Space spinoffs include many devices that are used in consumer products. The joystick controller is one example. The bar codes on every product you buy at a grocery store are another space spinoff. Similar bar codes were developed by NASA to keep an accurate inventory of the many parts used in spacecraft.

Cordless power tools were also originally developed for astronauts. There's no place to "plug in" a tool when repairing a satellite in space. Cordless, rechargeable tools met the need for work in space. Now they're very popular here on Earth. Other examples of consumer product spinoffs from the space program include scratch-resistant lenses, freeze-dried foods, shock-absorbing helmets, and smoke detectors.

▼ A metal alloy of nickel and titanium used in dental braces was originally developed for space equipment such as antennas.

New Materials A variety of materials were first developed by chemists and engineers for use in spacecraft. For example, flexible metal eyeglass frames are made with memory metals—metals that "remember" their former shapes when bent. The composite materials used in modern tennis rackets and golf clubs were developed to make spacecraft components lightweight yet strong. The athletic shoes you wear might contain a shock-absorbing material developed for astronauts' moon boots. A clear, ceramic material used for invisible dental braces was the result of research to make tough materials for spacecraft.

Highly efficient insulating materials were developed to protect spacecraft against radiation in space. These insulating materials are now being used in houses, cars, and trucks. Fire-resistant material developed for spacesuits is used in fireproof clothing and firefighter's suits.

Medical Devices Medical science has benefited greatly from the technology of the space program. Medical spinoffs include devices that use lasers to clean clogged arteries and pacemakers for hearts. These pacemakers use longer-life batteries originally developed for space power systems. Most hospitals use computer-aided imaging techniques developed for use on the moon during the Apollo program.

 Reading Checkpoint Why did NASA develop cordless power tools?

▼ Fire-resistant material developed for spacesuits is used in fireproof clothing such as suits worn by race-car drivers and firefighters.

◄ Many bicyclists use a lightweight, aerodynamic helmet with cooling vents that was developed with NASA's help.

◄ The design of the Apollo helmet, which gave the astronauts fog-free sight, has been adapted for use in ski goggles.

Chapter 2 J ◆ 61

Differentiated Instruction

Special Needs L1
Understanding Memory Metals Have each student squeeze a rubber ball and then release it. Ask: **What happened to the ball's shape when it was squeezed?** (*The shape changed.*) **What happened when the ball was released?** (*It regained its former shape.*) **How is the rubber ball like a memory metal?** (*They also regain their former shape after being compressed.*)
learning modality: kinesthetic

Less Proficient Readers L1
Comparing and Contrasting Ask students to use Figure 15 to make a two-column chart. In the first column, students write how each item is used in space. In the second column, students write how the item is used on Earth. Then have students read the passages about spinoffs and classify the spinoffs in the same way.
learning modality: visual

Lab zone Build Inquiry L2

Problem-Solving Space Challenges

Materials pen and paper
Time 30 minutes

Focus Ask students how many cordless tools are in their homes. Ask: **Why did NASA develop cordless tools?** (*There is no place to plug in a tool when you are repairing a satellite in outer space.*)

Teach Organize students into groups of four. Challenge each group to identify a problem faced by astronauts in space. Then have students develop and illustrate solutions.

Apply Have students describe how their solutions could be adapted for use on Earth.
learning modality: logical/mathematical

Satellites

Teach Key Concepts L2
Remote Sensing

Focus Remind students that observation satellites use remote sensing to gather data.

Teach Ask: **What types of data do the satellites collect?** (*Possible answers: Information about the atmosphere, such as weather systems; information about Earth's surface, such as patterns of rainfall*)

Apply Ask: **What might be the advantage of gathering such data from above Earth's surface?** (*Possible answer: More area is visible from above; large-scale patterns can be seen; no obstacles are in the way.*) **learning modality: logical/mathematical**

Writing Have each student write a paragraph that describes how space spinoffs have affected his or her life. Students can save their paragraphs in their portfolios. Portfolio

Answers
Figure 15 An astronaut on a spacewalk cannot remove his or her faceplate to clean it. On Earth, people engaging in activities requiring both hands and constant use of eye protection no longer need to stop what they are doing to clear fog from their goggles.

Reading Checkpoint There is no place to plug in a tool in space.

Monitor Progress ———— L2

Answers
Figure 16 Desert

Reading Checkpoint Gathering information about Earth's surface without being in direct contact with it

Assess

Reviewing Key Concepts

1. a. Near vacuum, temperature extremes, and microgravity **b.** Spacecraft are well insulated and airtight.
2. a. An item that was originally designed for use in space but has uses on Earth **b.** Medical spinoffs include devices that use lasers to clean clogged arteries, pacemakers that use longer-lasting batteries, and computer-aided imaging techniques.
c. Possible answer: Insulating materials that protect spacecraft from radiation are used on Earth in homes.
3. a. Possible answer: transmitting television signals, gathering weather data, and relaying computer data **b.** Because a geosynchronous satellite stays in the same place over Earth, signals to and from the satellite can always be directed to and from the same location in the sky. **c.** Scientists can examine satellite images of an area taken over a period of years to find out whether the area covered by rainforest is changing.

Reteach L1

Have students look at Figure 15 to describe conditions in space that have led to the development of space spinoffs.

Performance Assessment L2

Skills Check Have students make concept maps that show different space spinoffs and their uses.

All in One Teaching Resources

- Section Summary: *Using Space Science on Earth*
- Review and Reinforce: *Using Space Science on Earth*
- Enrich: *Using Space Science on Earth*

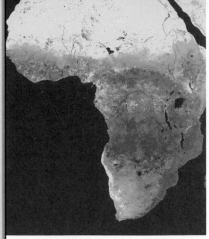

FIGURE 16
Remote Sensing
This satellite image shows patterns of vegetation in Africa. It is a false-color image, meaning that the colors have been adjusted to make certain features more obvious.
Inferring *What do you think the yellow areas in the image represent?*

Satellites

When a World Cup soccer final is played, almost the entire world can watch! Today, hundreds of satellites are in orbit around Earth, relaying television signals from one part of the planet to another. Satellites also relay telephone signals and computer data. **Satellites are used for communications and for collecting weather data and other scientific data.**

Observation satellites are used for many purposes, including tracking weather systems, mapping Earth's surface, and observing changes in Earth's environment. Observation satellites collect data using **remote sensing,** which is the collection of information about Earth and other objects in space without being in direct contact. Modern computers take the data collected by satellites and produce images for various purposes. For example, Figure 16 shows vegetation patterns in Africa. Satellite data might also be used to analyze the amount of rainfall over a wide area, or they might be used to discover where oil deposits lie underground.

Satellites are placed in different orbits depending on their purpose. Most communications satellites are placed in a geosynchronous orbit. In a **geosynchronous orbit,** a satellite orbits Earth at the same rate as Earth rotates and thus stays over the same place on Earth all the time. Read the *Technology and Society* feature on pages 64–65 to learn more about communications satellites.

Reading Checkpoint What is remote sensing?

Section 4 Assessment

Target Reading Skill Identifying Main Ideas Use your graphic organizer to help you answer Question 2 below.

Reviewing Key Concepts

1. a. Listing Name three ways that conditions in space are different from conditions on Earth.
   b. Relating Cause and Effect How have engineers designed spacecraft to operate in the special conditions of space?
2. a. Defining What is a space spinoff?
   b. Summarizing How has medical science benefited from the space program?
   c. Comparing and Contrasting Choose one space spinoff and compare how it is used in space and on Earth.

3. a. Listing Name three uses of satellites that affect everyday life.
   b. Inferring What advantage would there be to placing a satellite in geosynchronous orbit?
   c. Designing Experiments How could a scientist use satellites to determine whether a rain forest was becoming smaller over time?

Lab zone At-Home Activity

Spinoffs at Home Look back at the various space spinoffs discussed in the chapter. Then, with a family member, make a list of space spinoffs in your home.

Lab zone At-Home Activity

Spinoffs at Home L2 Before students conduct the activity at home, review with them the space spinoffs listed in this section. Additional space spinoffs can be found on the NASA web site. Along with a family member, each student can then check off a list of items found at home.

Lab zone Chapter Project

Keep Students on Track Check that students have built their model vehicles. Allow students to test their vehicles outside in an area that resembles the landscape of a barren or rocky planet. Before conducting the tests, have students review the criteria they will use to evaluate their vehicle's performance.

Space Spinoffs

Problem

Which blanket protects better against heat loss?

Skills Focus

graphing, drawing conclusions

Materials

- 1 foil blanket piece • 1 cloth blanket piece
- 3 thermometers • 1 beaker, 600 mL • ice
- 3 identical small test tubes • hot water
- 3 identical large test tubes • cotton balls
- cellophane tape or rubber bands • tap water

Procedure 🔬 🧤 🔧

1. On a separate sheet of paper, copy the data table below to record your observations.

2. Wrap the outside of one small test tube with the foil blanket piece. Wrap a second small test tube with the cloth blanket piece. Use tape or rubber bands to secure the blankets. Leave the third small test tube unwrapped.

3. Fill each of the three small test tubes half full with hot water. Be sure to use the same volume of water in each test tube. Insert a thermometer into each small test tube. Use cotton to "seal" the top of the small test tube and to hold the thermometer in place. Then, insert each small test tube into a large test tube.

4. Put ice in the beaker and fill the beaker two-thirds of the way with water.

5. Put the large test tubes into the ice water. Do not let water enter the test tubes. Record the starting temperatures of all three thermometers.

6. Allow the test tubes to sit in the ice water bath for about 10 minutes. Every minute note the temperature of each thermometer and record the results in your data table.

Analyze and Conclude

1. **Graphing** Graph the temperature over time for each of the thermometers.

2. **Calculating** Calculate the difference between the starting and ending temperatures of each thermometer. Which thermometer was best protected against heat loss?

3. **Controlling Variables** What was the purpose of the third, unwrapped small test tube?

4. **Drawing Conclusions** Which type of blanket protects better against heat loss? Explain.

5. **Communicating** Write an advertisement for the blanket that proved to be the best insulator. In the ad, describe the test procedures you used to justify your claim. Also explain why this blanket would benefit consumers.

Design an Experiment

The activity you just completed tested how well different materials protected against the loss of heat. Design an experiment that would test how well the same blankets would protect against an increase in heat. Obtain your teacher's approval before conducting your experiment.

Data Table

Time (minutes)	Temperature (°C)		
	Foil-Wrapped Thermometer	Cloth-Wrapped Thermometer	Unwrapped Thermometer
0			
1			

Space Spinoffs L2

Prepare for Inquiry

Skills Objectives

After this lab, students will be able to

- measure and compare temperatures at regular intervals
- interpret the data gathered to determine which type of blanket gives better protection against heat loss

🕐 **Prep Time** 30 minutes

Class Time 40 minutes

All in One **Teaching Resources**

- Lab Worksheet: *Space Spinoffs*

Safety

Advise students to use caution working with thermometers because these can easily roll off lab tables and break. Review the safety guidelines in Appendix A.

Guide Inquiry

Introduce the Procedure

- Describe the basic strategy of testing and measuring, and ask students how they will know which blanket is more effective. (*It will have the smallest temperature change over time.*)
- Students may work in groups or individually, depending on material availability.
- Tell students to stop testing if all thermometers reach a temperature of 0°C, the temperature of the ice bath.

Expected Outcome

The three thermometers will cool to well below room temperature, but not to 0°C. The cloth-wrapped thermometer protects against heat loss better than the foil-wrapped blanket.

Extend Inquiry

Design an Experiment

One possible design would be to place the thermometers under a light source rather than in ice to test heat gain. For this design, placing the thermometers in test tubes would be unnecessary. An alternative would be to repeat the experiment using hot water instead of cold water.

Analyze and Conclude

1. The graph should have time on the *x*-axis and temperature on the *y*-axis. All three thermometers can be graphed on the same graph. Each will have its own curved line.

2. Results will vary depending on room tempature and the amounts of insulating material and ice used. The cloth-wrapped thermometer protects best against heat loss.

3. The test tubes in which the unwrapped thermometer is placed also cools down. This test tube serves as a control to show the effects of the insulating materials on heat loss.

4. The cloth blanket protects against heat loss better than the foil blanket. Data show that the temperature did not drop as far when a thermometer was wrapped with cloth.

5. Answers will vary. Accept any creative advertisement that incorporates test procedures and provides data to support the claim.

Technology and Society

Communications Satellites

Key Concept
Technology has changed the way people around the world communicate.

Build Background Knowledge
Recalling Space Exploration Missions
Ask: **What was the purpose of the first satellites?** (*They intiated the space race between the United States and the Soviet Union. Their purpose was mainly scientific and experimental.*) **What are some purposes of satellites that have been launched since then?** (*Later satellites have been used for communications and for collecting weather data and other scientific data.*)

Introduce the Discussion
Tell students that most cell phones still use Earth-based towers for relaying signals. Explain that these towers are high because they depend on "line-of-sight" connections with cell phones. As a result, higher towers can relay signals from farther away; that is, higher towers cover more territory. Ask: **What would be the advantage of using a satellite instead of a tower for cell phones?** (*The satellite is thousands of kilometers above Earth's surface. The difference in height means that the territory covered by the satellite is many times greater than that covered by the tower.*)

Facilitate the Discussion
Have students read the feature and answer the first question in *Weigh the Impact*. Ask students to list and discuss ways in which communications satellites have affected their own lives. Many may immediately think of television. Prompt students to consider other examples in which instant communications may be important or even lifesaving. Some examples might be the onboard GPS systems now available in some cars or the network between hospitals that allows doctors to diagnose problems in remote areas.

Communications Satellites

What do watching TV, talking on a cellular phone, and sending e-mails have in common? Satellites orbiting Earth make these types of communication possible. Using microwaves, communications satellites receive and transmit radio, telephone, TV, computer data, and other signals. This technology has changed the way people around the globe communicate.

Orbiting Satellites

Communications satellites orbit Earth at different speeds and different altitudes. One type—geostationary satellites—are especially useful for long-distance communication because they orbit Earth at the same rate as Earth rotates. As a result, these satellites remain over fixed points on Earth. Geostationary satellites orbit at an altitude of about 35,880 km. Today there are more than 150 geostationary satellites located in a band around the Equator.

Bus
The bus is the satellite framework. It holds and protects the computer, the engine, and other equipment. Batteries in the bus store the energy that's used to power the satellite.

Kick Motor
The kick motor maintains the orbit of the satellite.

Receiving Antenna
This antenna receives signals sent from Earth and converts them to messages that the onboard computer understands.

Ground Station
These stations receive and transmit signals.

Background

History of Science The concept of communications satellites was first proposed by Arthur C. Clark in 1945. Clark, who would later become famous as a science fiction writer, was an electronics officer in the Royal Air Force in England at that time. He suggested that satellites in orbit around Earth could relay communications among the world's large landmasses. In 1962 the first operating communications satellite, *Telstar*, was launched into orbit. Unlike prior satellites, *Telstar* was privately sponsored. Its purpose was to allow instantaneous transoceanic television broadcasts. Because *Telstar* was not in a geostationary orbit, it could relay signals for only 20 minutes at a time. It completed its elliptical orbit every 2 hours and 37 minutes.

Solar Panels
Solar cells in the solar panels convert sunlight into electricity. Batteries store the energy that's used to power the satellite.

Transmitting Antenna
This antenna changes data into signals that can be sent to Earth.

Thermal Blanket
This thin foil protects the satellite from extreme temperatures.

Onboard Computer
A computer controls and monitors all parts of the satellite.

Ground Station

Cellular phone signals are sent by communications satellites.

The Cost of Going Global

Communications satellites can relay signals, allowing the immediate exchange of information worldwide. Like all technology, though, there are trade-offs to using satellites. Earth's atmosphere can interfere with signals, causing problems such as static and time delays. Satellites cost hundreds of millions of dollars to build and even more to launch into space. When they are no longer useful, many burn up in space or become space junk.

Weigh the Impact

1. Identify the Need
How have communications satellites changed people's lives?

2. Research
Research the uses of communications satellites over the last 20 years. List their influences on society.

3. Write
In several paragraphs, describe ways in which you and your family use this satellite technology in your daily lives.

Go Online
PHSchool.com
For: More on communications satellites
Visit: PHSchool.com
Web Code: cfh-5020

J ◆ 65

Go Online
PHSchool.com
For: More on communications satellites
Visit: PHSchool.com
Web Code: cfh-5020
Students can research communications satellites online.

Weigh the Impact

1. Students might suggest that people have more access to television broadcasts. They might also discuss how satellites are used for making many long-distance phone calls and for transmitting computer data and images.

2. Research should find at least four uses of communications satellites and their influence on society. Answers might include instant news broadcasting that allows people everywhere on Earth to react at once to events. Others might include the use of cell phones, pagers, faxes, or the Internet.

3. Students' paragraphs should describe ways in which students and their families use satellite technology in their daily lives.

Extend

Encourage students to research what scientists are predicting about the future of communications satellites. How will we be using them in 20 years? What effect will they have on the way we live?

Help Students Read

Building Vocabulary

Word Forms Students may have seen several of the key terms for this chapter used in different contexts. Help them relate these familiar meanings to section content. Ask: **What form might shuttles take in a city?** *(Buses and vans that move people between buildings or to and from an airport are sometimes referred to as shuttles.)* **What is a satellite medical facility?** *(A facility, such as a clinic, that is associated with a larger facility, such as a hospital)* Ask students to relate how the objects described by these terms are similar to the objects described by the terms in space science.

Paraphrasing Ask students to write the key terms on a sheet of paper. Instruct students to write a definition, in their own words, for each term. Then ask them to compare each of their own definitions with the definition given in the text. Tell students to revise their definitions, if necessary.

Connecting Concepts

Concept Maps Help students develop one way to show how the information in this chapter is related. Space exploration uses many technologies that benefit people on Earth and provide knowledge about our solar system and the universe. Have students brainstorm to identify the key concepts, key terms, details, and examples. Then ask students to write each item on a self-stick note, and attach the note at random on chart paper or on the board.

Point out that this concept map will be organized in hierarchical order. Tell students to begin at the top with the key concepts. To guide students to categorize the information on the self-stick notes, ask these questions:

1 The Science of Rockets

Key Concepts

- Rocket technology originated in China hundreds of years ago and gradually spread to other parts of the world.
- A rocket moves forward when gases shooting out the back of the rocket push it in the opposite direction.
- The main advantage of a multistage rocket is that the total weight of the rocket is greatly reduced as the rocket rises.

Key Terms

rocket
thrust
velocity
orbital velocity
escape velocity

2 The Space Program

Key Concepts

- The space race began in 1957 when the Soviets launched the satellite *Sputnik I* into orbit. The United States responded by speeding up its own space program.
- The American effort to land astronauts on the moon was named the Apollo program.

Key Term

satellite

3 Exploring Space Today

Key Concepts

- NASA has used space shuttles to perform many important tasks. These include taking satellites into orbit, repairing damaged satellites, and carrying astronauts and equipment to and from space stations.
- A space station provides a place where long-term observations and experiments can be carried out in space.
- Space probes contain a power system to produce electricity, a communication system to send and receive signals, and scientific instruments to collect data and perform experiments.

Key Terms

space shuttle
space station
space probe
rover

4 Using Space Science on Earth

Key Concepts

- Conditions in space that differ from those on Earth include the near vacuum, temperature extremes, and microgravity.
- The space program has developed thousands of products that affect many aspects of modern society, including consumer products, new materials, medical devices, and communications satellites.
- Satellites are used for communications and for collecting weather data and other scientific data.

Key Terms

vacuum
microgravity
space spinoff
remote sensing
geosynchronous orbit

What was the Apollo program? How are spacecrafts launched into space? What are space spinoffs?

Prompt students by using connecting words or phrases, such as "can be done using" and "can lead to," to indicate the basis for the organization of the map. The phrases should form a sentence that connects a set of concepts.

Answer Accept logical presentations by students.

All in One Teaching Resources

- Key Terms Review: *Exploring Space*

Review and Assessment

Organizing Information

Comparing and Contrasting Copy the graphic organizer onto a separate sheet of paper. Then complete it and add a title. (For more on Comparing and Contrasting, see the Skills Handbook.)

Astronaut	Year	Spacecraft	Accomplishment
Yuri Gagarin	1961	a. ___?___	First human in space
Alan Shepard	b. ___?___	Freedom 7	c. ___?___
d. ___?___	1962	Friendship 7	e. ___?___
Neil Armstrong	f. ___?___	g. ___?___	First human to walk on the moon

Reviewing Key Terms

Choose the letter of the best answer.

1. A device that expels gas in one direction to move in the opposite direction is a
   a. rocket. b. space probe.
   c. space station. d. rover.

2. To fly beyond a planet's gravitational pull, a spacecraft must reach
   a. velocity.
   b. orbital velocity.
   c. escape velocity.
   d. geosynchronous orbit.

3. Any object that revolves around another object in space is called a
   a. vacuum.
   b. space station.
   c. satellite.
   d. rocket.

4. A spacecraft that can carry a crew into space, return to Earth, and then be reused for the same purpose is a
   a. rover.
   b. space shuttle.
   c. space station.
   d. space probe.

5. Acquiring information about Earth and other objects in space without being in direct contact with these worlds is called
   a. microgravity.
   b. spinoff.
   c. thrust.
   d. remote sensing.

If the statement is true, write *true*. If it is false, change the underlined word or words to make the statement true.

6. The reaction force that propels a rocket forward is called <u>microgravity</u>.

7. The velocity a rocket must reach to establish an orbit in space is <u>escape velocity</u>.

8. A large artificial satellite on which people can live for long periods is a <u>space station</u>.

9. An item that has uses on Earth, but was originally developed for use in space is called a <u>space shuttle</u>.

10. A satellite in <u>geosynchronous orbit</u> stays over the same place on Earth all the time.

Writing in Science

Descriptive Paragraph Imagine that you are a scientist planning the first human expedition to Mars. In a detailed paragraph, list some of the major challenges that such a mission would face and provide possible solutions. Think about the physical stresses of space travel and how the crew's basic needs will be met.

Discovery CHANNEL SCHOOL

Exploring Space
Video Preview
Video Field Trip
▶ Video Assessment

Chapter 2 J ◆ 67

Go Online
PHSchool.com
For: Self-Assessment
Visit: PHSchool.com
Web Code: cfa-5020
Students can take an online practice test that is automatically scored.

 **Teaching Resources**
- Transparency J21
- Chapter Test
- Performance Assessment Teacher Notes
- Performance Assessment Teacher Worksheet
- Performance Assessment Scoring Rubric

ExamView® Computer Test Bank CD-ROM

Review and Assessment

Organizing Information
a. *Vostok 1*
b. 1961
c. First American in space
d. John Glenn
e. First American to orbit Earth
f. 1969
g. *Apollo 11* or *Eagle*

Reviewing Key Terms
1. a 2. c 3. c 4. b 5. d
6. thrust
7. orbital velocity
8. true
9. space spinoff
10. true

Writing in Science

Writing Mode: Description

Scoring Rubric

4 Exceeds criteria by including descriptive detail of challenges and providing novel solutions to the problems

3 Meets all criteria, but description lacks interest

2 Includes some challenges and solutions, but includes inaccurate information

1 Is incomplete and inaccurate

Discovery CHANNEL SCHOOL Video Assessment

Exploring Space

Show the Video Assessment to review chapter content and as a prompt for the writing assignment Discussion questions: **Describe the first manned space flight.** *(In 1961, Yuri Gagarin orbited once around Earth and returned to Earth 1 hour and 48 minutes later.)* **What makes a crewed trip to Mars a challenge?** *(Scientists are not yet sure of the long-term effects of extended space travel. Scientists are also working on the logistics of taking long space journeys, which include growing a sustainable food supply, recycling water, and producing oxygen to breathe.)*

Checking Concepts

11. Solid fuels and liquid fuels are used to power most rockets. Some rockets use gas ions to produce thrust.

12. Neil Armstrong said, "That's one small step for man, one giant leap for mankind."

13. The crew of the space shuttle takes satellites into orbit, repairs damaged satellites, and carries equipment to and from space.

14. The purpose of a space station is to provide a place where long-term observations and experiments can be carried out in space.

15. Possible answer: Computer-aided imaging techniques are a medical spinoff. Athletic shoes that contain shock-absorbing material are a materials spinoff. A joystick controller is a consumer spinoff.

Thinking Critically

16. The downward red arrow represents the action force of gas propelled out of the back of a rocket. The upward blue arrow represents the reaction force of the thrust that propels the rocket forward.

17. Yes. A rocket expels gas in one direction to move the device in the opposite direction.

18. Possible answer: The educators made that decision to ensure that U.S. students—the country's future scientists—understood and could contribute to space exploration and other areas of technological achievement.

19. Possible answer: Yes. The benefits outweighed the costs because we have learned much about the origins of Earth and the moon. We have also benefited from many space spinoffs.

20. Orbital velocity is the velocity a rocket must achieve to establish an orbit. Escape velocity is the velocity a rocket must reach to fly beyond a planet's gravitational pull. Escape velocity is much greater than orbital velocity.

21. Possible answer: Astronauts are conducting a variety of experiments on the International Space Station. This research may produce technological breakthroughs and a greater understanding of the effects of microgravity that will help the subsequent exploration of the solar system.

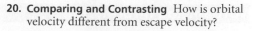
Checking Concepts

11. What are the two main types of rocket fuels?

12. What did Neil Armstrong say when he first set foot on the moon?

13. Describe some tasks carried out by the crew of the space shuttle.

14. What is the purpose of a space station?

15. Name a space spinoff in each of the following categories: medical devices, materials, and consumer products.

Thinking Critically

16. **Applying Concepts** The diagram below shows a rocket lifting off. What does each of the arrows represent?

17. **Classifying** A jet airplane usually uses liquid fuel that is burned with oxygen from the atmosphere. A jet engine expels hot gases to the rear, and the airplane moves forward. Is a jet a type of rocket? Explain.

18. **Relating Cause and Effect** When the Soviet Union launched *Sputnik I* into orbit in 1957, educators in the United States decided to improve math and science education in U.S. schools. Why do you think educators made that decision?

19. **Making Judgments** Do you think that the benefits of the Apollo program outweighed the program's costs? Explain.

20. **Comparing and Contrasting** How is orbital velocity different from escape velocity?

21. **Making Generalizations** How could the International Space Station help with further exploration of the solar system?

Applying Skills

Use the graph below to answer Questions 22–24.

The graph shows the amounts of time needed for satellites at different altitudes above Earth's surface to complete one orbit.

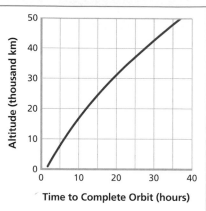

22. **Interpreting Diagrams** How long will a satellite orbiting at an altitude of 50,000 km take to complete one orbit?

23. **Applying Concepts** A geosynchronous satellite orbits Earth once every 24 hours. At what altitude does such a satellite orbit?

24. **Making Generalizations** What is the relationship between satellite altitude and the time needed to complete one orbit?

 **Chapter Project**

Performance Assessment Before testing your vehicle, list your design goals and criteria. Describe some of the challenges you faced. What could you change to improve your model?

 **Chapter Project**   **L3**

Project Wrap Up Give students the opportunity to explain their design goals and criteria. Criteria should focus on ease of navigation and include costs and benefits. Ask students to describe any challenges they faced and how they resolved them. For example, students might have changed the size of a model's wheels or its power source.

Reflect and Record Students will reflect that it is hard to design and build a vehicle that cannot be controlled directly—that is, they will grasp the difficulties inherent in controlling a vehicle from Earth that is moving on a distant planet or moon with a rough terrain.

Standardized Test Prep

Choose the letter of the answer that best answers the question or completes the statement.

1. Which of the following developments was most directly responsible for the creation of rockets that were capable to going to the moon?

   A gunpowder   B explosives
   C single-stage   D multistage rockets
     rockets

2. What force must a rocket overcome to be launched into space?
   F thrust   G gravity
   H orbital velocity   J escape velocity

3. During the space race, the former Soviet Union was the first to accomplish all of the following except
   A launching the first satellite into orbit.
   B sending the first living creature into space.
   C sending the first human into space.
   D landing the first human on the moon.

4. A satellite in geosynchronous orbit revolves around Earth once each
   F hour.   G week.
   H month.   J day.

The diagram below shows a rocket and the direction of four forces. Use the diagram and your knowledge of rockets to answer Question 5.

5. Which of the lettered forces shown in the diagram represents an equal and opposite force to the thrust of the rocket?
   A Force A   B Force B
   C Force C   D Force D

A

B   D

C

Earth

Constructed Response

6. Space probes have been used to explore all the planets except Pluto. Describe three types of information that a probe orbiting Pluto could gather about the planet.

Applying Skills

22. The satellite will take about 37 hours to complete one orbit.

23. The satellite orbits at an altitude of about 36,000 km.

24. In general, the higher a satellite's altitude is, the longer its orbital period.

Standardized Test Prep

1. D   **2.** G   **3.** D   **4.** J   **5.** C

6. Possible answer: The probe could take images of Pluto, which could be used to locate features on the planet's surface. The probe could also look for evidence of minerals or ices on Pluto's surface and gases in its thin atmosphere. It could examine how Pluto's surface temperature changes over time and at different locations. The probe could also map the planet's gravitational and magnetic fields.

Chapter at a Glance

PRENTICE HALL
TeacherEXPRESS™
Plan · Teach · Assess

Lab zone **Chapter Project** *Model of the Solar System*

Technology	Local Standards

All in One Teaching Resources
- Chapter Project Teacher Notes, pp. 164–165
- Chapter Project Student Overview, pp. 166–167
- Chapter Project Student Worksheets, pp. 168–169
- Chapter Project Scoring Rubric, p. 170

Discovery CHANNEL SCHOOL Video Preview

Section 1 **Observing the Solar System**

2 periods
1 block

J.3.1.1 Identify the geocentric and heliocentric systems.

J.3.1.2 Recognize how scientists such as Copernicus, Galileo, and Kepler contributed to acceptance of the heliocentric system.

J.3.1.3 Identify the objects that make up the solar system.

Go Online *active art*

Section 2 **The Sun**

2 periods
1 block

J.3.2.1 State the three layers of the sun's interior.

J.3.2.2 Identify the three layers of the sun's atmosphere.

J.3.2.3 Describe features that form on or above the sun's surface.

Go Online PLANET DIARY

Section 3 **The Inner Planets**

3 periods
1 1/2 blocks

J.3.3.1 Describe the characteristics that the inner planets have in common.

J.3.3.2 Identify the main characteristics that distinguish each of the inner planets.

Go Online SCiLINKS™ NSTA

Section 4 **The Outer Planets**

3 periods
1 1/2 blocks

J.3.4.1 Describe characteristics that the gas giants have in common.

J.3.4.2 Identify characteristics that distinguish each outer planet.

Go Online PHSchool.com

Section 5 **Comets, Asteroids, and Meteors**

1 period
1/2 block

J.3.5.1 Describe the characteristics of comets.

J.3.5.2 Identify where most asteroids are found.

J.3.5.3 Explain what meteoroids are and how they form.

Go Online SCiLINKS™ NSTA

Section 6 **Is There Life Beyond Earth?**

1 period
1/2 block

J.3.6.1 List the conditions that living things need to exist on Earth.

J.3.6.2 Recognize why scientists think Mars and Europa are good places to look for signs of life.

Go Online SCiLINKS™ NSTA

Review and Assessment

All in One Teaching Resources
- Key Terms Review, p. 218
- Transparency J34
- Performance Assessment Teacher Notes, p. 225

- Performance Assessment Scoring Rubric, p. 226
- Performance Assessment Student Worksheet, p. 227
- Chapter Test, pp. 228–231

Discovery CHANNEL SCHOOL Video Assessment

Go Online PHSchool.com

Test Preparation

Test Preparation Blackline Masters

Chapter Activities Planner

Lab zone

For more activities

LAB ZONE Easy Planner CD-ROM

Student Edition	Inquiry	Time	Materials	Skills	Resources
Chapter Project, p. 71	Open-Ended	4 weeks	**All in One** Teaching Resources See p. 164	Making models, calculating	Lab zone Easy Planner **All in One** Teaching Resources Support pp. 164–165
Section 1					
Discover Activity, p. 72	Directed	10 minutes	Flashlight	Drawing conclusions	Lab zone Easy Planner
Try This Activity, p. 75	Directed	15 minutes	White paper, corrugated cardboard, 30-cm string, 2 pushpins, ruler, pencil	Predicting	Lab zone Easy Planner
Section 2					
Discover Activity, p. 78	Directed	15 minutes	Binoculars, ring stand, ruler, thin cardboard, scissors, tape, paper	Observing	Lab zone Easy Planner
Try This Activity, p. 80	Guided	10 minutes per day for 10 days	Binoculars, ring stand, ruler, thin cardboard, scissors, tape, paper	Interpreting data	Lab zone Easy Planner
Skills Lab, p. 83	Directed	30 minutes	Graph paper, pencil, ruler	Graphing, interpreting data	Lab zone Easy Planner Lab Activity Video **All in One** Teaching Resources Skills Lab: *Stormy Sunspots, pp. 184–185*
Section 3					
Discover Activity, p. 84	Guided	10 minutes	White paper, compass, ruler	Observing	Lab zone Easy Planner
Try This Activity, p. 88	Guided	20 minutes	Plastic wrap, 2 glass jars, 2 thermometers	Observing	Lab zone Easy Planner
Try This Activity, p. 90	Guided	15 minutes	Paper, goggles, tape	Drawing conclusions	Lab zone Easy Planner
Section 4					
Discover Activity, p. 94	Guided	15 minutes	Quarter, metric ruler, lined paper, butcher paper or poster board, compass, pushpin, string	Classifying	Lab zone Easy Planner
Skills Activity, p. 98	Guided	20 minutes	8-cm plastic foam sphere, clear plastic sheet, ruler, scissors, compass, 5 toothpicks, tape, baking soda, peppercorn, glue (optional)	Making models	Lab zone Easy Planner
Design Your Own Lab, pp. 102–103	Guided	45 minutes	1.5-m string, one-hole rubber stopper, 6-cm plastic tube, stopwatch, meter stick, weight or several washers	Developing hypotheses, making models, designing experiments	Lab zone Easy Planner Lab Activity Video **All in One** Teaching Resources Design Your Own Lab: *Speeding Around the Sun, pp. 202–204*
Section 5					
Discover Activity, p. 104	Guided	10 minutes	Modeling clay, pencil, 3 10-cm lengths of string, small fan	Inferring	Lab zone Easy Planner
Try This Activity, p. 106	Guided	45 minutes	String, magnet, plastic bag, microscope slides, petroleum jelly, microscope	Estimating	Lab zone Easy Planner
Section 6					
Discover Activity, p. 108	Directed	15 minutes	Yeast, warm water, bowl, thermometer, spoon, sugar, or clock	Forming operational definitions	Lab zone Easy Planner
Skills Activity, p. 109	Open-Ended	15 minutes	None	Communicating	Lab zone Easy Planner

Section 1 Observing the Solar System

🕐 *2 periods, 1 block*

ABILITY LEVELS
L1 Basic to Average
L2 For All Students
L3 Average to Advanced

Objectives

J.3.1.1 Identify the geocentric and heliocentric systems.

J.3.1.2 Recognize how scientists such as Copernicus, Galileo, and Kepler contributed to acceptance of the heliocentric system.

J.3.1.3 Identify the objects that make up the solar system.

Key Terms

• geocentric • heliocentric • ellipse

Local Standards

Preteach

Build Background Knowledge

Use a photograph of the night sky and identify the objects.

Lab zone Discover Activity *What Is at the Center?* L2

Targeted Print and Technology Resources

All in One Teaching Resources

L2 Reading Strategy Transparency J22: Previewing Visuals

◉ **Presentation-Pro CD-ROM**

Instruct

Earth at the Center Analyze the movement of the planets in a geocentric system.

Sun at the Center Examine a diagram of the heliocentric system and describe the contributions of scientists to this model.

Modern Discoveries Discuss planets and other objects in the solar system that have been discovered since Galileo's time.

Targeted Print and Technology Resources

All in One Teaching Resources

L2 Guided Reading, pp. 173–175

PHSchool.com Web Code: cfp-5031

◉ **Student Edition on Audio CD**

Assess

Section Assessment Questions

↻ Have students use their graphic organizers with the questions and answers they prepared from previewing visuals to answer the questions.

Reteach

Students use a mnemonic device to learn the proper order of planets from the sun.

Targeted Print and Technology Resources

All in One Teaching Resources

• Section Summary, p. 172
L1 Review and Reinforce, p. 176
L3 Enrich, p. 177

Section 2 The Sun

🕐 *2 periods, 1 block*

Objectives

J.3.2.1 Name the three layers of the sun's interior.
J.3.2.2 Identify the three layers of the sun's atmosphere.
J.3.2.3 Describe features that form on or above the sun's surface.

Local Standards

Key Terms

• core • nuclear fusion • radiation zone • convection zone • photosphere
• chromosphere • corona • solar wind • sunspot • prominence • solar flare

Preteach

Build Background Knowledge

Students describe what a sunburn feels like and then discuss that the sun gives light and heat.

Lab zone Discover Activity *How Can You Safely Observe the Sun?* **L2**

Targeted Print and Technology Resources

All in One Teaching Resources
L2 Reading Strategy Transparency J23: Outlining

💿 **Presentation-Pro CD-ROM**

Instruct

The Sun's Interior Consider properties of the sun's interior layers.

The Sun's Atmosphere Discuss the layers of the sun and indicate which layer we see when we look at an image of the sun.

Features on the Sun Make a table that compares and contrasts features on the sun.

Lab zone Skills Lab *Stormy Sunspots* **L2**

Targeted Print and Technology Resources

All in One Teaching Resources
L2 Guided Reading, pp. 180–181
L2 Transparency J24
L2 Skills Lab: *Stormy Sunspots,* pp. 184–185

📼 **Lab Activity Video/DVD**
Skills Lab: *Stormy Sunspots*

PHSchool.com Web Code: cfd-5032

💿 **Student Edition on Audio CD**

Assess

Section Assessment Questions

🔊 Have students use their outlines to answer the questions.

Reteach

Students look at the diagrams in this section to review key terms.

Targeted Print and Technology Resources

All in One Teaching Resources
• Section Summary, p. 179
L1 Review and Reinforce, p. 182
L3 Enrich, p. 183

Section 3 **The Inner Planets**

🕐 *3 periods, 1 1/2 blocks*

Objectives

J.3.3.1 Describe the characteristics that the inner planets have in common.

J.3.3.2 Identify the main characteristics that distinguish each of the inner planets.

Key Terms

• terrestrial planets • greenhouse effect

Local Standards

Preteach

Build Background Knowledge

Identify Earth from a drawing based on its characteristic color.

Lab zone **Discover Activity** *How Does Mars Look From Earth?* **L1**

Targeted Print and Technology Resources

All in One Teaching Resources

L2 Reading Strategy Transparency J25: Using Prior Knowledge

💿 **Presentation-Pro CD-ROM**

Instruct

Earth Compare Earth to other planets, focusing on distance from the sun and period of revolution.

Mercury Compare and contrast Mercury to Earth's moon.

Venus Compare and contrast Earth and Venus, and identify their rotations as you use globes to demonstrate.

Mars Compare and contrast Mars to the other inner planets.

Targeted Print and Technology Resources

All in One Teaching Resources

L2 Guided Reading, pp. 188–191
L2 Transparencies J26, J29

www.SciLinks.org Web Code: scn-0633

💿 **Student Edition on Audio CD**

Assess

Section Assessment Questions

🔄 Have students use their graphic organizers that they completed, based on prior knowledge, to answer the questions.

Reteach

Students imagine that they are scientists and explain the relative difficulties of viewing the inner planets.

Targeted Print and Technology Resources

All in One Teaching Resources

• Section Summary, p. 187
L1 Review and Reinforce, p. 192
L3 Enrich, p. 193

Section 4 The Outer Planets

🕐 *3 periods, 1 1/2 blocks*

Objectives

J.3.4.1 Describe characteristics that the gas giants have in common.

J.3.4.2 Identify characteristics that distinguish each outer planet.

Key Terms

• gas giant • ring

Local Standards

Preteach

Build Background Knowledge

Have students write what they know about the outer planets.

Lab zone Discover Activity *How Big Are the Planets?* L2

Targeted Print and Technology Resources

All in One Teaching Resources

L2 Reading Strategy Transparency J27: Identifying Main Ideas

⊙ **Presentation-Pro CD-ROM**

Instruct

Gas Giants and Pluto Discuss the atmospheres and cores of the outer planets.

Jupiter Analyze Jupiter's atmosphere.

Saturn Consider why Saturn's rings look different from Earth than they do up close.

Uranus Use a diagram to examine Uranus's axis of rotation.

Neptune Discuss Neptune's moons.

Pluto Identify what makes Pluto different from the other outer planets.

Lab zone Design Your Own Lab *Speeding Around the Sun* L3

Targeted Print and Technology Resources

All in One Teaching Resources

L2 Guided Reading, pp. 196–199
L2 Transparencies J28, J29, J30
L3 Design Your Own Lab: *Speeding Around the Sun,* pp. 202–204

📼 **Lab Activity Video/DVD**
Skills Lab: *Speeding Around the Sun*

PHschool.com Web Code: ced-5034

⊙ **Student Edition on Audio CD**

Assess

Section Assessment Questions

Have students use their main ideas and details to answer the questions.

Reteach

Students examine what they wrote in the Background activity and make corrections as needed.

Targeted Print and Technology Resources

All in One Teaching Resources

• Section Summary, p. 195
L1 Review and Reinforce, p. 200
L3 Enrich, p. 201

Section 5 Comets, Asteroids, and Meteors

🕐 *1 period, 1/2 block*

ABILITY LEVELS
L1 Basic to Average
L2 For All Students
L3 Average to Advanced

Objectives

J.3.5.1 Describe the characteristics of comets.

J.3.5.2 Identify where most asteroids are found.

J.3.5.3 Explain what meteoroids are and how they form.

Local Standards

Key Terms

• comet • coma • nucleus • Kuiper belt • Oort cloud • asteroid • asteroid belt
• meteoroid • meteor • meteorite

Preteach

Build Background Knowledge

Talk about experiences of seeing "shooting stars."

Lab zone **Discover Activity** *Which Way Do Comet Tails Point?* **L1**

Targeted Print and Technology Resources

All in One Teaching Resources

L2 Reading Strategy Transparency J31: Comparing and Contrasting

💿 **Presentation-Pro CD-ROM**

Instruct

Comets Examine orbits of Earth and comets.

Asteroids Consider what happens to asteroids that land on Earth.

Meteors Define meteoroid, meteor, and meteorite.

Targeted Print and Technology Resources

All in One Teaching Resources

L2 Guided Reading, pp. 207–208

L2 Transparency J32

www.SciLinks.org Web Code: scn-0635

💿 **Student Edition on Audio CD**

Assess

Section Assessment Questions

🔄 Have students use their graphic organizers comparing and contrasting comets, asteroids, and meteoroids to answer the questions.

Reteach

Students discuss the structure of a comet.

Targeted Print and Technology Resources

All in One Teaching Resources

• Section Summary, p. 206

L1 Review and Reinforce, p. 209

L3 Enrich, p. 210

Section 6 Is There Life Beyond Earth?

1 period, 1/2 block

Objectives

J.3.6.1 List the conditions that living things need to exist on Earth.

J.3.6.2 Recognize why scientists think Mars and Europa are good places to look for signs of life.

Key Terms

• extraterrestrial life

Local Standards

Preteach

Build Background Knowledge

Compare and contrast living and nonliving things.

Lab zone Discover Activity *Is Yeast Alive or Not?* **L2**

Targeted Print and Technology Resources

All in One Teaching Resources

L2 Reading Strategy Transparency J33: Asking Questions

⊙ **Presentation-Pro CD-ROM**

Instruct

Life on Earth Discuss conditions on Earth that make life possible.

Life Elsewhere in the Solar System? Consider the findings of *Viking* spacecraft, which were sent to Mars to find evidence of life. Speculate on the kinds of life forms that might be found on Europa.

Targeted Print and Technology Resources

All in One Teaching Resources

L2 Guided Reading, pp. 213–215

www.SciLinks.org Web Code: scn-0636

⊙ **Student Edition on Audio CD**

Assess

Section Assessment Questions

Have students use their graphic organizer with their questions and answers to answer the questions.

Reteach

Students list the evidence for life on Mars and Europa.

Targeted Print and Technology Resources

All in One Teaching Resources

• Section Summary, p. 212

L1 Review and Reinforce, p. 216

L3 Enrich, p. 217

Chapter 3 **Content Refresher**

Go Online

NSTA-PDi LINKS

For: Professional development support
Visit: NSTA.org
Web Code: scf-0630

Professional Development

Section 1 **Observing the Solar System**

Motion Until the early 1600s, scientists dating back to the ancient Greeks assumed that all of the planets moved in perfect circles, which were considered to be the most perfect geometric shape. From 1576 to 1597, the Danish astronomer Tycho Brahe made very detailed measurements of planetary positions. Tycho's assistant, Johannes Kepler, used this data to develop three laws of planetary motion.

Kepler found that Tycho's data was inconsistent with the assumption that the planets moved in circulara orbits. However, Kepler discovered that his calculations matched Tycho's observations if he assumed that the planets moved in elliptical orbits. He thus formulated his first law: *The orbit of each planet around the sun is an ellipse, with the sun at one of the foci of the ellipse.*

Kepler's calculations told him something else that seemed surprising. The speed of a planet as it orbits the sun is not constant. A planet moves faster when it is closer to the sun and slower when it is farther away. This led him to his second law: *A planet sweeps out equal areas in equal times as it orbits the sun.* The illustration shows how that law works.

Kepler also noticed that the planets all moved at different speeds. At first he tried to come up with a simple relationship between the respective speeds. But after much calculation, the simplest terms he could come to gave him his third law: *The square of the period of a planet orbiting the sun is proportional to the cube of its mean (average) distance from the sun.*

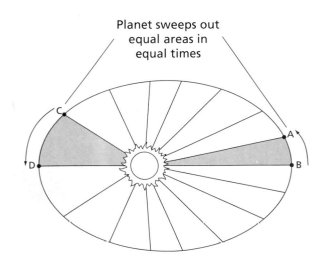

Planet sweeps out
equal areas in
equal times

Kepler could say *how* the planets moved, but not *why.* Then, in 1687, 57 years after Kepler died, Isaac Newton provided the explanation in his book, *Philosophiae naturalis principia mathematica.* Newton's three laws of motion and the law of universal gravitation provide the physical explanation for Kepler's laws and the movement of the planets.

Section 2 **The Sun**

Sunspot Cycles Some scientists theorize that sunspot cycles influence Earth's climate. Among the evidence for this hypothesis is the so-called Little Ice Age, which occurred from approximately 1550 until 1850. During this time, most parts of the world experienced cooler and harsher weather.

The Little Ice Age has been associated with a period of low sunspot activity that occurred between 1645 and 1715. This period is known as the Maunder minimum after the English astronomer who described it. Sunspots were first detected around 1600, but there are few recorded sightings during the Maunder minimum. Sunspot sightings resumed after 1715.

There is evidence that times of low sunspot activity occur in cycles of 500 years. If true, another "Little Ice Age" could possibly begin in about 2050.

Section 3 **The Inner Planets**

Exploring Venus Because of Venus's extreme heat, high atmospheric pressure, and clouds of sulfuric acid, it would be almost impossible for astronauts to go there. To gather information about Venus, scientists rely on uncrewed space probes. The Soviet Union was the first nation to attempt interplanetary exploration. In 1961 it launched the probe *Venera 1,* which passed within 100,000 km of Venus but did not transmit information back to Earth. In 1966 the Soviets launched *Venera 3,* the first spacecraft to crash-land on another planet. In 1967 *Venera 4* parachuted a capsule of instruments to Venus's surface. *Venera 7* (1970) detected radioactive isotopes on Venus's surface. In 1975 *Venera 9* sent back the first close-up photographs of the surface of Venus.

Section 4 The Outer Planets

Discovery of Pluto The American astronomer Clyde Tombaugh discovered Pluto in 1930. He was only 24 years old. Tombaugh had been fascinated by astronomy since he was a child. Soon after high school, he built his own telescope. When he sent sketches of his observations of Jupiter and Mars to the Lowell Observatory, they offered him a job: finding Pluto.

Astronomers had predicted the existence of Pluto based on calculations that indicated that a distant planet was disturbing the orbits of Uranus and Neptune. Scientists now know that Pluto's small mass could not have caused the disturbance. Regardless, Tombaugh spent 10 months looking at hundreds of thousands of images and, despite all odds, found Pluto.

Section 5 Comets, Asteroids, and Meteors

Ceres The first asteroid discovered, Ceres, is the largest known asteroid. It was discovered twice. The first sighting was made by Giuseppe Piazzi on January 1, 1801, in Palermo, Sicily. Piazzi named the asteroid *Ceres* after the Roman goddess of grain, who also happened to be the patron saint of Sicily. Piazzi observed the asteroid for roughly one month before it moved into the daytime sky. The German astronomer Franz von Zach rediscovered Ceres exactly one year later.

When Piazzi named the asteroid, he began the asteroid-naming tradition still in use today—asteroids are named *by* their discoverers, unlike comets, which are named *for* their discoverers.

Section 6 Is There Life Beyond Earth?

Europa Jupiter's moon Europa is five times farther from the sun than Earth is. The *Galileo* probe verified that Europa's surface is water ice. More surprisingly, the probe indicated liquid water beneath the ice. But, how could liquid water exist on a moon so far away from the sun? Why isn't all of Europa's water frozen? Something must be heating Europa.

> ⚑ **Address Misconceptions**
>
> *Some students may think that extraterrestrial life is limited to only intelligent life forms. However, extraterrestrial life, if found, would include any living thing, no matter how small or simple.* For a strategy for overcoming this misconception, see **Address Misconceptions** in *Is There Life Beyond Earth*?

That something turns out to be tidal forces. Europa is squeezed and stretched in different directions by Jupiter's tremendous gravitational force and by the gravity of Jupiter's other moons. This constant "tidal flexing" causes ridges and cracks in Europa's surface ice. Beneath the ice, the heat caused by the flexing allows water to exist in its liquid state.

Help Students Read

KWL (Know-Want to Know-Learned)
What I Know/What I Want to Know/What I Learned

Strategy Help students access prior knowledge, set a purpose for reading, recall what has been read, and link new information to prior knowledge. The KWL strategy has students create and complete a three-column chart. As students read, they complete the Learned column. Assign a section from this chapter, such as *Comets, Asteroids, and Meteors* for students to read.

Example
1. Pre-reading Have students fill in the first column with information about the topic that they already know. Next, have them preview the section and generate questions they would like to have answered during reading.

2. Reading Have students read the section, filling in the third column with the answers to their questions, along with information that was new to them.

3. Post-reading Below their KWL chart, have students use the information they've written in the Learned column to make a list headed New Information I Was Surprised to Learn.

Interactive Textbook
- Complete student edition
- Video and audio
- Simulations and activities
- Section and chapter activities

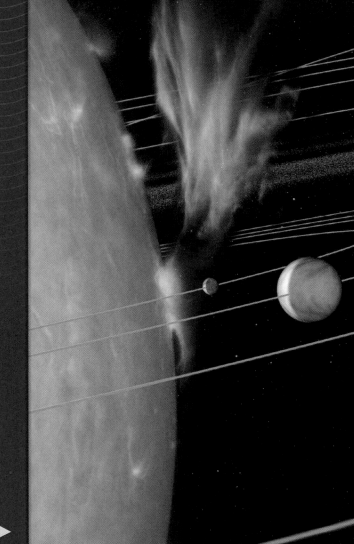

Interactive Textbook

This illustration shows the planets in orbit around the sun. ▶

Lab zone Chapter **Project** [L3]

Objectives
This project will help students understand that the distances between planets are very large relative to the sizes of the planets. After this Chapter Project, students will be able to
- make scale models to show the actual size of the solar system
- calculate and convert large numbers to an established scale
- compare scaled distances and diameters to familiar distances and diameters
- communicate the features of their models in a class presentation

Skills Focus
making models, calculating, comparing and contrasting, communicating

Project Time Line 4 weeks

 **Teaching Resources**
- Chapter Project Teacher Notes
- Chapter Project Worksheet 1
- Chapter Project Worksheet 2
- Chapter Project Scoring Rubric

Developing a Plan
Models should be completed sequentially, beginning with the planet sizes, then moving to the distance between the planets, and ending with the combination model. Have students complete the appropriate portions of the worksheets and get approval from you before they begin each phase of the model building.

Possible Materials
- Provide a wide variety of materials for model planets, such as tennis balls, beach balls, pieces of fruit, marbles, dried beans, and ball bearings.
- Students will need meter sticks or metric rulers and calculators to build their models.

The Solar System

Show the Video Preview to introduce the Chapter Project and present an overview of the chapter content. Discussion question: **What are the common characteristics of the inner planets?** *(They are relatively small, dense, and have rocky surfaces.)*

Lab zone™ Chapter **Project**

Build a Model of the Solar System

The solar system is a vast region containing the sun, planets, and many other objects. To help you understand the huge distances involved, you will design three different scale models of the solar system.

Your Goal To design scale models of the solar system

To complete this project, you will

- design a model to show the planets' distances from the sun
- design a model to show the planets' sizes compared to the sun
- test different scales to see if you can use the same scale for both size and distance in one model

Plan It! Begin by previewing the planet tables on pages 85 and 95. With a group of classmates, brainstorm how to build your models. Then design two models—one to show distances and one to show diameters. Next, design a third model that uses the same scale for both size and distance. Try several different scales to find which works best. Prepare a data table to record your calculations.

Possible Shortcuts

Because many distances in the solar system are given in astronomical units, a convenient scale is 1 AU = 1 m. (An AU, or astronomical unit, is the average distance between Earth and the sun.) Allow students to work in groups when calculating distances and building models.

Launching the Project

Bring in a scale model of an object familiar to all students, such as the Statue of Liberty. Take measurements of features of the model, and compare these to measurements on the actual object. Ask: **How does the size of this model compare to the real object?** *(It is smaller but proportional.)* Take the opportunity to discuss both scales and distances, using maps of your local community.

Performance Assessment

The Chapter Project Scoring Rubric will help you evaluate how well students complete the Chapter Project. Share the rubric with students at the beginning of the project so they will know what is expected. Students will be assessed on

- how accurately they did their mathematical calculations
- how well they selected model scales
- how well they can discuss the concepts of size and scaling
- the thoroughness and organization of their presentations

Portfolio

Objectives

After this lesson, students will be able to
J.3.1.1 Identify the geocentric and heliocentric systems.
J.3.1.2 Recognize how scientists such as Copernicus, Galileo, and Kepler contributed to acceptance of the heliocentric system.
J.3.1.3 Identify the objects that make up the solar system.

Target Reading Skill 🔁

Previewing Visuals Explain that looking at visuals before they read helps students activate prior knowledge and predict what they are about to read.

Answers

Possible Answers
Q: What is a geocentric model?
A: A model that shows Earth at the center of the revolving planets and stars
Q: What is a heliocentric system?
A: A model that shows Earth and the other planets revolving around the sun

All in One Teaching Resources

• Transparency J22

Preteach

Build Background Knowledge   L2

Night Sky

Let students examine a photograph of the night sky that shows stars and the moon. Ask them to identify the objects they see. Then ask: **Where was the sun when this picture was taken?** *(The sun could not be seen from the spot where the picture was taken because it was on the other side of Earth.)* Reinforce the idea that the objects in our solar system are moving.

Reading Preview

Key Concepts

• What are the geocentric and heliocentric systems?
• How did Copernicus, Galileo, and Kepler contribute to our knowledge of the solar system?
• What objects make up the solar system?

Key Terms

• geocentric • heliocentric
• ellipse

🔁 Target Reading Skill

Previewing Visuals Preview Figure 2 and Figure 3. Then write two questions that you have about the diagrams in a graphic organizer. As you read, answer your questions.

Models of the Universe

Q. What is a geocentric model?
A.
Q.

Lab zone Discover **Activity**

What Is at the Center?

1. Stand about 2 meters from a partner who is holding a flashlight. Have your partner shine the flashlight in your direction. Tell your partner not to move the flashlight.
2. Continue facing your partner, but move sideways in a circle, staying about 2 meters away from your partner.
3. Record your observations about your ability to see the light.
4. Repeat the activity, but this time remain stationary and continually face one direction. Have your partner continue to hold the flashlight toward you and move sideways around you, remaining about 2 meters from you.
5. Record your observations about your ability to see the light.

Think It Over
Drawing Conclusions Compare your two sets of observations. If you represent Earth and your partner represents the sun, is it possible, just from your observations, to tell whether Earth or the sun is in the center of the solar system?

Have you ever gazed up at the sky on a starry night? If you watch for several hours, the stars seem to move across the sky. The sky seems to be rotating right over your head. In fact, from the Northern Hemisphere, the sky appears to rotate completely around the North Star once every 24 hours.

Now think about what you see every day. During the day, the sun appears to move across the sky. From here on Earth, it seems as if Earth is stationary and that the sun, moon, and stars are moving around Earth. But is the sky really moving above you? Centuries ago, before there were space shuttles or even telescopes, there was no easy way to find out.

FIGURE 1
Star Trails
This photo was made by exposing the camera film for several hours. Each star appears as part of a circle, and all the stars seem to revolve around the North Star.

72 ◆ J

Lab zone Discover **Activity**

Skills Focus drawing conclusions
Materials flashlight
Time 10 minutes

Tips Darken the room before students conduct the activity. Let students take turns representing the sun and Earth.

L2 **Expected Outcome** The student who represents Earth will find it difficult to see the light when moving behind the student who represents the sun. The same student will find it difficult to see the light when the "sun" moves behind him or her.

Think It Over It would be difficult if not impossible to tell whether Earth or the sun were the center of the solar system.

Earth at the Center

When the ancient Greeks watched the stars move across the sky, they noticed that the patterns of the stars didn't change. Although the stars seemed to move, they stayed in the same position relative to one another. These patterns of stars, called constellations, kept the same shapes from night to night and from year to year.

Greek Observations As the Greeks observed the sky, they noticed something surprising. Several points of light seemed to wander slowly among the stars. The Greeks called these objects *planets,* from the Greek word meaning "wanderers." The Greeks made careful observations of the motions of the planets that they could see. You know these planets by the names the ancient Romans later gave them: Mercury, Venus, Mars, Jupiter, and Saturn.

Most early Greek astronomers believed the universe to be perfect, with Earth at the center. The Greeks thought that Earth is inside a rotating dome they called the celestial sphere. Since *geo* is the Greek word for "Earth," an Earth-centered model is known as a **geocentric** (jee oh SEN trik) system. **In a geocentric system, Earth is at the center of the revolving planets and stars.**

Ptolemy's Model About A.D. 140, the Greek astronomer Ptolemy (TAHL uh mee) further developed the geocentric model. Like the earlier Greeks, Ptolemy thought that Earth is at the center of a system of planets and stars. In Ptolemy's model, however, the planets move on small circles that move on bigger circles.

Even though Ptolemy's geocentric model was incorrect, it explained the motions observed in the sky fairly accurately. As a result, the geocentric model of the universe was widely accepted for nearly 1,500 years after Ptolemy.

Reading Checkpoint What is a geocentric system?

FIGURE 2
Geocentric System
In a geocentric system, the planets and stars are thought to revolve around a stationary Earth. In the 1500s, an astronomy book published the illustration of Ptolemy's geocentric system shown below.
Interpreting Diagrams *Where is Earth located in each illustration?*

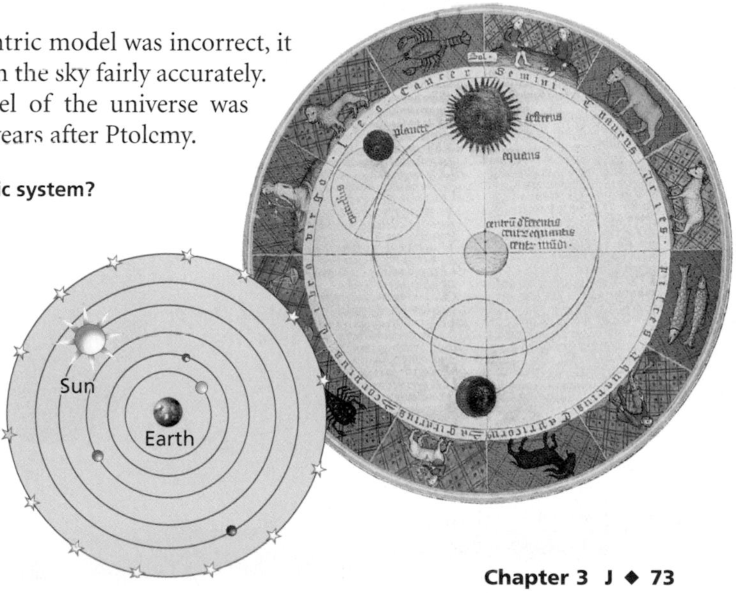

Chapter 3 J ◆ 73

J ● 73

Sun at the Center

Teach Key Concepts
Scientific Contributions

Focus Ask: **How do Earth and the other planets move in the heliocentric system?** *(They revolve around the sun.)*

Teach Ask: **Describe Copernicus's contribution to the heliocentric system.** *(Copernicus worked out the arrangement of the known planets and many details of how they moved around the sun.)*

Apply Have students examine the top model in Figure 3.
Ask: **Does this diagram reflect Kepler's contribution to the heliocentric system? How do you know?** *(It reflects Kepler's contribution to the heliocentric system because the orbits of the planets are ellipses rather than circles.)* **learning modality: visual**

Modeling the Movements of the Inner Planets

Materials chalk, metric ruler

Time 15 minutes

Focus Place students in groups of four. Have each group use chalk to draw concentric circles in a playground or a parking lot of radii 3.5 m, 5.0 m, and 7.5 m. Tell students they will represent the sun, Venus, Earth, and Mars, respectively.

Teach Ask: **Where will the sun stand?** *(In the center)* **Where will the other planets stand?** *(Inner circle: Venus; middle circle: Earth; outer circle: Mars)* Have students model the movements of the planets by walking around the "sun."

Apply Ask: **If everyone moved at a constant speed, which planet circled the sun the fastest?** *(Venus)* **The slowest?** *(Mars)* **learning modality: kinesthetic**

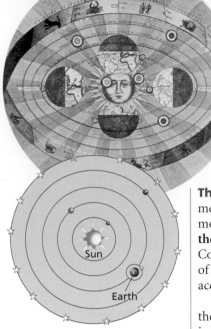

FIGURE 3
Heliocentric System
In a heliocentric system, Earth and the other planets revolve around the sun. The illustration by Andreas Cellarius (top) was made in the 1660s.
Interpreting Diagrams *In a heliocentric model, what revolves around Earth?*

Sun at the Center

Not everybody believed in the geocentric system. An ancient Greek scientist developed another explanation for the motion of the planets. This sun-centered model is called a **heliocentric** (hee lee oh SEN trik) system. *Helios* is Greek for "sun." **In a heliocentric system, Earth and the other planets revolve around the sun.** This model was not well received in ancient times, however, because people could not accept that Earth is not at the center of the universe.

The Copernican Revolution In 1543, the Polish astronomer Nicolaus Copernicus further developed the heliocentric model. **Copernicus was able to work out the arrangement of the known planets and how they move around the sun.** Copernicus's theory would eventually revolutionize the science of astronomy. But at first, many people were unwilling to accept his theory. They needed more evidence to be convinced.

In the 1500s and early 1600s, most people still believed in the geocentric model. However, evidence collected by the Italian scientist Galileo Galilei gradually convinced others that the heliocentric model was correct.

Galileo's Evidence **Galileo used the newly invented telescope to make discoveries that supported the heliocentric model.** For example, in 1610, Galileo used a telescope to discover four moons revolving around Jupiter. The motion of these moons proved that not everything in the sky revolves around Earth.

Nicolaus Copernicus
1473–1543

Galileo Galilei
1564–1642

▼ A reconstruction of Galileo's telescope

FIGURE 4
Major Figures in the History of Astronomy

74 ◆ J

Galileo's observations of Venus also supported the heliocentric system. Galileo knew that Venus is always seen near the sun. He discovered that Venus goes through a series of phases similar to those of Earth's moon. But Venus would not have a full set of phases if it circled around Earth. Therefore, Galileo reasoned, the geocentric model must be incorrect.

Tycho Brahe's Observations Copernicus correctly placed the sun at the center of the planets. But he incorrectly assumed that the planets travel in orbits that are perfect circles. Copernicus had based his ideas on observations made by the ancient Greeks.

In the late 1500s, the Danish astronomer Tycho Brahe (TEE koh BRAH uh) and his assistants made much more accurate observations. For more than 20 years, they carefully observed and recorded the positions of the planets. Surprisingly, these observations were made without using a telescope. Telescopes had not yet been invented!

Kepler's Calculations Tycho Brahe died in 1601. His assistant, Johannes Kepler, went to work analyzing the observations. Kepler began by trying to figure out the shape of Mars's orbit. At first, he assumed that the orbit was circular. But his calculations did not fit the observations. Kepler eventually found that Mars's orbit was a slightly flattened circle, or ellipse. An **ellipse** is an oval shape, which may be elongated or nearly circular.

After years of detailed calculations, Kepler reached a remarkable conclusion about the motion of the planets. **Kepler found that the orbit of each planet is an ellipse.** Kepler had used the evidence gathered by Tycho Brahe to disprove the long-held belief that the planets move in perfect circles.

Reading Checkpoint What is an ellipse?

Tycho Brahe
1546–1601

◀ Brahe's observatory on an island between Denmark and Sweden

Johannes Kepler
1571–1630

Chapter 3 J ◆ 75

J ● 75

Modern Discoveries

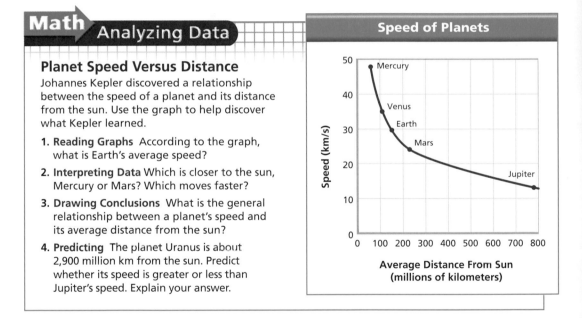

Mercury 58,000,000 km
Venus 108,000,000 km
Earth 150,000,000 km
Mars 228,000,000 km

Jupiter 779,000,000 km

Saturn 1,434,000,000 km

FIGURE 5
The Sun and Planets
This illustration shows the average distances of the nine planets from the sun. These distances are drawn to scale, but the sizes of the planets are not drawn to the same scale. **Observing** *Which planet is closest to the sun?*

Modern Discoveries

Today, people talk about the "solar system" rather than the "Earth system." This shows that people accept the idea that Earth and the other planets revolve around the sun.

Since Galileo's time, our knowledge of the solar system has increased dramatically. Galileo knew the same planets that the ancient Greeks had known—Mercury, Venus, Earth, Mars, Jupiter, and Saturn. Since Galileo's time, astronomers have discovered three more planets—Uranus, Neptune, and Pluto. Astronomers have also identified many other objects in the solar system, such as comets and asteroids. **Today we know that the solar system consists of the sun, nine planets and their moons, and several kinds of smaller objects that revolve around the sun.**

Math ▶ Analyzing Data

Planet Speed Versus Distance

Johannes Kepler discovered a relationship between the speed of a planet and its distance from the sun. Use the graph to help discover what Kepler learned.

1. **Reading Graphs** According to the graph, what is Earth's average speed?

2. **Interpreting Data** Which is closer to the sun, Mercury or Mars? Which moves faster?

3. **Drawing Conclusions** What is the general relationship between a planet's speed and its average distance from the sun?

4. **Predicting** The planet Uranus is about 2,900 million km from the sun. Predict whether its speed is greater or less than Jupiter's speed. Explain your answer.

Speed of Planets

(graph: Speed (km/s) vs. Average Distance From Sun (millions of kilometers); points labeled Mercury, Venus, Earth, Mars, Jupiter)

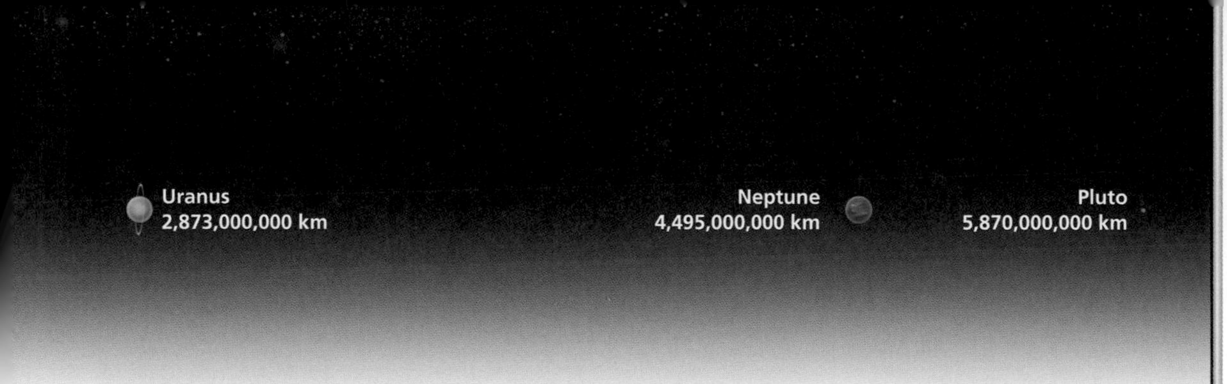

Uranus	Neptune	Pluto
2,873,000,000 km	4,495,000,000 km	5,870,000,000 km

Go Online *active art*

For: Solar System activity
Visit: PHSchool.com
Web Code: cfp-5031

Students can interact with the art of the solar system online.

Galileo used a telescope to observe the solar system from Earth's surface. Astronomers today still use telescopes located on Earth, but they have also placed telescopes in space to gain a better view of the universe beyond Earth. Scientists have also sent astronauts to the moon and launched numerous space probes to explore the far reaches of the solar system. Our understanding of the solar system continues to grow every day. Who knows what new discoveries will be made in your lifetime!

Go Online *active art*

For: Solar System activity
Visit: PHSchool.com
Web Code: cfp-5031

✔ **Reading Checkpoint** Which six planets were known to the ancient Greeks?

Section 1 Assessment

➲ **Target Reading Skill** **Previewing Visuals** Refer to your questions and answers about Figure 2 and Figure 3 to help you answer Question 1 below.

Reviewing Key Concepts

1. a. Explaining What are the geocentric and heliocentric systems?
  b. Comparing and Contrasting How was Copernicus's model of the universe different from Ptolemy's model?
  c. Drawing Conclusions What discoveries by Galileo support the heliocentric model?
  d. Applying Concepts People often say the sun rises in the east, crosses the sky, and sets in the west. Is this literally true? Explain.
2. a. Interpreting Data How did Kepler use Tycho Brahe's data?
  b. Describing What did Kepler discover about the orbits of the planets?
  c. Inferring How did Tycho Brahe and Kepler employ the scientific method?

3. a. Describing What objects make up the solar system?
  b. Listing What are the nine planets, in order of increasing distance from the sun?
  c. Interpreting Diagrams Use Figure 5 to find the planet with the closest orbit to Earth.

Writing in Science

Dialogue Write an imaginary conversation between Ptolemy and Galileo about the merits of the geocentric and heliocentric systems. Which system would each scientist favor? What evidence could each offer to support his view? Do you think that one scientist could convince the other to change his mind? Use quotation marks around the comments of each scientist.

Monitor Progress [L1]

Answers
Figure 5 Mercury

✔ **Reading Checkpoint** Mercury, Venus, Earth, Mars, Jupiter, Saturn

Assess

Reviewing Key Concepts

1. a. Geocentric: Earth is at the center of the solar system. Heliocentric: the sun is at the center. **b.** Ptolemy thought that the planets, moon, and sun revolved around Earth. Copernicus thought that the sun was in the middle and that the planets revolved around the sun. **c.** Moons revolving around Jupiter and the phases of Venus **d.** No; Earth is rotating from west to east. This causes the sun to appear to move across the sky.
2. a. To describe the motion of the planets **b.** They are elliptical. **c.** Brahe observed and recorded his observations. Kepler used the evidence gathered by Brahe to form a hypothesis about planetary orbits. Then he made predictions and confirmed or revised his hypothesis on the basis of his observations.
3. a. The sun, nine planets and their moons, and other smaller objects **b.** Mercury, Venus, Earth, Mars, Jupiter, Saturn, Uranus, Neptune, Pluto **c.** Venus

Reteach [L1]

Use a mnemonic device to help students remember the planets in order from the sun. Example: Many Very Eager Monkeys Jump Skyward Until Night Passes.

All in One Teaching Resources [L2]

- Section Summary: *Observing the Solar System*
- Review and Reinforce: *Observing the Solar System*
- Enrich: *Observing the Solar System*

Lab zone Chapter Project

Keep Students on Track Have students begin by making a table that shows the distances of the planets from the sun. They should then decide on a scale for their model. If students have difficulty developing a scale, suggest that they try 1: 10,000,000. Also, suggest that they use lined paper to keep their calculations neat and easy to follow.

Writing in Science

Writing Skill Description
Scoring Rubric
4 Exceeds criteria, includes the system favored by each scientist and supporting evidence is lively and entertaining
3 Meets all criteria but does not go beyond requirements
2 Meets only some criteria
1 Is inaccurate and incomplete

Section 2 — The Sun

Objectives

After this lesson, students will be able to
J.3.2.1 Name the three layers of the sun's interior.
J.3.2.2 Identify the three layers of the sun's atmosphere.
J.3.2.3 Describe features that form on or above the sun's surface.

Target Reading Skill

Outlining Explain that using an outline format helps students organize information by main topic, subtopic, and details.

Answers

The Sun
  I. The Sun's Interior
     A. The Core
     B. The Radiation Zone
     C. The Convection Zone
 II. The Sun's Atmosphere
     A. The Photosphere
     B. The Chromosphere
     C. The Corona
III. Features on the Sun
     A. Sunspots
     B. Prominences
     C. Solar Flares
     D. Solar Wind

All in One Teaching Resources

• Transparency J23

Preteach

Build Background Knowledge   L2

Solar Radiation

Invite students who have been sunburned to tell about their experiences. Encourage all students to imagine going outside on a clear, hot day and feeling the warmth of the sun. Ask: **What do we receive from the sun?** *(Possible answers: Light, heat)*

Reading Preview

Key Concepts

• What are the three layers of the sun's interior?
• What are the three layers of the sun's atmosphere?
• What features form on or above the sun's surface?

Key Terms

• core
• nuclear fusion
• radiation zone
• convection zone
• photosphere
• chromosphere
• corona
• solar wind
• sunspot
• prominence
• solar flare

Target Reading Skill

Outlining As you read, make an outline about the sun that you can use for review. Use the red headings for main topics and the blue headings for subtopics.

The Sun
I. The sun's interior
A. The core
B.
C.
II. The sun's atmosphere
A. The photosphere

Lab zone — Discover Activity

How Can You Safely Observe the Sun?

1. Clamp a pair of binoculars to a ring stand as shown in the photo.
2. Cut a hole in a 20-cm by 28-cm sheet of thin cardboard so that it will fit over the binoculars, as shown in the photo. The cardboard should cover one lens, but allow light through the other lens. Tape the cardboard on securely.
3. Use the binoculars to project an image of the sun onto a sheet of white paper. The cardboard will shade the white paper. Change the focus and move the paper back and forth until you get a sharp image.
   CAUTION: *Never look directly at the sun. You will hurt your eyes if you do. Do not look up through the binoculars.*

Think It Over
Observing Draw what you see on the paper. What do you see on the surface of the sun?

Suppose you are aboard a spaceship approaching the solar system from afar. Your first impression of the solar system might be that it consists of a single star with a few tiny objects orbiting around it. Your first impression wouldn't be that far off. In fact, the sun accounts for 99.8 percent of the solar system's total mass. As a result of its huge mass, the sun exerts a powerful gravitational force throughout the solar system. Although this force decreases rapidly with distance, it is strong enough to hold all the planets and other distant objects in orbit.

FIGURE 6
Active Sun
The sun is a huge, hot ball of glowing gas.

Lab zone — Discover Activity

Skills Focus observing   L2

Materials binoculars, ring stand, ruler, thin cardboard, scissors, masking tape, white paper

Time 15 minutes

Tips If binoculars are not available, make a pinhole in a sheet of cardboard and project the sun's image through the hole

onto the white paper. A small telescope can also be used to project the image.
CAUTION: *The image of the sun focused to a point can cause burns and ignite paper.*

Expected Outcome Students will see an image of the sun and perhaps sunspots.

Think It Over A large bright circle will appear on the paper. Sunspots may also be visible.

The Sun's Interior

Unlike Earth, the sun does not have a solid surface. Rather, the sun is a ball of glowing gas through and through. About three fourths of the sun's mass is hydrogen and one fourth is helium. There are also small amounts of other elements. Like Earth, the sun has an interior and an atmosphere. **The sun's interior consists of the core, the radiation zone, and the convection zone.**

The Core The sun produces an enormous amount of energy in its **core,** or central region. This energy is not produced by burning fuel. Rather, the sun's energy comes from nuclear fusion. In the process of **nuclear fusion,** hydrogen atoms join together to form helium. Nuclear fusion occurs only under conditions of extremely high temperature and pressure. The temperature inside the sun's core reaches about 15 million degrees Celsius, high enough for nuclear fusion to take place.

The total mass of the helium produced by nuclear fusion is slightly less than the total mass of the hydrogen that goes into it. What happens to this mass? It is changed into energy. This energy slowly moves outward from the core, eventually escaping into space.

The Radiation Zone The energy produced in the sun's core moves outward through the middle layer of the sun's interior, the radiation zone. The **radiation zone** is a region of very tightly packed gas where energy is transferred mainly in the form of electromagnetic radiation. Because the radiation zone is so dense, energy can take more than 100,000 years to move through it.

The Convection Zone The **convection zone** is the outermost layer of the sun's interior. Hot gases rise from the bottom of the convection zone and gradually cool as they approach the top. Cooler gases sink, forming loops of gas that move energy toward the sun's surface.

 **Reading Checkpoint** What is nuclear fusion?

Go Online PLANET DIARY
For: More on the sun
Visit: PHSchool.com
Web Code: cfd-5032

 J ◆ 79

Differentiated Instruction

Special Needs L1
Interpreting Diagrams Show students color photographs of the sun at various stages of an eclipse. Point out the photosphere, the chromosphere, and the corona. Using the photographs as a guide, have students draw their own diagrams and label them appropriately. **learning modality: visual**

Less Proficient Readers L1
Understanding Key Ideas Have students look up the meanings of the word *corona* and the prefixes *chromo-* and *photo-*. Ask: **Why is the core called a core?** *(Because it's at the center)* Explain to students that the chromosphere lies just above the photosphere and has an intense red color when seen during an eclipse. **learning modality: verbal**

Go Online PLANET DIARY
For: More on the sun
Visit: PHSchool.com
Web Code: cfd-5032
Students can review the sun in an online interactivity.

Instruct

The Sun's Interior

Teach Key Concepts L2
Properties of the Sun's Interior Layers

Focus Remind students that the sun does not have a solid surface.

Teach Ask: **In what layer does nuclear fusion occur?** *(The core)* **How is energy transferred in the radiation zone?** *(Mainly in the form of electromagnetic radiation)* **What happens to the temperature of gases as they reach the top of the convection zone?** *(It becomes lower.)*

Apply Ask: **Why do you think that nuclear fusion is not used as an energy source on Earth?** *(Nuclear fusion occurs only under conditions of extremely high temperature and pressure. We do not currently have the technology to produce electricity by fusion.)* **learning modality: logical/mathematical**

Help Students Read
Relate Cause and Effect Cause-and-effect relationships are integral to scientific discovery. Ask: **What causes sunspots to look darker than surrounding areas on the sun's surface?** *(Sunspots are areas of cooler gases, which don't give off as much light as hotter gases.)*

Independent Practice L2
All in One Teaching Resources
• Guided Reading and Study Worksheet: *The Sun*

💿 **Student Edition on Audio CD**

Monitor Progress L2
Drawing Have students diagram the sun's interior and atmosphere.

Answer
✓ **Reading Checkpoint** A process in the sun's core in which hydrogen joins to form helium, releasing energy in the process

The Sun's Atmosphere

Teach Key Concepts [L1]

Layers of the Sun's Atmosphere

Focus Remind students that Earth's atmosphere is divided into layers.

Teach Ask: **What are the layers of the sun's atmosphere from innermost to outermost?** (*The photosphere, the chromosphere, and the corona*)

Apply Ask: **If you look at a typical image of the sun, which layer do you see?** (*The photosphere*) **learning modality: logical/mathematical**

Lab zone Teacher **Demo**

Energy From the Sun [L1]

Materials 2 glass jars with lids, 2 plastic thermometers, black plastic, waterproof glue (hot glue works well)

Time 45 minutes

Focus Remind students that most energy on Earth comes from the sun.

Teach Glue black plastic on one-half of the *inside* of each jar. Glue a plastic thermometer to the inside of each jar so that it can be read without opening the jar. Fill the jars with cold water, leaving 1.0 cm for expansion, and cap tightly. Take the class outside and place one jar in a shady spot and the other in direct sun, propped up so that sunlight fully illuminates the inside of the jar. Read the temperature of each jar every five minutes for thirty minutes. Back in the classroom, have students graph the temperature versus time for each container.

Apply Ask: **What happened to the temperature of the jars?** (*Shady jar may have gone up or down slightly; sunny jar rose several degrees*) **What caused the temperature to rise?** (*Energy from the sun*) **learning modality: logical/mathematical**

FIGURE 7
The Sun's Corona
During a total solar eclipse, you can see light from the corona, the outer layer of the sun's atmosphere around the dark disk of the moon.

Lab zone Try This **Activity**

Viewing Sunspots
You can observe changes in the number of sunspots.

1. Make a data table to record the number of sunspots you see each day.
2. Decide on a time to study sunspots each day.
3. View the sun's image in the way described in the Discover activity on page 78. **CAUTION:** *Never look directly at the sun. You will hurt your eyes if you do.*
4. Make and record your observations.

Interpreting Data How much did the number of sunspots change from day to day?

80 ◆ J

The Sun's Atmosphere

The sun's atmosphere includes the photosphere, the chromosphere, and the corona. Each layer has unique properties.

The Photosphere The inner layer of the sun's atmosphere is called the **photosphere** (FOH tuh sfeer). The Greek word *photos* means "light," so *photosphere* means the sphere that gives off visible light. The sun does not have a solid surface, but the gases of the photosphere are thick enough to be visible. When you look at an image of the sun, you are looking at the photosphere. It is considered to be the sun's surface layer.

The Chromosphere During a total solar eclipse, the moon blocks light from the photosphere. The photosphere no longer produces the glare that keeps you from seeing the sun's faint, outer layers. At the start and end of a total eclipse, a reddish glow is visible just around the photosphere. This glow comes from the middle layer of the sun's atmosphere, the **chromosphere** (KROH muh sfeer). The Greek word *chroma* means "color," so the chromosphere is the "color sphere."

The Corona During a total solar eclipse an even fainter layer of the sun becomes visible, as you can see in Figure 7. This outer layer, which looks like a white halo around the sun, is called the **corona,** which means "crown" in Latin. The corona extends into space for millions of kilometers. It gradually thins into streams of electrically charged particles called the **solar wind.**

✓ **Reading Checkpoint** During what event could you see the sun's corona?

Features on the Sun

For hundreds of years, scientists have used telescopes to study the sun. They have spotted a variety of features on the sun's surface. **Features on or just above the sun's surface include sunspots, prominences, and solar flares.**

Sunspots Early observers noticed dark spots on the sun's surface. These became known as sunspots. Sunspots look small. But in fact, they can be larger than Earth. **Sunspots** are areas of gas on the sun's surface that are cooler than the gases around them. Cooler gases don't give off as much light as hotter gases, which is why sunspots look darker than the rest of the photosphere. Sunspots seem to move across the sun's surface, showing that the sun rotates on its axis, just as Earth does. The number of sunspots on the sun varies over a period of about 11 years.

Lab zone Try This **Activity**

Skills Focus interpreting data [L3]

Materials binoculars, ring stand, ruler, thin cardboard, scissors, masking tape, white paper

Time 10 minutes per day for 10 days

Tips Suggest that students look for sunspots two or three times per day for ten days. Their data tables should include the number of sunspots recorded at each interval as well as the average number of sunspots per day.

Extend Have students compile class results and evaluate the class average for the number of sunspots observed in a ten-day period. If findings vary, ask students to infer why. **learning modality: visual**

FIGURE 8

The Layers of the Sun

The sun has an interior and an atmosphere, each of which consists of several layers. The diameter of the sun (not including the chromosphere and the corona) is about 1.4 million kilometers. *Interpreting Diagrams* Name the layers of the sun's interior, beginning at its center.

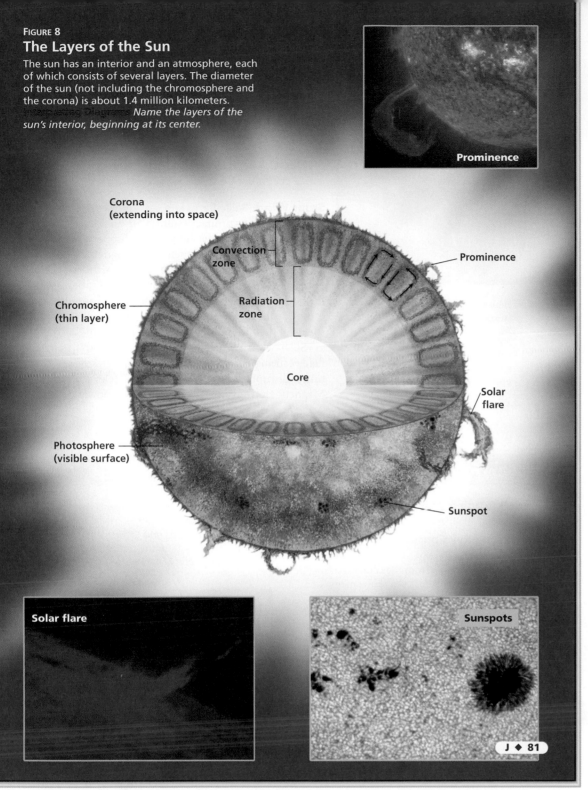

Prominence

Corona
(extending into space)

Convection
zone

Prominence

Radiation
zone

Chromosphere
(thin layer)

Core

Solar
flare

Photosphere
(visible surface)

Sunspot

Solar flare

Sunspots

J ◆ 81

Features on the Sun

Teach Key Concepts L2

Sunspots, Prominences, and Solar Flares

Focus Show students images or illustrations of the sun. Features such as sunspots, prominences, and solar flares should be visible.

Teach Ask students to make a table that compares and contrasts sunspots, prominences, and solar flares.

Apply Have students identify the features they saw on the sun's image from the results of the Discover activity. *(Sunspots)* **learning modality: visual**

Use Visuals: Figure 8 L2

The Layers of the Sun

Focus Have students look up the meanings of the word *corona* and the prefixes *chromo-* and *photo-*.

Teach As students examine Figure 8, ask: **Why is the corona called a corona?** *(It surrounds the sun like a crown.)* **Why is the core called a core?** *(Because it's at the center)* **What is the source of light that reaches Earth from the sun?** *(The photosphere)* **What is the source of energy for the energy produced by the sun?** *(Nuclear fusion)*

Apply Explain to students that the chromosphere lies just above the photosphere and has an intense red color when seen during an eclipse. **learning modality: visual**

All in One **Teaching Resources**

• Transparency J24

Differentiated Instruction

Less Proficient Readers L1
Analyzing Words The words used to describe the sun's features may be unfamiliar to some students. Point out that terms such as *sunspot* and *solar flare* are descriptive. Have students separate these terms into their parts. *(sun + spot; solar + flare)* Tell students to look up the words

and word parts in the dictionary. Encourage students to explain how the terms help describe the features of the sun. *(A sunspot is a spot on the sun. A solar flare is a flare or an explosion on the sun.)* **learning modality: verbal**

Monitor Progress L2

Drawing Have students draw and label a diagram of the surface of the sun.

Answers
Figure 8 Core, radiation zone, convection zone

✓ Reading Checkpoint   Total solar eclipse

Monitor Progress _____ L2

Answer

✓ **Reading Checkpoint**   A huge, reddish loop of gas on the sun's surface

Assess

Reviewing Key Concepts

1. a. Core, radiation zone, convection zone **b.** In the core **c.** In the radiation zone, energy is transferred mainly in the form of electromagnetic radiation. In the convection zone, hot gases transport energy toward the sun's surface.

2. a. Photosphere, chromosphere, and corona **b.** Photosphere **c.** The glare from the photosphere blocks out the fainter corona.

3. a. Sunspots: cooler, darker areas on sun's surface; prominences: reddish loops of gas that sometimes connect sunspots; and solar flares: gas eruptions reaching into space **b.** Sunspots are cooler than the surrounding photosphere.

Reteach   L1

Use the diagrams in this section to review key terms.

Performance Assessment   L3

Writing Have students create a travel brochure for an imaginary vacation to the sun. The brochure should include sites to visit, a map, and travel tips.

All in One Teaching Resources

- Section Summary: *The Sun*
- Review and Reinforce: *The Sun*
- Enrich: *The Sun*

FIGURE 9
Auroras
Auroras such as this can occur near Earth's poles when particles of the solar wind strike gas molecules in Earth's upper atmosphere.

Prominences Sunspots usually occur in groups. Huge, reddish loops of gas called **prominences** often link different parts of sunspot regions. When a group of sunspots is near the edge of the sun as seen from Earth, these loops can be seen extending over the edge of the sun.

Solar Flares Sometimes the loops in sunspot regions suddenly connect, releasing large amounts of magnetic energy. The energy heats gas on the sun to millions of degrees Celsius, causing the gas to erupt into space. These eruptions are called **solar flares.**

Solar Wind Solar flares can greatly increase the solar wind from the corona, resulting in an increase in the number of particles reaching Earth's upper atmosphere. Normally, Earth's atmosphere and magnetic field block these particles. However, near the North and South poles, the particles can enter Earth's atmosphere, where they create powerful electric currents that cause gas molecules in the atmosphere to glow. The result is rippling sheets of light in the sky called auroras.

Solar wind particles can also affect Earth's magnetic field, causing magnetic storms. Magnetic storms sometimes disrupt radio, telephone, and television signals. Magnetic storms can also cause electrical power problems.

✓ **Reading Checkpoint**   What is a prominence?

Section 2 Assessment

🎯 **Target Reading Skill Outlining** Use your outline to help answer the questions below.

Reviewing Key Concepts

1. a. Listing List the three layers of the sun's interior, starting from the center.
   b. Explaining Where is the sun's energy produced?
   c. Comparing and Contrasting Compare how energy moves through the radiation zone and the convection zone.

2. a. Listing What three layers make up the sun's atmosphere?
   b. Identifying Which of the sun's layers produces its visible light?
   c. Relating Cause and Effect Why is it usually impossible to see the sun's corona from Earth?

3. a. Describing Describe three features found on or just above the sun's surface.
   b. Relating Cause and Effect Why do sunspots look darker than the rest of the sun's photosphere?

Lab zone At-Home **Activity**

Sun Symbols As the source of heat and light, the sun is an important symbol in many cultures. With family members, look around your home and neighborhood for illustrations of the sun on signs, flags, clothing, and in artwork. Which parts of the sun's atmosphere do the illustrations show?

82 ◆ J

Lab zone At-Home **Activity**

Sun Symbols L1 Suggest that students prepare photo essays or sketchbook collections of the items identified by their families. Some places to look for sun imagery include watches and clocks, artwork, product labels, and book illustrations.

Stormy Sunspots

Problem

How are magnetic storms on Earth related to sunspot activity?

Skills Focus

graphing, interpreting data

Materials

- graph paper
- ruler

Procedure

1. Use the data in the table of Annual Sunspot Numbers to make a line graph of sunspot activity between 1972 and 2002.
2. On the graph, label the x-axis "Year." Use a scale with 2-year intervals, from 1972 to 2002.
3. Label the y-axis "Sunspot Number." Use a scale of 0 through 160 in intervals of 10.
4. Graph a point for the Sunspot Number for each year.
5. Complete your graph by drawing lines to connect the points.

Analyze and Conclude

1. **Graphing** Based on your graph, which years had the highest Sunspot Number? The lowest Sunspot Number?
2. **Interpreting Data** How often does the cycle of maximum and minimum activity repeat?
3. **Interpreting Data** When was the most recent maximum sunspot activity? The most recent minimum sunspot activity?
4. **Inferring** Compare your sunspot graph with the magnetic storms graph. What relationship can you infer between periods of high sunspot activity and magnetic storms? Explain.

Annual Sunspot Numbers			
Year	Sunspot Number	Year	Sunspot Number
1972	68.9	1988	100.2
1974	34.5	1990	142.6
1976	12.6	1992	94.3
1978	92.5	1994	29.9
1980	154.6	1996	8.6
1982	115.9	1998	64.3
1984	45.9	2000	119.6
1986	13.4	2002	104.0

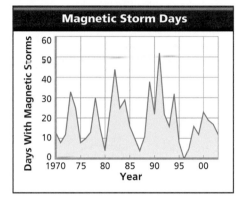

Magnetic Storm Days

5. **Communicating** Suppose you are an engineer working for an electric power company. Write a brief summary of your analysis of sunspot data. Explain the relationship between sunspot number and electrical disturbances on Earth.

More to Explore

Using the pattern of sunspot activity you found, predict the number of peaks you would expect in the next 30 years. Around which years would you expect the peaks to occur?

Stormy Sunspots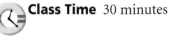

Prepare for Inquiry

Skills Objectives

After this lab, students will be able to

- Make a graph showing the average sunspot number per year
- Compare a graph of sunspot activity to a graph of number of magnetic storms on Earth during the same period

🕐 **Class Time** 30 minutes

All in One Teaching Resources

- Lab Worksheet: *Stormy Sunspots*

Guide Inquiry

Invitation

Tell students that a magnetic storm is defined as a brief disturbance in Earth's magnetic field.

Introduce the Procedure

Explain that *sunspot number* is a technical term that takes into account both the number of sunspot groups and the number of individual sunspots.

Expected Outcome

- Students will draw a graph that shows three peaks and three valleys in sunspot activity from 1972 to 2002.
- The sunspot activity valleys seem to coincide with valleys in the magnetic storm data.

Analyze and Conclude

1. Highest: 1980, 1990, and 2000; lowest: 1976, 1986, and 1996

2. Every 10–11 years

3. Most recent maximum sunspot activity: 2000; most recent minimum sunspot activity: 1996

4. Periods of high sunspot activity correspond to an increase in magnetic storms. Periods of low sunspot activity correspond to a decrease in magnetic storms.

5. Each summary should include examples and a clear explanation of the relationship among the sunspot number for the year, the number of days in that year with magnetic storms, and the occurrence of electrical disturbances.

Extend Inquiry

More to Explore Three more peaks should occur over the next 30 years. They should occur around 2010–2012, 2020–2023, and 2030–2033.

Objectives

After this lesson, students will be able to
J.3.3.1 Describe the characteristics that the inner planets have in common.
J.3.3.2 Identify the main characteristics that distinguish each of the inner planets.

Target Reading Skill

Using Prior Knowledge Explain that using prior knowledge helps students connect what they already know to what they are about to read.

Answers

Possible answers include the following:

What You Know
1. Most of Earth is covered with water.
2. Mercury is closest to the sun.
3. Venus is very hot.
4. Mars is called the "red planet."

What You Learned
1. Earth is unique in our solar system for having liquid water at its surface.
2. Mercury has a greater temperature range than any of the other planets.
3. A day on Venus is longer than its year.
4. The reddish tinge on Mars is caused by the breakdown of iron-rich rocks.

All in One Teaching Resources
• Transparency J25

Preteach

Build Background Knowledge L2

The Blue Planet
Show students a colored drawing of the solar system with the names of the planets covered. Ask: **Which planet is Earth?** (*The third planet from the sun*) **How do you know?** (*Possible answer: The third planet appears blue, and Earth has liquid water on its surface, which makes it look blue from space.*)

Section
3 The Inner Planets

Reading Preview

Key Concepts
• What characteristics do the inner planets have in common?
• What are the main characteristics that distinguish each of the inner planets?

Key Terms
• terrestrial planets
• greenhouse effect

Target Reading Skill

Using Prior Knowledge Look at the section headings and visuals to see what this section is about. Then write what you know about the inner planets in a graphic organizer like the one below. As you read, write what you learn.

What You Know
1. Most of Earth is covered with water.
2.

What You Learned
1.
2.

Lab zone Discover Activity

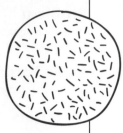

How Does Mars Look From Earth?

1. Work in pairs. On a sheet of paper, draw a circle 20 cm across to represent Mars. Draw about 100 small lines, each about 1 cm long, at random places inside the circle.
2. Have your partner look at your drawing of Mars from the other side of the room. Your partner should draw what he or she sees.
3. Compare your original drawing with what your partner drew. Then look at your own drawing from across the room.

Think It Over
Observing Did your partner draw any connecting lines that were not actually on your drawing? What can you conclude about the accuracy of descriptions of other planets based on observations from Earth?

Where could you find a planet whose atmosphere has almost entirely leaked away into space? How about a planet whose surface is hot enough to melt lead? And how about a planet with volcanoes higher than any on Earth? Finally, where could you find a planet with oceans of water brimming with fish and other life? These are descriptions of the four planets closest to the sun, known as the inner planets.

Earth and the three other inner planets—Mercury, Venus, and Mars—are more similar to each other than they are to the five outer planets. **The four inner planets are small and dense and have rocky surfaces.** The inner planets are often called the **terrestrial planets,** from the Latin word *terra,* which means "Earth." Figure 10 summarizes data about the inner planets.

Earth

As you can see in Figure 11, Earth has three main layers—a crust, a mantle, and a core. The crust includes the solid, rocky surface. Under the crust is the mantle, a layer of hot molten rock. When volcanoes erupt, this hot material rises to the surface. Earth has a dense core made of mainly iron and nickel. The outer core is liquid, but the inner core is solid.

Lab zone Discover Activity

Skills Focus observing
Materials white paper, compass, ruler
Time 10 minutes
Tips Tell students to make the small lines dark enough to be seen from a distance. To minimize confusion, suggest that they label the drawings as *Original* and *Copied From a Distance.*

L1

Think It Over The partner may see and draw patterns and lines that are not in the original drawing. The view from across the room is not an accurate representation of what the original drawing looked like.

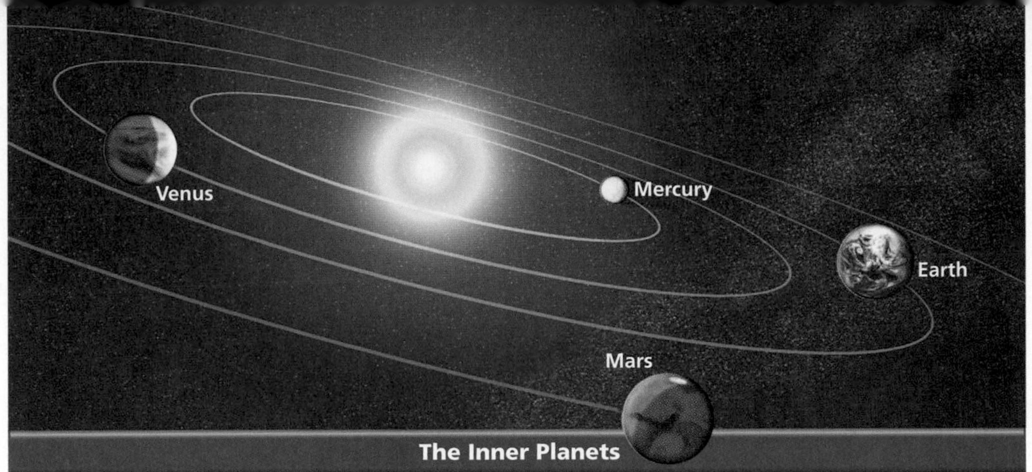

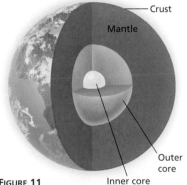

The Inner Planets

Planet	Diameter (kilometers)	Period of Rotation (Earth days)	Average Distance From Sun (kilometers)	Period of Revolution (Earth years)	Number of Moons
Mercury	4,879	59	58,000,000	0.24	0
Venus	12,104	243	108,000,000	0.62	0
Earth	12,756	1	150,000,000	1	1
Mars	6,794	1.03	228,000,000	1.9	2

Water Earth is unique in our solar system in having liquid water at its surface. In fact, most of Earth's surface, about 70 percent, is covered with water. Perhaps our planet should be called "Water" instead of "Earth"! Earth has a suitable temperature range for water to exist as a liquid, gas, or solid. Water is also important in shaping Earth's surface, wearing it down and changing its appearance over time.

Atmosphere Earth has enough gravity to hold on to most gases. These gases make up Earth's atmosphere, which extends more than 100 kilometers above its surface. Other planets in the solar system have atmospheres too, but only Earth has an atmosphere that is rich in oxygen. The oxygen you need to live makes up about 20 percent of Earth's atmosphere. Nearly all the rest is nitrogen, with small amounts of other gases such as argon and carbon dioxide. The atmosphere also includes varying amounts of water in the form of a gas. Water in a gaseous form is called water vapor.

 Reading Checkpoint What two gases make up most of Earth's atmosphere?

FIGURE 10
The inner planets take up only a small part of the solar system. Note that sizes and distances are not drawn to scale.

- Crust
- Mantle
- Outer core
- Inner core

FIGURE 11
Earth's Layers
Earth has a solid, rocky surface.
Interpreting Diagrams What are Earth's three main layers?

Earth

Teach Key Concepts   L1
Comparing Other Inner Planets to Earth

Focus Have students examine Figure 10, which shows characteristics of the inner planets.

Teach Ask: **Which planet is most similar in size to Earth?** (*Venus*) **How many times does Mercury revolve around the sun during one Earth year?** (*About four*)

Apply Challenge students to make a generalization about a planet's distance from the sun and its period of revolution. (*The farther a planet is from the sun, the longer it takes to complete one period of revolution.*)
learning modality: visual

All in One Teaching Resources
- Transparencies J26, J29

Independent Practice   L2
All in One Teaching Resources
- Guided Reading and Study Worksheet: *The Inner Planets*

Student Edition on Audio CD

Differentiated Instruction

Gifted and Talented   L3
Creating a Diagram Have students use a computer graphics program to create a scale diagram showing Earth's layers. Have students label the diagram and add pertinent information, such as the depth of each layer, gathered from independent research. **learning modality: visual**

Special Needs   L1
Identifying Earth's Layers Place a hard-boiled egg on a paper towel spread on your desk. Use a knife to slice the shelled egg crosswise. Ask students to identify what each part of the egg represents. (*Shell—crust; white—mantle; yolk—core*) **learning modality: visual**

Monitor Progress   L1

Drawing Have students draw a cross-section of Earth and its atmosphere and label the crust, the mantle, the outer core, the inner core, and the atmosphere. Have students save their drawings in their portfolios.

Answers
Figure 11 Crust, mantle, and core

Reading Checkpoint Nitrogen and oxygen

Mercury

Teach Key Concepts L1

Mercury's Characteristics

Focus Show students images of Mercury and Earth's moon.

Teach Ask students to describe the features shared by the moon and Mercury. *(Heavily cratered surface, little atmosphere, no liquid water, little erosion)* Ask: **What difference do you see between the surface of Earth's moon and that of Mercury?** *(Mercury's surface has no maria.)*

Apply Tell students that in some ways, Mercury has more features in common with Earth's moon than with Earth and the other inner planets. **learning modality: visual**

Build Inquiry L2

Observing Mercury

Materials coin, desk lamp, ruler
Time 20 minutes

Focus Have students write inferences regarding why scientists have a difficult time making observations of Mercury. After completing this activity, have students revise their inferences.

Teach Pair students. Have one student hold a coin about 10 cm in front of a dim desk lamp. The head side of the coin should face away from the bulb. Challenge the other student to determine the date on the coin. Caution the student not to look directly at the light bulb.

Apply Ask: **What do you observe about the coin?** *(The brightness of the bulb makes it impossible to see the date.)* **How is this similar to problems encountered by scientists who want to observe features on Mercury?** *(The brightness of the sun makes it hard to see Mercury's surface features.)*
learning modality: visual

Size of Mercury
compared to Earth

FIGURE 12
Mercury
This image of Mercury was produced by combining a series of smaller images made by the *Mariner 10* space probe.
Interpreting Photographs *How is Mercury's surface different from Earth's?*

Mercury

Mercury is the smallest terrestrial planet and the planet closest to the sun. Mercury is not much larger than Earth's moon and has no moons of its own. The interior of Mercury is probably made up mainly of the dense metal iron.

Exploring Mercury Because Mercury is so close to the sun, it is hard to see from Earth. Much of what astronomers know about Mercury's surface came from a single probe, *Mariner 10*. It flew by Mercury three times in 1974 and 1975. Two new missions to Mercury are planned. The first of these, called *MESSENGER*, is scheduled to go into orbit around Mercury in 2009.

Mariner 10's photographs show that Mercury has many flat plains and craters on its surface. The large number of craters shows that Mercury's surface has changed little for billions of years. Many of Mercury's craters have been named for artists, writers, and musicians, such as the composers Bach and Mozart.

Mercury's Atmosphere Mercury has virtually no atmosphere. Mercury's high daytime temperatures cause gas particles to move very fast. Because Mercury's mass is small, its gravity is weak. Fast-moving gas particles can easily escape into space. However, astronomers have detected small amounts of sodium and other gases around Mercury.

Mercury is a planet of extremes, with a greater temperature range than any other planet in the solar system. It is so close to the sun that during the day, the side facing the sun reaches temperatures of 430°C. Because Mercury has almost no atmosphere, at night its heat escapes into space. Then its temperature drops below −170°C.

✓ **Reading Checkpoint** Compare daytime and nighttime temperatures on Mercury.

86 ◆ J

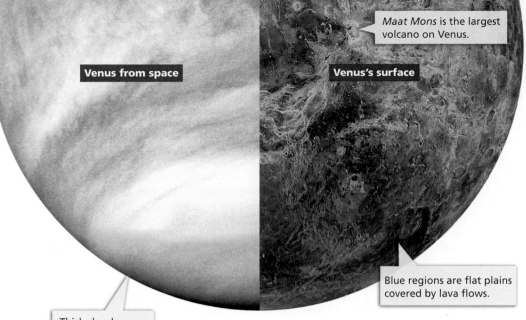

Maat Mons is the largest volcano on Venus.

Venus from space

Venus's surface

Thick clouds cover the surface.

Blue regions are flat plains covered by lava flows.

FIGURE 13
Venus
This figure combines images of Venus taken from space with a camera (left) and radar (right). The camera image shows Venus's thick atmosphere. Radar is able to penetrate Venus's clouds to reveal the surface. Both images are false color.

Venus

You can sometimes see Venus in the west just after sunset. When Venus is visible in that part of the sky, it is known as the "evening star," though of course it really isn't a star at all. At other times, Venus rises before the sun in the morning. Then it is known as the "morning star."

Venus is so similar in size and mass to Earth that it is sometimes called "Earth's twin." **Venus's density and internal structure are similar to Earth's. But, in other ways, Venus and Earth are very different.**

Venus's Rotation Venus takes about 7.5 Earth months to revolve around the sun. It takes about 8 months for Venus to rotate once on its axis. Thus, Venus rotates so slowly that its day is longer than its year! Oddly, Venus rotates from east to west, the opposite direction from most other planets and moons. Astronomers hypothesize that this unusual rotation was caused by a very large object that struck Venus billions of years ago. Such a collision could have caused Venus to change its direction of rotation. Another hypothesis is that Venus's thick atmosphere could have somehow altered its rotation.

Size of Venus compared to Earth

Go **Online**
SCI**LINKS** NSTA

For: Links on the planets
Visit: www.SciLinks.org
Web Code: scn-0633

Chapter 3 J ◆ 87

Venus

Teach Key Concepts　L2
Venus's Rotation

Focus Remind students that most planets, including Earth, rotate from west to east.

Teach Place a globe on a table and spin it so that it turns from west to east. Place a second globe on the table and spin it very slowly so that it turns from east to west. Ask: **Which globe represented Earth?** *(The first; Earth rotates from west to east.)* **What did the other globe represent?** *(Venus; it rotates very slowly from east to west.)*

Apply Ask students to compare and contrast Earth and Venus. *(They are similar in density and internal structure. They have different atmospheres and rotations.)*
learning modality: visual

Help Students Read　L1
Visualizing Have students close their books and listen while you read the paragraph about Venus's rotation. Ask them to describe how they visualize what caused this unusual rotation. Then ask students to work in pairs and discuss how they visualized the process.

Monitor Progress ———— L2

Writing Have students write paragraphs describing how sunrise on Venus differs from sunrise on Earth.

Answers
Figure 12 Mercury's surface is heavily cratered and barren.

✓ **Reading Checkpoint** Temperatures on Mercury vary from 430°C on the sunlit side to below −170°C at night.

Differentiated Instruction

**Less Proficient Readers　L1
Comparing and Contrasting Inner Planets** Suggest that students use Venn diagrams to compare and contrast each inner planet with Earth. Demonstrate how to use a Venn diagram to compare and contrast two subjects. First, have volunteers read aloud the information about Earth and Venus in the section. Then draw a Venn diagram on the chalkboard. As students name similarities between Venus and Earth, write these in the overlapping portion of the diagram. Then have students name differences and record these in the outer portions of the circles. Instruct students to complete additional Venn diagrams for the remaining inner planets and Earth. **learning modality: visual**

Use Visuals: Figure 14
Radar Images

Focus Tell students that radar images are formed when radio waves are bounced off a surface.

Teach Have students infer why scientists used radar to obtain images of volcanoes on Venus. *(They could not see the volcanoes because the thick atmosphere of Venus blocked the view.)* Explain that radar images sometimes exaggerate the heights of objects such as volcanoes. Ask: **Why might astronomers want to use an exaggerated scale when examining an image?** *(Possible answer: Astronomers increase the scale of an image so that they can examine details more clearly.)*

Apply Inform students that the colors in the figure are generated by the computer-imaging process. The actual volcano colors vary; they appear more like those of volcanoes on Earth. **learning modality: visual**

Lab zone Build Inquiry L3

Interpreting the Greenhouse Effect

Materials photograph of a greenhouse

Time 20 minutes

Focus Show students a photograph of a greenhouse with plants growing inside. Explain that a greenhouse lets in sunlight and prevents convection from carrying away heat. The plants stay warm inside.

Teach Place students in pairs and have them create flowcharts or sketches that compare the path of light and heat energy in a greenhouse with the path of light and heat energy on Venus.

Apply Have students discuss possible environmental problems caused by changes in Earth's greenhouse effect. **learning modality: logical/mathematical**

Lab zone Try This Activity

Greenhouse Effect

How can you measure the effect of a closed container on temperature?

1. 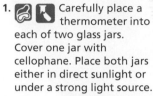 Carefully place a thermometer into each of two glass jars. Cover one jar with cellophane. Place both jars either in direct sunlight or under a strong light source.

2. Observe the temperature of both thermometers when you start. Check the temperatures every 5 minutes for a total of 20 minutes. Record your results in a data table.

Inferring Compare how the temperature changed in the uncovered jar and the covered jar. What do you think is the reason for any difference in the temperatures of the two jars? Which jar is a better model of Venus's atmosphere?

Venus's Atmosphere Venus's atmosphere is so thick that it is always cloudy there. From Earth or space, astronomers can see only a smooth cloud cover over Venus. The clouds are made mostly of droplets of sulfuric acid.

If you could stand on Venus's surface, you would quickly be crushed by the weight of its atmosphere. The pressure of Venus's atmosphere is 90 times greater than the pressure of Earth's atmosphere. You couldn't breathe on Venus because its atmosphere is mostly carbon dioxide.

Because Venus is closer to the sun than Earth is, it receives more solar energy than Earth does. Much of this radiation is reflected by Venus's atmosphere. However, some radiation reaches the surface and is later given off as heat. The carbon dioxide in Venus's atmosphere traps heat so well that Venus has the hottest surface of any planet. At 460°C, its average surface temperature is hot enough to melt lead. This trapping of heat by the atmosphere is called the **greenhouse effect**.

Exploring Venus Many space probes have visited Venus. The first probe to land on the surface and send back data, *Venera 7*, landed in 1970. It survived for only a few minutes because of the high temperature and pressure. Later probes were more durable and sent images and data back to Earth.

The *Magellan* probe reached Venus in 1990, carrying radar instruments. Radar works through clouds, so *Magellan* was able to map nearly the entire surface. The *Magellan* data confirmed that Venus is covered with rock. Venus's surface has many volcanoes and broad plains formed by lava flows.

✓ **Reading Checkpoint** What are Venus's clouds made of?

FIGURE 14
Maat Mons
Scientists used radar data to develop this computer image of the giant volcano *Maat Mons*. The height of the mountains is exaggerated to make them stand out.

88 ◆ J

Lab zone Try This Activity

Skills Focus inferring   L2

Materials plastic wrap, two glass jars, two thermometers

Time 20 minutes

Tips Place jars and thermometers in a position so that thermometers can be read without touching the jars or disturbing them in any way.

Expected Outcome The temperature in the covered jar should rise faster.

Extend Have students infer normal working of Earth's atmosphere. That is, how a similar greenhouse effect keeps Earth warm. **learning modality: kinesthetic**

Mars

Mars is called the "red planet." When you see it in the sky, it has a slightly reddish tinge. This reddish color is due to the breakdown of iron-rich rocks, which creates a rusty dust that covers much of Mars's surface.

Mars's Atmosphere The atmosphere of Mars is more than 95 percent carbon dioxide. It is similar in composition to Venus's atmosphere, but much thinner. You could walk around on Mars, but you would have to wear an airtight suit and carry your own oxygen, like a scuba diver. Mars has few clouds, and they are very thin compared to clouds on Earth. Mars's transparent atmosphere allows people on Earth to view its surface with a telescope. Temperatures on the surface range from −140°C to 20°C.

Water on Mars In 1877, an Italian astronomer named Giovanni Schiaparelli (sky ah puh REL ee) announced that he had seen long, straight lines on Mars. He called them *canale*, or channels. In the 1890s and early 1900s, Percival Lowell, an American astronomer, convinced many people that these lines were canals that had been built by intelligent Martians to carry water. Astronomers now know that Lowell was mistaken. There are no canals on Mars.

Images of Mars taken from space do show a variety of features that look as if they were made by ancient streams, lakes, or floods. There are huge canyons and features that look like the remains of ancient coastlines. **Scientists think that a large amount of liquid water flowed on Mars's surface in the distant past.** Scientists infer that Mars must have been much warmer and had a thicker atmosphere at that time.

At present, liquid water cannot exist for long on Mars's surface. Mars's atmosphere is so thin that any liquid water would quickly turn into a gas. So where is Mars's water now? Some of it is located in the planet's two polar ice caps, which contain frozen water and carbon dioxide. A small amount also exists as water vapor in Mars's atmosphere. Some water vapor has probably escaped into space. But scientists think that a large amount of water may still be frozen underground.

Size of Mars compared to Earth

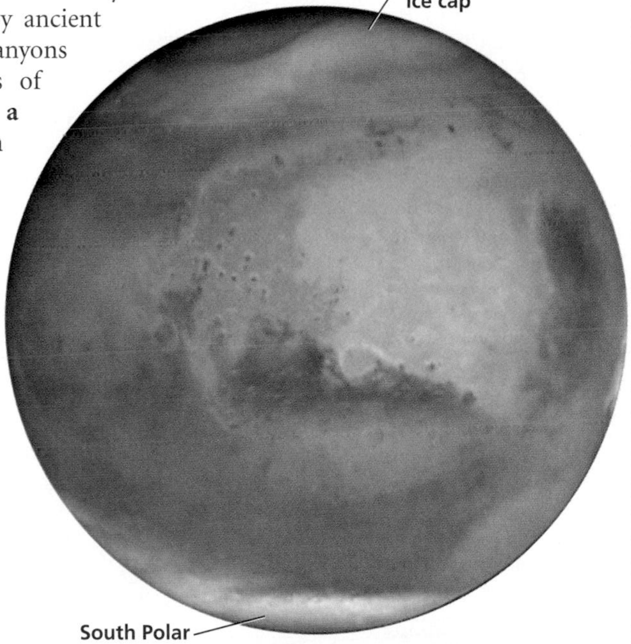

FIGURE 15
Mars
Because of its thin atmosphere and its distance from the sun, Mars is quite cold. Mars has ice caps at both poles. *Inferring Why is it easy to see Mars's surface from space?*

North Polar ice cap

South Polar ice cap

Mars

Teach Key Concepts L1
Exploring Mars

Focus Explain to students that people on Earth can view the surface of Mars with a telescope.

Teach Ask: **What does Mars have in common with the other inner planets?** (*It has seasons, volcanoes, and polar caps like Earth. It may have had liquid water in the past. The composition of its atmosphere is similar to that of Venus. It is barren like Mercury.*) Ask: **What distinguishes Mars from the other inner planets?** (*Unlike Venus and Earth, Mars has a very thin atmosphere. Mars has two moons.*)

Apply Ask: **What challenges might astronauts face if they went to Mars?** (*Possible answer: Lack of oxygen in the atmosphere, distance from Earth, extreme temperatures, lack of liquid water*) **learning modality: verbal**

Address Misconceptions
Science or Science Fiction?

Focus Students' ideas about the features and history of Mars may be partly based on science-fiction stories, television shows, and movies.

Teach Have each student prepare a Fact/Fiction sheet to distinguish scientific findings about Mars from science fiction.

Apply Have students share their sheets with partners and discuss whether they agree on what is fact and what is fiction. **learning modality: verbal**

Monitor Progress L2

Oral Presentation Have students work in groups of four. Assign each member of the group an inner planet. Have each student read the information about the assigned planet in the text and then teach the other members of the group what he or she has learned.

Answers
Figure 15 Mars has a thin, transparent atmosphere.

✓ **Reading Checkpoint** Mostly droplets of sulfuric acid

Differentiated Instruction

Gifted and Talented L3
Musical Planets The English composer Gustav Holst, who lived from 1874 to 1934, composed a group of pieces for orchestra entitled *The Planets*. The seven pieces describe musically the planets Mercury, Venus, Mars, Jupiter, Saturn, Uranus, and Neptune. Have interested students listen to one of the pieces. Ask each to write a brief paragraph describing how Holst used music to represent the planet. Encourage students to use descriptive terms, such as *eerie* and *brash*. **learning modality: verbal**

The Solar System

Show the Video Field Trip to let students experience exploring the inner planets. Discussion questions: **Name the inner planets of our solar system.** (*Mercury, Venus, Earth, and Mars*) **Describe one unique characteristic of each inner planet.** (*Possible answers: Mercury—closest planet to sun, on Mercury there are only one and one-half days per year; Venus—covered with thick, swirling clouds; brightest planet in Earth's sky; Venus's year is shorter than its day; its rotation is in opposite direction from that of other planets; Earth—has life, liquid water, protective atmosphere; Mars—red planet; has water as ice on surface near poles*)

Lab zone Build **Inquiry** L2

Modeling Channels

Materials sand, rectangular baking pans, large beaker, bucket for sand disposal

Time 15 minutes

Focus Remind students that water changes geologic features through the process of erosion.

Teach Place large buckets in strategic locations around the room for sand disposal. Warn students to keep the sand out of the sinks. Have pairs of students build slopes with moist sand in one end of a rectangular metal baking pan. The sand should slope from just below the rim on one end to about the middle of the pan. Have students pour a slow, steady stream of water onto the top of the slope and observe what happens as the water runs down the slope. Have students continue pouring until there is about 1 cm of water in the pan.

Apply Ask: **How did the flowing water change the surface of the sand?** (*It formed channels.*) Ask students to infer why scientists believe water once flowed on Mars. (*Channels on Mars look similar to channels formed by flowing water on Earth.*) **learning modality: kinesthetic**

Lab zone Try This **Activity**

Remote Control

How hard is it to explore another planet by remote control?

1. Tape a piece of paper over the front of a pair of goggles. Have your partner put them on.
2. 🖐 Walk behind your partner and direct him or her to another part of the room. **CAUTION:** *Do not give directions that would cause your partner to walk into a wall or a corner, trip on an obstacle, or bump into anything.*
3. Trade places and repeat Steps 1 and 2.

Drawing Conclusions Which verbal directions worked best? How quickly could you move? How is this activity similar to the way engineers have moved rovers on Mars? How fast do you think such a rover could move?

Seasons on Mars Because Mars has a tilted axis, it has seasons just as Earth does. During the Martian winter, an ice cap grows larger as a layer of frozen carbon dioxide covers it. Because the northern and southern hemispheres have opposite seasons, one ice cap grows while the other one shrinks.

As the seasons change on the dusty surface of Mars, windstorms arise and blow the dust around. Since the dust is blown off some regions, these regions look darker. A hundred years ago, some people thought these regions looked darker because plants were growing there. Astronomers now realize that the darker color is often just the result of windstorms.

Exploring Mars Many space probes have visited Mars. The first ones seemed to show that Mars is barren and covered with craters like the moon. In 2004, two new probes landed on Mars's surface. NASA's *Spirit* and *Opportunity* rovers explored opposite sides of the planet. They examined a variety of rocks and soil samples. At both locations, the rovers found strong evidence that liquid water was once present. The European Space Agency's *Mars Express* probe orbited overhead, finding clear evidence of frozen water (ice). However, the *Mars Express* lander failed.

Volcanoes on Mars Some regions of Mars have giant volcanoes. Astronomers see signs that lava flowed from the volcanoes in the past, but the volcanoes are no longer active. *Olympus Mons* on Mars is the largest volcano in the solar system. It covers a region as large as the state of Missouri and is nearly three times as tall as Mount Everest, the tallest mountain on Earth!

Lab zone Try This **Activity**

Skills Focus drawing conclusions L2

Materials paper, goggles, tape

Time 15 minutes

Tips Perform this activity in a large, open area with no obstacles.

Expected Outcome Clear simple directions worked best. Students could not move quickly. In a similar way, rovers must be given simple directions, and they move slowly.

Extend Have students infer difficulties that NASA encountered when trying to get rovers to perform tasks on Mars. **learning modality: kinesthetic**

FIGURE 16
Mars's Surface
As the large photo shows, the surface of Mars is rugged and rocky. Mars has many large volcanoes. The volcano *Olympus Mons* (inset) rises about 27 km from the surface. It is the largest volcano in the solar system.

Mars's Moons Mars has two very small moons. Phobos, the larger moon, is only 27 kilometers in diameter, about the distance a car can travel on the highway in 20 minutes. Deimos is even smaller, only 15 kilometers in diameter. Like Earth's moon, Phobos and Deimos are covered with craters. Phobos, which is much closer to Mars than Deimos is, is slowly spiraling down toward Mars. Astronomers predict that Phobos will smash into Mars in about 40 million years.

 Reading Checkpoint How many moons does Mars have? What are their names?

Section 3 Assessment

🎯 **Target Reading Skill** **Using Prior Knowledge** Review your graphic organizer about the inner planets and revise it based on what you just learned in the section.

Reviewing Key Concepts

1. **a. Listing** List the four inner planets in order of size, from smallest to largest.
   b. Comparing and Contrasting How are the four inner planets similar to one another?
2. **a. Describing** Describe an important characteristic of each inner planet.
   b. Comparing and Contrasting Compare the atmospheres of the four inner planets.
   c. Relating Cause and Effect Venus is much farther from the sun than Mercury is. Yet average temperatures on Venus's surface are much higher than those on Mercury. Explain why.

Writing in Science

Travel Brochure Select one of the inner planets other than Earth. Design a travel brochure for your selected planet, including basic facts and descriptions of places of interest. Also include a few sketches or photos to go along with your text.

Chapter 3 J ◆ 91

 **Chapter Project**

Keep Students on Track Students should now design a model that shows the relative diameters of the planets. If students have trouble finding a scale that works, suggest 1 cm = 10,000 km. At this scale, Mercury would be about the size of a pea and the sun would be about the size of an easy chair.

Writing in Science

Writing Mode Persuasion
Scoring Rubric
4 Exceeds criteria, includes complete descriptions, basic facts, and photos; brochure is colorful and entertaining
3 Meets all criteria but does not go beyond requirements
2 Includes only brief descriptions
1 Is inaccurate or incomplete

Science and Society

Space Exploration—Is It Worth the Cost?

Key Concept
Space exploration is expensive and poses risks and danger to human explorers.

Build Background Knowledge
Recalling Space Exploration Missions
Help students recall that many successful probes have been sent to planets and moons in our solar system. Ask: **How many of the planets in our solar system have been photographed up close or visited by space probes from Earth?** (All except Pluto) **What have we learned about them that couldn't be learned with Earth-based observations?** (Surface features, existence of minor moons, existence of rings, properties such as magnetic fields, composition of rocks, and so on) Remind students that some missions included astronauts. Ask: **Have any of the moons or planets in the solar system been explored by astronauts?** (Yes; Earth's moon) **Why did astronauts go to the moon?** (The moon landing was part of the "space race." Some responses may also include that the landings were missions of discovery.)

Introduce the Panel Discussion
Ask: **What value is there in exploring space?** (To learn about the universe and solar system and how they formed; to learn new ideas in science and technology that can be applied on Earth) **If there is value in exploring space, is there any real value in sending people to explore space?** (Accept all answers. Possible answers: No; uncrewed probes can learn everything we need to know. Yes; crewmembers can respond better than machines to unusual situations or make immediate decisions in response to unplanned occurrences.)

Facilitate the Panel Discussion
- Have students complete the first two steps under "You Decide" as a way to prepare themselves for taking part in the discussion.
- After the discussion, have students complete step three, using what they learned in the discussion to find solutions to the problem.

Space Exploration—Is It Worth the Cost?

Imagine that your spacecraft has just landed on the moon or on Mars. You've spent years planning for this moment. Canyons, craters, plains, and distant mountains stretch out before you. Perhaps a group of scientists has already begun construction of a permanent outpost. You check your spacesuit and prepare to step out onto the rocky surface.

Is such a trip likely? Would it be worthwhile? How much is space flight really worth to human society? Scientists and public officials have already started to debate such questions. Space exploration can help us learn more about the universe. But exploration can be risky and expensive. Sending people into space costs billions of dollars and risks the lives of astronauts. How can we balance the costs and benefits of space exploration?

▼ **Moon Landing**
A rocket is preparing to dock with a lander on the moon's surface in this imaginative artwork.

The Issues

Should Humans Travel Into Space?

Many Americans think that Neil Armstrong's walk on the moon in 1969 was one of the great moments in history. Learning how to keep people alive in space has led to improvements in everyday life. Safer equipment for firefighters, easier ways to package frozen food, and effective heart monitors have all come from space program research.

What Are the Alternatives?

Space exploration can involve a project to establish a colony on the moon or Mars. It also can involve a more limited use of scientific instruments near Earth, such as the Hubble Space Telescope. Instead of sending people, we could send space probes like *Cassini* to other planets.

Background

NASA has included a detailed justification of space exploration on the Web site. NASA argues that the basic knowledge about the universe gained through space exploration gives us a better understanding of Earth. Space exploration has also allowed application in satellite communication. Many technological breakthroughs have come as a result of the space program. The space program supports many jobs and is thus good for the economy. The exploration of space serves as an inspiration to humans to explore the unknown and push back boundaries. Additional information is available at **www.nasa.gov.**

◀ **Lunar Outpost**
A mining operation on the moon is shown in this imaginative artwork. Such a facility may someday harvest oxygen from the moon's soil.

◀ **Lunar Module**
This artwork shows a futuristic vehicle that may one day be used to explore the moon and Mars. The vehicle serves as a combination lander, rover, and habitat for astronauts.

Is Human Space Exploration Worth the Cost?

Scientists who favor human travel into space say that only people can collect certain kinds of information. They argue that the technologies developed for human space exploration will have many applications on Earth. But no one knows if research in space really provides information more quickly than research that can be done on Earth. Many critics of human space exploration think that other needs are more important. One United States senator said, "Every time you put money into the space station, there is a dime that won't be available for our children's education or for medical research."

You Decide

1. Identify the Problem
In your own words, list the various costs and benefits of space exploration.

2. Analyze the Options
Make a chart of three different approaches to space exploration: sending humans to the moon or another planet, doing only Earth-based research, and one other option. What are the benefits and drawbacks of each of these approaches?

3. Find a Solution
Imagine that you are a member of Congress who has to vote on a new budget. There is a fixed amount of money to spend, so you have to decide which needs are most important. Make a list of your top ten priorities. Explain your decisions.

Go Online
PHSchool.com

For: More on space exploration
Visit: PHSchool.com
Web Code: cfh-5030

Go Online
PHSchool.com

For: More on space exploration
Visit: PHSchool.com
Web Code: cfh-5030

Students can research this issue online.

You Decide

1. Costs may include the monetary expense as well as the possible cost in human lives. The benefits may include the knowledge gained, the spinoff technology, and the jobs that result from building and launching spacecraft.

2. Option charts should include three approaches. Possible answer for human exploration approach: People can interpret situations in different ways and extend their research; for example, if a test indicates that certain chemicals on a planet's surface might have been produced by a life form, a human explorer can devise further testing to reach more exact conclusions. Possible answer for Earth-based approach: Better ways to refine instruments are found every day. Possible answer for other option approach: Unpiloted probes could be designed that would be able to make the types of analyses and decisions that currently only the human brain can make.

3. Students may set priorities for Congress's budget in many different ways. Many may put financing education or researching diseases near the top of the list and space exploration near the bottom.

Extend

Ask students to come up with several questions concerning space exploration that they could ask their family or community members in order to gain other insights into the space program and its potential benefits. For example, students may not realize how inspiring Neil Armstrong's first steps on the moon were unless they talk to someone who witnessed the moon landing on television in 1969.

Section 4 — The Outer Planets

Objectives
After this lesson, students will be able to
J.3.4.1 Describe characteristics that the gas giants have in common.
J.3.4.2 Identify characteristics that distinguish each outer planet.

Target Reading Skill
Identifying Main Ideas Explain that identifying main ideas and details helps students sort the facts into groups.

Answers
Possible answers include the following:
Detail: Structure—they do not have a solid surface
Detail: Atmosphere—thick and made up mainly of hydrogen and helium
Detail: Rings—each is surrounded by a set of rings
Detail: Size and mass—each is very large and massive

All in One Teaching Resources
• Transparency J27

Preteach

Build Background Knowledge L2

Knowledge About Outer Planets
Divide the class into groups of five. Give each student in a group an index card with the name of a different outer planet written on it. Have each student write three things that he or she believes to be true about the planet. When students have finished, they can share their cards within each group. Collect the cards and use them to review the material when students have finished the section.

Reading Preview

Key Concepts
• What characteristics do the gas giants have in common?
• What characteristics distinguish each of the outer planets?

Key Terms
• gas giant • ring

Target Reading Skill
Identifying Main Ideas As you read the *Gas Giants and Pluto* section, write the main idea—the biggest or most important idea—in a graphic organizer like the one below. Then write three supporting details that further explain the main idea.

Main Idea

| The four gas giants are similar in . . . |

| Detail | Detail | Detail |

Lab zone — Discover Activity

How Big Are the Planets?
The table shows the diameters of the outer planets compared to Earth. For example, Jupiter's diameter is about 11 times Earth's diameter.

Planet	Diameter (Earth = 1)
Earth	1.0
Jupiter	11.2
Saturn	9.4
Uranus	4.0
Neptune	3.9
Pluto	0.2

1. Measure the diameter of a quarter in millimeters. Trace the quarter to represent Earth.
2. If Earth were the size of a quarter, calculate how large Jupiter would be. Now draw a circle to represent Jupiter.
3. Repeat Step 2 for each of the other planets in the table.

Think It Over
Classifying List the outer planets in order from largest to smallest. What is the largest outer planet? Which outer planet is much smaller than Earth?

Imagine you are in a spaceship approaching Jupiter. You'll quickly discover that Jupiter is very different from the terrestrial planets. The most obvious difference is Jupiter's great size. Jupiter is so large that more than 1,300 Earths could fit within it!

As your spaceship enters Jupiter's atmosphere, you encounter thick, colorful bands of clouds. Next, you sink into a denser and denser mixture of hydrogen and helium gas. Eventually, if the enormous pressure of the atmosphere does not crush your ship, you'll reach an incredibly deep "ocean" of liquid hydrogen and helium. But where exactly is Jupiter's surface? Surprisingly, there isn't a solid surface. Like the other giant planets, Jupiter has no real surface, just a solid core buried deep within the planet.

◀ An illustration of the space probe *Galileo* approaching the cloud-covered atmosphere of Jupiter.

Lab zone — Discover Activity

Skills Focus classifying

Materials quarter, metric ruler, lined paper, butcher paper or poster board, compass, pushpin, string

Time 15 minutes

L2 **Tips CAUTION:** *Compasses have sharp points and can cause injury.* A quarter has a diameter of 24 mm. Jupiter and Saturn will be too large to draw with a compass, so use a pin and string for them. Have students locate the center of each circle in the same place. They will need to use large paper to fit the larger circles onto one sheet.

Expected Outcome Diameters of circles: Earth 24 mm, Jupiter 264 mm, Saturn 226 mm, Uranus 96 mm, Neptune 94 mm, Pluto 4 mm

Think It Over Jupiter, Saturn, Uranus, Neptune, Earth, Pluto; Jupiter; Pluto

The Outer Planets

Planet	Diameter (kilometers)	Period of Rotation (Earth days)	Average Distance From Sun (kilometers)	Period of Revolution (Earth years)	Number of Moons
Jupiter	143,000	0.41	779,000,000	12	60+
Saturn	120,500	0.45	1,434,000,000	29	31+
Uranus	51,100	0.72	2,873,000,000	84	25+
Neptune	49,500	0.67	4,495,000,000	164	13+
Pluto	2,400	6.4	5,870,000,000	248	1

Gas Giants and Pluto

Jupiter and the other planets farthest from the sun are called the outer planets. **The first four outer planets—Jupiter, Saturn, Uranus, and Neptune—are much larger and more massive than Earth, and they do not have solid surfaces.** Because these four planets are all so large, they are often called the **gas giants.** The fifth outer planet, Pluto, is small and rocky like the terrestrial planets. Figure 17 provides information about these planets.

Like the sun, the gas giants are composed mainly of hydrogen and helium. Because they are so massive, the gas giants exert a much stronger gravitational force than the terrestrial planets. Gravity keeps the giant planets' gases from escaping, so they have thick atmospheres. Despite the name "gas giant," much of the hydrogen and helium is actually in liquid form because of the enormous pressure inside the planets. The outer layers of the gas giants are extremely cold because of their great distance from the sun. Temperatures increase greatly within the planets.

All the gas giants have many moons. In addition, each of the gas giants is surrounded by a set of rings. A **ring** is a thin disk of small particles of ice and rock.

FIGURE 17
The outer planets are much farther apart than the inner planets. Note that planet sizes and distances are not drawn to scale.
Observing Which outer planet has the most moons?

Go Online
PHSchool.com

For: More on the planets
Visit: PHSchool.com
Web Code: ced-5034

Differentiated Instruction

English Learners/Beginning Comprehension: Key Concept L1 On the board, rewrite the boldface sentence as three sentences, for example: **The first four outer planets are Jupiter, Saturn, Uranus, and Neptune. These planets are much larger and more massive than Earth. None of these planets has a solid surface.** Discuss each sentence, and then help students organize the information in the text in a graphic organizer that lists main ideas and supporting details. **learning modality: verbal**

English Learners/Intermediate Comprehension: Key Concept L2 Have pairs of students rewrite the boldface sentence as three sentences and then organize the information in the text in a graphic organizer. **learning modality: verbal**

Go Online
PHSchool.com

For: More on the planets
Visit: PHSchool.com
Web Code: ced-5034

Students can review the planets in an online interactivity.

Instruct

Gas Giants and Pluto

Teach Key Concepts L2
Characteristics of Outer Planets

Focus Tell students to imagine that a space probe is exploring a gas giant.

Teach Ask students to describe what the probe would encounter as it approached the visible surface. *(There is no solid surface; the atmosphere just gets thicker. Eventually, the combination of heat and pressure would probably cause the probe to fail.)*

Apply Ask: **Could the probe penetrate to the solid part of the planet?** *(Not likely; the solid core is buried deep inside the planet.)*
learning modality: logical/mathematical

Use Visuals: Figure 17 L2

Focus Have students use their fingers to trace the orbit of each planet.

Teach Ask: **Which planet has an orbit that crosses the orbit of another?** *(Pluto crosses the orbit of Neptune.)* Refer students to the data table. Ask: **Which planet is about twice as far from the sun as Jupiter?** *(Saturn)* **About six times as far from the sun as Jupiter?** *(Neptune)*

Apply Have students use the data table to identify additional differences among the outer planets. **learning modality: visual**

All in One Teaching Resources
• Transparency J28

Independent Practice L2

All in One Teaching Resources
• Guided Reading and Study Worksheet: *The Outer Planets*

Monitor Progress _____ L2

Skills Check Have students compare and contrast Earth to the outer planets.

Answer
Figure 17 Jupiter

Jupiter

Teach Key Concepts [L3]

Characteristics of Jupiter

Focus Remind students that Jupiter is the largest planet.

Teach Ask: **Why is it somewhat misleading to call Jupiter a "gas" giant?** (*Much of the planet is mainly liquid.*) Remind students that hydrogen and helium occur naturally as gases on Earth. Ask: **Why are much of the hydrogen and helium on Jupiter in the liquid state?** (*The force of gravity on Jupiter is immense because Jupiter is so massive. Therefore, the hydrogen and helium are under a great pressure, which causes them to be compressed into the liquid state as their molecules slow down and are forced into a smaller volume.*)

Apply Ask: **In addition to Jupiter and other gas giants, what object or objects in our solar system are made up mainly of hydrogen and helium?** (*The sun*) **learning modality: logical/mathematical**

All in One Teaching Resources

• Transparency J28, J29

Help Students Read

Active Comprehension Before students read about Jupiter, ask them what they would like to know about this planet. Write a few of their questions on the board, such as "What is the Great Red Spot?" and "How do astronomers know what Jupiter is made of?" After students finish reading the selection, ask them to answer the questions.

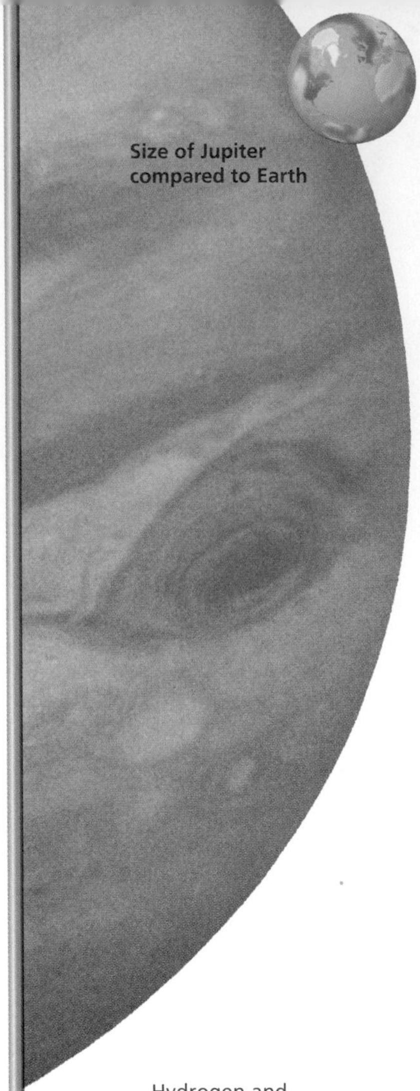

Jupiter

Jupiter is the largest and most massive planet. Jupiter's enormous mass dwarfs the other planets. In fact, its mass is about $2\frac{1}{2}$ times that of all the other planets combined!

Jupiter's Atmosphere Like all of the gas giants, Jupiter has a thick atmosphere made up mainly of hydrogen and helium. An especially interesting feature of Jupiter's atmosphere is its Great Red Spot, a storm that is larger than Earth! The storm's swirling winds blow hundreds of kilometers per hour, similar to a hurricane. But hurricanes on Earth weaken quickly as they pass over land. On Jupiter, there is no land to weaken the huge storm. The Great Red Spot, which was first observed in the mid-1600s, shows no signs of going away soon.

Jupiter's Structure Astronomers think that Jupiter, like the other giant planets, probably has a dense core of rock and iron at its center. As shown in Figure 18, a thick mantle of liquid hydrogen and helium surrounds this core. Because of the crushing weight of Jupiter's atmosphere, the pressure at Jupiter's core is estimated to be about 30 million times greater than the pressure at Earth's surface.

Jupiter's Moons Recall that Galileo discovered Jupiter's four largest moons. These moons, which are highlighted in Figure 19, are named Io (EYE oh), Europa, Ganymede, and Callisto. All four are larger than Earth's own moon. However, they are very different from one another. Since Galileo's time, astronomers have discovered dozens of additional moons orbiting Jupiter. Many of these are small moons that have been found in the last few years thanks to improved technology.

Reading Checkpoint What is Jupiter's atmosphere composed of?

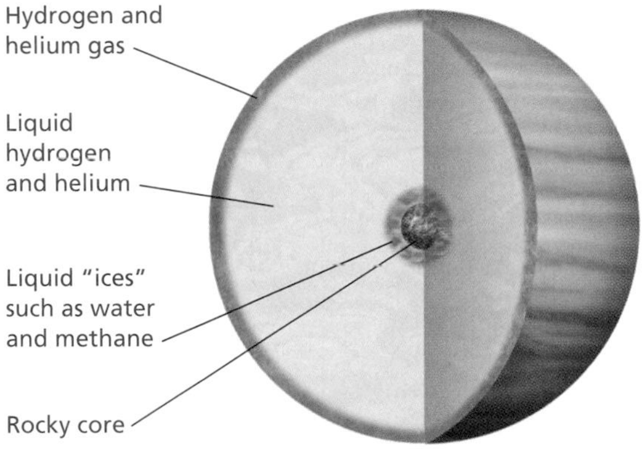

Hydrogen and helium gas

Liquid hydrogen and helium

Liquid "ices" such as water and methane

Rocky core

FIGURE 18
Jupiter's Structure
Jupiter is composed mainly of the elements hydrogen and helium. Although Jupiter is often called a "gas giant," much of it is actually liquid.
Comparing and Contrasting *How does the structure of Jupiter differ from that of a terrestrial planet?*

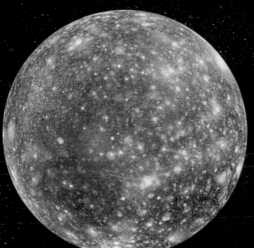

FIGURE 19
Jupiter's Moons
The astronomer Galileo discovered Jupiter's four largest moons. These images are not shown to scale.
Interpreting Photographs *Which is the largest of Jupiter's moons?*

Callisto's surface is icy and covered with craters. ▼

▲ Io's surface is covered with large, active volcanoes. An eruption of sulfur lava can be seen near the bottom of this photo. Sulfur gives Io its unusual colors.

Ganymede is the largest moon in the solar system. It is larger than either Mercury or Pluto. ▼

Europa ▼

Astronomers suspect that Europa's icy crust covers an ocean of liquid water underneath. This illustration shows Europa's icy surface.

Lab zone Teacher Demo

Modeling the Great Red Spot L1

Materials water, pepper, funnel or spoon, clear plastic 1-L bottle with lid

Time 10 minutes

Focus Point out the resemblance between the Great Red Spot and a hurricane on Earth. If necessary, show students images of hurricanes taken by satellites orbiting above Earth.

Teach Half fill a clear plastic bottle with water. Using a funnel or spoon, pour in a spoonful of pepper. Seal the bottle and swirl the water forcefully. Ask: **What happens to the pepper grains?** *(They spin in a large swirl.)*

Apply Have students compare the appearance of the spinning pepper grains to the images of the Great Red Spot. Ask: **What forces are causing the Great Red Spot to swirl?** *(Possible answer: Differences in pressure in Jupiter's atmosphere)* **What kind of data would you need to test your inferences?** *(Possible answer: Data that show the pressure of the atmosphere around the Great Red Spot)* **learning modality: visual**

Differentiated Instruction

Less Proficient Readers L1

Interpreting Visuals Refer students to Figure 19 and its captions. Help them interpret the visual by asking: How do the images relate to the captions? How do the captions help me understand the images? What do I already know about the information in the images and captions? What else do I want to learn about the subjects of these images? **learning modality: visual**

Monitor Progress L2

Oral Presentation Have students describe what they would see if they stood on the surfaces of Jupiter's four largest moons.

Answers

Figure 18 The terrestrial planets are small and rocky. Jupiter is large and mainly liquid with a solid core.

Figure 19 Ganymede

Reading Checkpoint Mainly hydrogen and helium

Saturn

Saturn's Rings

Focus Ask: **In your view, what is the most distinguishing characteristic of Saturn?** *(Possible answer: The rings)*

Teach Ask: **What are the rings made of?** *(Chunks of ice and rock)* **How do the rings appear from Earth?** *(It looks as if Saturn has only a few rings.)* **How do the rings look up close?** *(The obvious rings are divided into many smaller rings that are broad and thin.)*

Apply Tell students that the particles of Saturn's rings create an image of a solid surface when viewed from a distance, similar to the *pointillist* style of art or some computer graphics. Obtain and show an example of a pointillist painting or computer graphics with tiny dots showing an image. **learning modality: visual**

Build Inquiry   L2

Comparing and Contrasting Planets

Materials none

Time 15 minutes

Focus Ask students to note similarities and differences between Saturn and Jupiter as they read about Saturn.

Teach Have students make a table comparing and contrasting Saturn and Jupiter. The table should include size, density, appearance, composition, and any other features students wish to include.

Apply Have students write a paragraph describing the similarities and differences between Jupiter and Saturn. **learning modality: verbal**

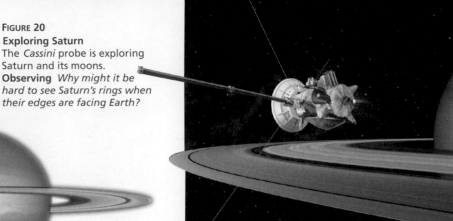

FIGURE 20
Exploring Saturn
The *Cassini* probe is exploring Saturn and its moons.
Observing *Why might it be hard to see Saturn's rings when their edges are facing Earth?*

Size of Saturn compared to Earth

Lab zone Skills Activity

Making Models

1. Use a plastic foam sphere 8 cm in diameter to represent Saturn.
2. Use an overhead transparency to represent Saturn's rings. Cut a circle 18 cm in diameter out of the transparency. Cut a hole 9 cm in diameter out of the center of the circle.
3. Stick five toothpicks into Saturn, spaced equally around its equator. Put the transparency on the toothpicks and tape it to them. Sprinkle baking soda on the transparency.
4. Use a peppercorn to represent Titan. Place the peppercorn 72 cm away from Saturn on the same plane as the rings.
5. What do the particles of baking soda represent?

98 ◆ J

Saturn

The second-largest planet in the solar system is Saturn. The *Voyager* probes showed that Saturn, like Jupiter, has a thick atmosphere made up mainly of hydrogen and helium. Saturn's atmosphere also contains clouds and storms, but they are less dramatic than those on Jupiter. Saturn is the only planet whose average density is less than that of water.

Saturn's Rings When Galileo first looked at Saturn with a telescope, he could see something sticking out on the sides. But he didn't know what it was. A few decades later, an astronomer using a better telescope discovered that Saturn had rings around it. These rings are made of chunks of ice and rock, each traveling in its own orbit around Saturn.

Saturn has the most spectacular rings of any planet. From Earth, it looks as though Saturn has only a few rings and that they are divided from each other by narrow, dark regions. The *Voyager* spacecraft discovered that each of these obvious rings is divided into many thinner rings. Saturn's rings are broad and thin, like a compact disc.

Saturn's Moons Saturn's largest moon, Titan, is larger than the planet Mercury. Titan was discovered in 1665 but was known only as a point of light until the *Voyager* probes flew by. The probes showed that Titan has an atmosphere so thick that little light can pass through it. Four other moons of Saturn are each over 1,000 kilometers in diameter.

Reading Checkpoint What are Saturn's rings made of?

Lab zone Skills Activity

Skills Focus making models   L1

Materials 8-cm plastic foam sphere, clear plastic sheet, ruler, scissors, compass, 5 toothpicks, tape, baking soda, peppercorn, glue (optional)

Time 20 minutes

Tips You may want to cut circles from the center of the transparencies yourself so that students do not need to use sharp scissors.

Expected Outcome The particles of baking soda represent the chunks of ice and rock that make up Saturn's rings.

Extend Have students use their model to demonstrate why the rings of Saturn are occasionally invisible from Earth. **learning modality: kinesthetic**

Uranus

Although the gas giant Uranus (YOOR uh nus) is about four times the diameter of Earth, it is still much smaller than Jupiter and Saturn. Uranus is twice as far from the sun as Saturn, so it is much colder. Uranus looks blue-green because of traces of methane in its atmosphere. Like the other gas giants, Uranus is surrounded by a group of thin, flat rings, although they are much darker than Saturn's rings.

Discovery of Uranus In 1781, Uranus became the first new planet discovered since ancient times. Astronomer William Herschel, in England, found a fuzzy object in the sky that did not look like a star. At first he thought it might be a comet, but it soon proved to be a planet beyond Saturn. The discovery made Herschel famous and started an era of active solar system study.

Exploring Uranus About 200 years after Herschel's discovery, *Voyager 2* arrived at Uranus and sent back close-up views of that planet. Images from *Voyager 2* show only a few clouds on Uranus's surface. But even these few clouds allowed astronomers to calculate that Uranus rotates in about 17 hours.

Uranus's axis of rotation is tilted at an angle of about 90 degrees from the vertical. Viewed from Earth, Uranus is rotating from top to bottom instead of from side to side, the way most of the other planets do. Uranus's rings and moons rotate around this tilted axis. Astronomers think that billions of years ago Uranus was hit by an object that knocked it on its side.

Uranus's Moons Photographs from *Voyager 2* show that Uranus's five largest moons have icy, cratered surfaces. The craters show that rocks from space have hit the moons. Uranus's moons also have lava flows on their surfaces, suggesting that material has erupted from inside each moon. *Voyager 2* images revealed 10 moons that had never been seen before. Recently, astronomers discovered several more moons, for a total of at least 25.

✓ **Reading Checkpoint** Who discovered Uranus?

Size of Uranus compared to Earth

FIGURE 21
Uranus
The false color image of Uranus below was taken by the Hubble Space Telescope. Unlike most other planets, Uranus rotates from top to bottom rather than side to side.
Inferring How must Uranus's seasons be unusual?

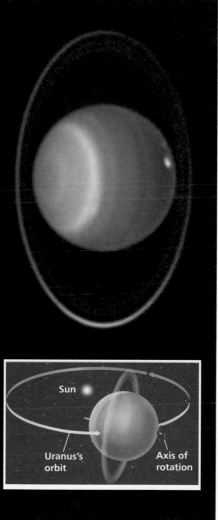

Sun

Uranus's orbit

Axis of rotation

Uranus

Teach Key Concepts   L1
Uranus's Axis of Rotation

Focus Remind students that Earth rotates on its axis from west to east.

Teach Ask: **How is Uranus's rotation different from that of the other planets?** *(It rotates from top to bottom instead of from side to side.)* **What do astronomers think caused this?** *(Uranus was probably hit by a large object that knocked it on its side.)*

Apply Tell students to examine the bottom image in Figure 21. Have them lay a pencil over the axis of rotation and then trace the orbit of Uranus by moving the pencil. Ask: **In which direction does the pencil point?** *(The pencil always points to the left edge of the paper.)* **Does the axis of rotation of Uranus always point to the sun?** *(No)* **learning modality: kinesthetic**

All in One Teaching Resources

• Transparency J28, J30

Monitor Progress _____ L2

Skills Check Have students create two fact sheets about Uranus. The first should include facts known about the planet before the *Voyager* missions. The second should include facts learned since the *Voyager* missions.

Answers
Figure 20 The rings are so thin that when their edges face Earth they are nearly invisible.
Figure 21 During spring and fall, all parts of the planet experience equal hours of sunlight and darkness. During winter and summer, one hemisphere is always in darkness while the other is always in sunlight.

✓ **Reading Checkpoint** Chunks of ice and rock

✓ **Reading Checkpoint** William Herschel

Differentiated Instruction

Gifted and Talented   L3
Researching Planet Names The ancient Romans named the planets they knew after the gods they worshipped. Mercury was the fast, winged messenger of the gods. Venus was the goddess of beauty, and Mars was the god of war. The planets and moons discovered in the last 200 years have also been named after ancient gods. Have students research the origin of the names of Jupiter, Saturn, Uranus, Neptune, or Pluto. Students can make posters describing the character of the god. *(Jupiter was the king of the Roman gods. Saturn was the god of agriculture. Uranus was the Greek god who was the husband of Gaea, Earth. Neptune was the Roman god of the sea. Pluto was the Roman god of the underworld.)* **learning modality: verbal**

Neptune

Teach Key Concepts

Neptune's Moons

Focus Have a student volunteer read aloud "Neptune's Moons."

Teach Ask: **How many moons does Neptune have?** *(At least 13)* **What is the name of Neptune's largest moon?** *(Triton)* **What is unusual about a region near Triton's south pole?** *(It may be covered by nitrogen ice; dark material erupts from under the ice.)*

Apply Tell students that the eruptions on Triton may be caused by geysers. On Earth, geysers are linked to tectonic activity. On Triton, geysers may be caused by sunlight warming the nitrogen gas; the resulting vapor rises through cracks in the icy surface. **learning modality: verbal**

Math Skills Formulas and Equations

Focus Have students recall that circumference is the perimeter of a circle.

Teach Point out that π is a constant, which means that its value does not vary.

Answer
$2 \times 3.14 \times 60{,}250 \text{ km} = \text{about } 378{,}800 \text{ km}$

Pluto

Teach Key Concepts

Classifying Pluto

Focus Remind students that Pluto is unique among the planets.

Teach Ask: **What makes Pluto different from the outer planets? The inner planets?** *(Pluto is much smaller than the outer planets and less dense than the inner planets.)*

Apply Remind students that Pluto is only twice the size of its own moon, Charon. Point out that Pluto and Charon may be two of many similar objects waiting to be discovered in the Kuiper belt. Challenge students to write a paragraph about whether Pluto should be classified as a planet, a Kuiper belt object, or some other type of object. **learning modality: verbal**

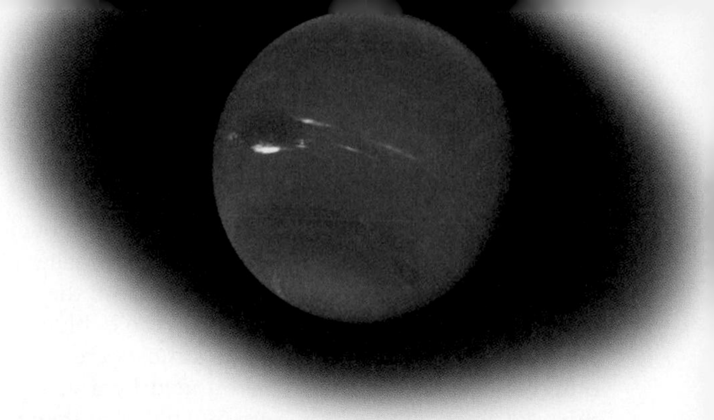

FIGURE 22
Neptune
The Great Dark Spot was a giant storm in Neptune's atmosphere. White clouds, probably made of methane ice crystals, can also be seen in the photo.

Size of Neptune compared to Earth

Circumference

To calculate the circumference of a circle, use this formula:

$$C = 2\pi r$$

In the formula, $\pi \approx 3.14$, and r is the circle's radius, which is the distance from the center of the circle to its edge. The same formula can be used to calculate the circumference of planets, which are nearly spherical.

Neptune's radius at its equator is about 24,800 km. Calculate its circumference.

$$C = 2\pi r$$
$$= 2.00 \times 3.14 \times 24{,}800 \text{ km}$$
$$= 156{,}000 \text{ km}$$

Practice Problem Saturn's radius is 60,250 km. What is its circumference?

Neptune

Neptune is even farther from the sun than Uranus. In some ways, Uranus and Neptune look like twins. They are similar in size and color. **Neptune is a cold, blue planet. Its atmosphere contains visible clouds.** Scientists think that Neptune, shown in Figure 22, is slowly shrinking, causing its interior to heat up. As this energy rises toward Neptune's surface, it produces clouds and storms in the planet's atmosphere.

Discovery of Neptune Neptune was discovered as a result of a mathematical prediction. Astronomers noted that Uranus was not quite following the orbit predicted for it. They hypothesized that the gravity of an unseen planet was affecting Uranus's orbit. By 1846, mathematicians in England and France had calculated the orbit of this unseen planet. Shortly thereafter, an observer saw an unknown object in the predicted area of the sky. It was the new planet, now called Neptune.

Exploring Neptune In 1989, *Voyager 2* flew by Neptune and photographed a Great Dark Spot about the size of Earth. Like the Great Red Spot on Jupiter, the Great Dark Spot was probably a giant storm. But the storm didn't last long. Images taken five years later showed that the Great Dark Spot was gone. Other, smaller spots and regions of clouds on Neptune also seem to come and go.

Neptune's Moons Astronomers have discovered at least 13 moons orbiting Neptune. The largest moon is Triton, which has a thin atmosphere. The *Voyager* images show that the region near Triton's south pole is covered by nitrogen ice.

Reading Checkpoint Before they could see Neptune, what evidence led scientists to conclude that it existed?

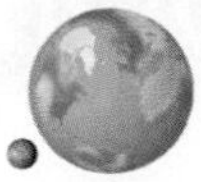

Size of Pluto compared to Earth

Pluto

Pluto is very different from the gas giants. **Pluto has a solid surface and is much smaller and denser than the other outer planets.** In fact, Pluto is smaller than Earth's moon.

Pluto has a single moon of its own, Charon. Since Charon is more than half the size of Pluto, some astronomers consider them to be a double planet instead of a planet and a moon.

Pluto's Orbit Pluto is so far from the sun that it revolves around the sun only once every 248 Earth years. Pluto's orbit is very elliptical, bringing it closer to the sun than Neptune on part of its orbit.

Is Pluto Really a Planet? Pluto is so small that many astronomers do not think it is worthy of being called a planet at all. Pluto may be merely the largest of tens of thousands of objects made of ice, rock, and dust that revolve around the sun beyond Neptune. If astronomers had found these other objects before they found Pluto, they might not have called Pluto a planet.

 Reading Checkpoint How long does it take Pluto to revolve around the sun?

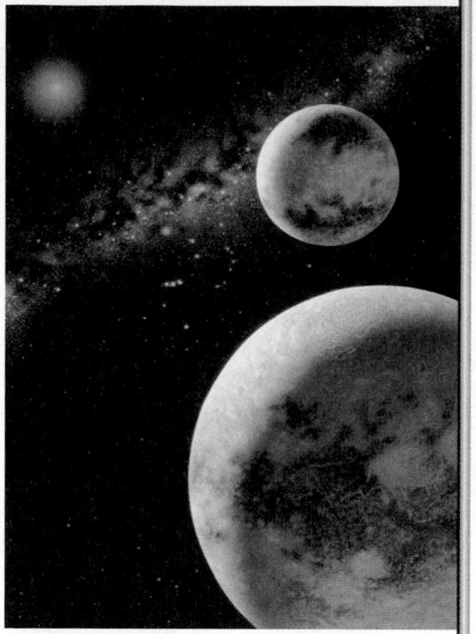

FIGURE 23
Pluto and Charon
The illustration above shows Pluto (lower right) and its moon Charon. *Inferring Why do astronomers often call Pluto and Charon a double planet?*

Section 4 Assessment

Target Reading Skill Identifying Main Ideas
Use your graphic organizer about the structure of the gas giants to help you answer Question 1 below.

Reviewing Key Concepts

1. **a. Describing** How are the gas giants similar to one another?
   b. Explaining Why do all of the gas giants have thick atmospheres?
   c. Listing List the outer planets in order of size, from smallest to largest.
   d. Comparing and Contrasting Compare the structure of a typical terrestrial planet with that of a gas giant.

2. **a. Describing** Describe an important characteristic of each outer planet that helps to distinguish it from the other outer planets.
   b. Comparing and Contrasting How is Pluto different from the gas giants?
   c. Classifying Why do some astronomers think that Pluto should not be classified as a planet?

 **Math Practice**

3. **Circumference** The radius of Jupiter at its equator is about 71,490 km. What is its circumference?

Chapter 3   J ◆ 101

Speeding Around the Sun

 **Design Your Own Lab**

Speeding Around the Sun 〖L3〗

Prepare for Inquiry

Skills Objectives
After this lab, students will be able to
- Develop hypotheses concerning the revolution of a planet around the sun
- Make a model planet to test their hypotheses

⏱ **Class Time** 45 minutes

All in One Teaching Resources
- Lab Worksheet: *Speeding Around the Sun*

Alternative Materials
In place of a stopper, use a tennis ball with rubber bands around it. In place of the plastic tube, use a pen tube with smooth ends.

Safety
The stopper should be swung in an open space that is clear of all students and objects. Make sure that the object on the opposite end of the string from the stopper cannot be pulled through the tube. Check the strength of the string to make sure that it will not break. Tell students to wear eye protection throughout the lab. Review the safety guidelines in Appendix A.

Guide Inquiry

Invitation
Discuss the difference between a hypothesis and a scientific fact. A hypothesis is a possible explanation for a set of observations or an answer to a scientific question.

Problem
How does a planet's distance from the sun affect its period of revolution?

Skills Focus
making models, developing hypotheses, designing experiments

Materials
- string, 1.5 m
- plastic tube, 6 cm
- meter stick
- weight or several washers
- one-hole rubber stopper
- stopwatch or watch with second hand

Procedure

PART 1 **Modeling Planetary Revolution**

1. Copy the data table onto a sheet of paper.

Data Table				
Distance (cm)	Period of Revolution			
	Trial 1	Trial 2	Trial 3	Average
20				
40				
60				

2. Make a model of a planet orbiting the sun by threading the string through the rubber stopper hole. Tie the end of the string to the main part of the string. Pull tightly to make sure that the knot will not become untied.

3. Thread the other end of the string through the plastic tube and tie a weight to that end. Have your teacher check both knots.

4. Pull the string so the stopper is 20 cm away from the plastic tube. Hold the plastic tube in your hand above your head. Keeping the length of string constant, swing the rubber stopper in a circle above your head just fast enough to keep the stopper moving. The circle represents a planet's orbit, and the length of string from the rubber stopper to the plastic tube represents the distance from the sun.
CAUTION: *Stand away from other students. Make sure the swinging stopper will not hit students or objects. Do not let go of the string.*

5. Have your lab partner time how long it takes for the rubber stopper to make ten complete revolutions. Determine the period for one revolution by dividing the measured time by ten. Record the time in the data table.

6. Repeat Step 5 two more times. Be sure to record each trial in a data table. After the third trial, calculate and record the average period of revolution.

Introduce the Procedure
- Have students think of the inward pull of the string as gravity.
- The activity should give students a "feel" for the effects of gravity and the increased speed of objects as their orbits get smaller.

Troubleshooting the Experiment
- Students may have to practice keeping the stopper moving at a constant speed.

PART 2 Designing an Experiment

7. Write your hypothesis for how a planet's period of revolution would be affected by changing its distance from the sun.

8. Design an experiment that will enable you to test your hypothesis. Write the steps you plan to follow to carry out your experiment. As you design your experiment, consider the following factors:
   • What different distances will you test?
   • What variables are involved in your experiment and how will you control them?
   • How many trials will you run for each distance?

9. Have your teacher review your step-by-step plan. After your teacher approves your plan, carry out your experiment.

Analyze and Conclude

1. **Making Models** In your experiment, what represents the planet and what represents the sun?

2. **Making Models** What force does the pull on the string represent?

3. **Interpreting Data** What happened to the period of revolution when you changed the distance in Part 2? Did your experiment prove or disprove your hypothesis?

4. **Drawing Conclusions** Which planets take less time to revolve around the sun—those closer to the sun or those farther away? Use the model to support your answer.

5. **Designing Experiments** As you were designing your experiment, which variable was the most difficult to control? How did you design your procedure to control that variable?

6. **Communicating** Write a brief summary of your experiment for a science magazine. Describe your hypothesis, procedure, and results in one or two paragraphs.

More to Explore

Develop a hypothesis for how a planet's mass might affect its period of revolution. Then, using a stopper with a different mass, modify the activity to test your hypothesis. Before you swing your stopper, have your teacher check your knots.

Chapter 3 J ◆ 103

Expected Outcome

• It takes longer for a single revolution when the string is longer.

• Tell students that as distance from the sun increases, the gravitational pull of the sun on a planet decreases. In addition, the circumference of the orbit increases as distance from the sun increases. This means that the planet is traveling more slowly over a greater distance.

Analyze and Conclude

1. The plastic tube represented the sun. The rubber stopper represented the planet.

2. The pull on the string represents the force of gravity.

3. The period of revolution should have increased as the length of string increased. This result may support or disprove students' hypotheses.

4. Planets closer to the sun revolve around the sun in less time. Students should support this conclusion by noting that when the string was short in the model, the period of revolution was also short.

5. Students may cite such variables as mass or angle of rotation. Make sure students designed their experiment to take into account a way to control that variable.

6. Check students' articles for accuracy. Make sure they included the requested information.

Extend Inquiry

More to Explore By adding additional rubber stoppers, the mass of the swinging object is increased. By repeating the swing of the increased mass in the same orbit, students will find that planets have the same period at the same distance. They may also notice that the inward pull of the string has to be greater with more stoppers. The force of gravity between the sun and a planet is related to the mass of the planet. The inertia of a planet is also related to its mass. Thus, the effect of increasing the mass is to increase both the pull of the sun's gravity and the ability of the planet to withstand that pull through inertia. The resulting speed of the planet is the same, regardless of mass.

Sample Data Table				
Distance	Trial 1	Trial 2	Trial 3	Average
(cm)	(s)	(s)	(s)	(s)
20	0.4	0.5	0.4	0.43
40	0.6	0.6	0.7	0.63
60	0.8	0.8	0.8	0.8

Objectives

After this lesson, students will be able to
J.3.5.1 Describe the characteristics of comets.
J.3.5.2 Identify where most asteroids are found.
J.3.5.3 Explain what meteoroids are and how they form.

Target Reading Skill

Comparing and Contrasting Explain that comparing and contrasting information shows how ideas, facts, and events are similar and different. The results of the comparison can have importance.

Answers

Possible answers include the following:
Comets: Origin—Kuiper belt and Oort cloud; Size—excluding the tail, about the size of a mountain; Composition—ice, dust, small rocky particles
Asteroids: Origin—between the orbits of Mars and Jupiter; Size—typically less than 1 km; some are more than 300km in diameter; Composition—rock
Meteoroids: Origin—comets or asteroids; Size—smaller than comets or asteroids; Composition—rock or dust

All in One Teaching Resources

• Transparency J31

Preteach

Build Background Knowledge L2

Shooting Stars

Ask students whether they have ever seen a "shooting star." Ask them to describe what it looked like. What did they think it was? After the discussion, tell students that in this section, they will investigate the nature of comets, asteroids, and shooting stars, which are actually meteors.

Reading Preview

Key Concepts
- What are the characteristics of comets?
- Where are most asteroids found?
- What are meteoroids and how do they form?

Key Terms
- comet • coma • nucleus
- Kuiper belt • Oort cloud
- asteroid • asteroid belt
- meteoroid • meteor
- meteorite

Target Reading Skill
Comparing and Contrasting
As you read, compare and contrast comets, asteroids, and meteoroids by completing a table like the one below.

Comets, Asteroids, and Meteoroids

Feature	Comets	Asteroids
Origin	Kuiper belt and Oort cloud	
Size		
Composition		

FIGURE 24
Structure of a Comet
The main parts of a comet are the nucleus, the coma, and the tail. The nucleus is deep within the coma. Most comets have two tails—a bluish gas tail and a white dust tail.

Lab zone Discover Activity

Which Way Do Comet Tails Point?

1. Form a small ball out of modeling clay to represent a comet.
2. Using a pencil point, push three 10-cm lengths of string into the ball. The strings represent the comet's tail. Stick the ball onto the pencil point, as shown.
3. Hold the ball about 1 m in front of a fan. The air from the fan represents the solar wind. Move the ball toward the fan, away from the fan, and from side to side.
   CAUTION: *Keep your fingers away from the fan blades.*

Think It Over
Inferring How does moving the ball affect the direction in which the strings point? What determines which way the tail of a comet points?

Imagine watching a cosmic collision! That's exactly what happened in July 1994. The year before, Eugene and Carolyn Shoemaker and David Levy discovered a comet that had previously broken into pieces near Jupiter. When their orbit passed near Jupiter again, the fragments crashed into Jupiter. On Earth, many people were fascinated to view images of the huge explosions—some were as large as Earth!

As this example shows, the sun, planets, and moons aren't the only objects in the solar system. There are also many smaller objects moving through the solar system. These objects are classified as comets, asteroids, or meteoroids.

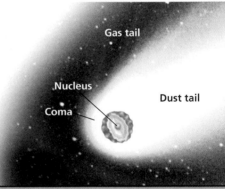

Gas tail

Nucleus

Dust tail

Coma

Lab zone Discover Activity

Skills Focus inferring

Materials modeling clay, pencil, 3 10-cm lengths of string, small fan

Time 10 minutes

Tips You may wish to have more than one fan available and allow two or three students to test their models at the same time.

L1

Expected Outcome The strings point away from the fan, behind the ball of clay.

Think It Over Moving the ball does not change the direction in which the strings point. A comet's tail always points away from the sun.

Comets

One of the most glorious things you can see in the night sky is a comet. But what exactly is a comet? You can think of a **comet** as a "dirty snowball" about the size of a mountain. **Comets are loose collections of ice, dust, and small rocky particles whose orbits are usually very long, narrow ellipses.**

A Comet's Head When a comet gets close enough to the sun, the energy in the sunlight turns the ice into gas, releasing gas and dust. Clouds of gas and dust form a fuzzy outer layer called a **coma.** Figure 24 shows the coma and the **nucleus,** the solid inner core of a comet. The brightest part of a comet, the comet's head, is made up of the nucleus and coma.

A Comet's Tail As a comet approaches the sun and heats up, some of its gas and dust stream outward, forming a tail. The name *comet* means "long-haired star" in Greek. Most comets have two tails—a gas tail and a dust tail. Both tails usually point away from the sun, as shown in Figure 25.

A comet's tail can be more than 100 million kilometers long and stretch across most of the sky. The material is stretched out very thinly, however, so there is little mass in a comet's tail.

Origin of Comets Most comets are found in one of two distant regions of the solar system: the Kuiper belt and the Oort cloud. The **Kuiper belt** is a doughnut-shaped region that extends from beyond Neptune's orbit to about 100 times Earth's distance from the sun. The **Oort cloud** is a spherical region of comets that surrounds the solar system out to more than 1,000 times the distance between Pluto and the sun.

Reading Checkpoint What is the Oort cloud?

For: Links on comets, asteroids, and meteors
Visit: www.SciLinks.org
Web Code: scn-0635

FIGURE 25
Comet Orbits
Most comets revolve around the sun in very long, narrow orbits. Gas and dust tails form as the comet approaches the sun. **Observing** *What shape is a comet's orbit?*

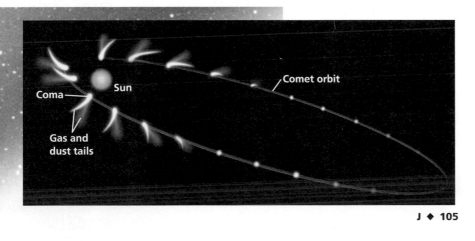

Coma
Sun
Comet orbit
Gas and dust tails

J ◆ 105

For: Links on comets, asteroids, and meteors
Visit: www.SciLinks.org
Web Code: scn-0635

Download a worksheet that will guide students' review of Internet resources on comets, asteroids, and meteors.

Instruct

Comets

Teach Key Concepts L2
Viewing Comets

Focus Remind students that astronomers can calculate the orbits of many comets.

Teach Point out the coma and the nucleus of the comet shown in Figure 24. Have students examine the orbits of Earth and the comet. Ask: **How does the orbit of the comet differ from the orbit of a planet?** *(The orbits of most comets are much longer and narrower than the orbits of planets.)*

Apply **Are you likely to see Halley's comet? Explain your answer.** *(Yes, Halley's comet, which appears approximately every 76 years, last appeared in 1986.)* **When will Halley's comet next appear?** *(2062)* **How old will you be?** *(Answers will vary.)* **learning modality: logical/mathematical**

Independent Practice L2

All in One Teaching Resources

- Guided Reading and Study Worksheet: *Comets, Asteroids, and Meteors*

Monitor Progress _____ L2

Writing Have students tell how the coma and the tail of a comet are formed.

Answers
Figure 25 Typically a long, narrow ellipse

Reading Checkpoint A spherical region of comets that surrounds the solar system out to more than 1,000 times the distance between Pluto and the sun

---

Differentiated Instruction

Less Proficient Readers L1
Creating Flashcards Provide each student with three note cards. Have each write *comet*, *asteroid*, and *meteor* on the cards, one term per card. As students read the section, have them list the characteristics of each object on the opposite side of the appropriate card. Then have partners take turns using their flashcards for testing each other's knowledge of comets, asteroids, and meteors. **learning modality: visual**

Gifted and Talented L3
Researching the First Asteroid Ask interested students to research and write about Ceres, the first asteroid to be discovered. *(It was discovered twice and is the largest known asteroid.)* **learning modality: verbal**

Asteroids

Teach Key Concepts L2

Asteroid Strike

Focus Show the Yucatan Peninsula of Mexico on a world map. Explain that an asteroid struck near there 65 million years ago.

Teach Tell students that asteroids and other objects from space that land on Earth usually explode into dust or vapor. Ask: **Where are most asteroids found in space?** *(Between the orbits of Mars and Jupiter.)*

Apply Ask: **What may have happened to the dust from the asteroid that hit the Yucatan?** *(Possible answer: It fell into the ocean, settled on the ocean floor, was buried by layers of sediment, and eventually turned back into rock.)* **learning modality: logical/mathematical**

All in One Teaching Resources
• Transparency J32

Meteors

Teach Key Concepts L1

Meteors

Focus Remind students of the difference between a meteoroid, a meteor, and a meteorite.

Teach Ask: **What do you see when a meteor burns up in Earth's atmosphere?** *(A bright streak of light)*

Apply Ask: **What causes the streak of light to appear?** *(Friction with the air creates heat; the air becomes white-hot.)* **learning modality: verbal**

🔘 **Student Edition on Audio CD**

Help Students Read

KWL Refer to the Content Refresher for guidelines on KWL. Have students fill out the K column. Then have them scan the section and ask them to think of questions they may have about comets, asteroids, and meteors. Those questions will form the basis for what they write in the W column. As students read, have them write answers to their questions in the L column.

Micrometeorites

An estimated 300 tons of material from space fall on Earth each day. Much of this is micrometeorites, tiny, dust-sized meteorites.

1. To gather magnetic micrometeorites, tie a string to a small, round magnet and place the magnet in a plastic freezer bag. Lower the magnet close to the ground as you walk along sidewalk cracks, drain spouts, or a parking lot.

2. To gather nonmagnetic and magnetic micrometeorites, cover one side of a few microscope slides with petroleum jelly. Leave the slides outside for several days in a place where they won't be disturbed.

3. Use a microscope to examine the materials you have gathered. Any small round spheres you see are micrometeorites.

Estimating Which technique allows you to gather a more complete sample of micro-meteorites? Were all the particles that were gathered in Step 2 micrometeorites? How could you use the method described in Step 2 to estimate the total number of micrometeorites that land on Earth each day?

Asteroids

Between 1801 and 1807, astronomers discovered four small objects between the orbits of Mars and Jupiter. They named the objects Ceres, Pallas, Juno, and Vesta. Over the next 80 years, astronomers found 300 more. These rocky objects, called **asteroids,** are too small and too numerous to be considered full-fledged planets. **Most asteroids revolve around the sun between the orbits of Mars and Jupiter.** This region of the solar system, shown in Figure 26, is called the **asteroid belt.**

Astronomers have discovered more than 100,000 asteroids, and they are constantly finding more. Most asteroids are small—less than a kilometer in diameter. Only Ceres, Pallas, and Vesta are more than 300 kilometers across. At one time, scientists thought that asteroids were the remains of a shattered planet. However, the combined mass of all the asteroids is too small to support this idea. Scientists now hypothesize that the asteroids are leftover pieces of the early solar system that never came together to form a planet.

Some asteroids have very elliptical orbits that bring them closer to the sun than Earth's orbit. Someday, one of these asteroids could hit Earth. One or more large asteroids did hit Earth about 65 million years ago, filling the atmosphere with dust and smoke and blocking out sunlight around the world. Scientists hypothesize that many species of organisms, including the dinosaurs, became extinct as a result.

✓ **Reading Checkpoint** Name the three largest asteroids.

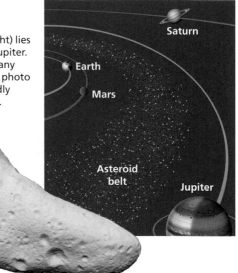

FIGURE 26
Asteroids
The asteroid belt (right) lies between Mars and Jupiter. Asteroids come in many sizes and shapes. The photo below shows the oddly shaped asteroid Eros.

Lab zone Try This **Activity**

Skill Focus estimating L2

Materials string; small, round magnet; plastic freezer bag; microscope slides; petroleum jelly; microscope

Time 45 minutes

Tips Stay in open areas away from trees and other overhead obstructions. Use the magnet in low spots where runoff from rain will have washed micrometeorites into one place.

Expected Outcome Most of the debris will be dust, pollen, and other microscopic objects. But some will be micrometeorites.

Extend Collect samples from several distinct areas and compare results. Have students hypothesize about their findings. **learning modality: kinesthetic**

Meteors

It's a perfect night for stargazing—dark and clear. Suddenly, a streak of light flashes across the sky. For an hour or so, you see a streak at least once a minute. You are watching a meteor shower. Meteor showers happen regularly, several times a year.

Even when there is no meteor shower, you often can see meteors if you are far from city lights and the sky is not cloudy. On average, a meteor streaks overhead every 10 minutes.

A **meteoroid** is a chunk of rock or dust in space. **Meteoroids come from comets or asteroids.** Some meteoroids form when asteroids collide in space. Others form when a comet breaks up and creates a cloud of dust that continues to move through the solar system. When Earth passes through one of these dust clouds, bits of dust enter Earth's atmosphere.

When a meteoroid enters Earth's atmosphere, friction with the air creates heat and produces a streak of light in the sky—a **meteor.** If the meteoroid is large enough, it may not burn up completely. Meteoroids that pass through the atmosphere and hit Earth's surface are called **meteorites.** The craters on the moon were formed by meteoroids.

FIGURE 27
Meteors
Meteoroids make streaks of light called meteors, like the one above, as they burn up in the atmosphere.

Reading Checkpoint What is a meteorite?

Section 5 Assessment

Target Reading Skill Comparing and Contrasting Use the information in your table about comets, asteroids, and meteoroids to help you answer the questions below.

Reviewing Key Concepts

1. **a. Defining** What is a comet?
   b. Listing What are the different parts of a comet?
   c. Relating Cause and Effect How does a comet's appearance change as it approaches the sun? Why do these changes occur?
2. **a. Describing** What is an asteroid?
   b. Explaining Where are most asteroids found?
   c. Summarizing How did the asteroids form?
3. **a. Describing** What is a meteoroid?
   b. Explaining What are the main sources of meteoroids?
   c. Comparing and Contrasting What are the differences between meteoroids, meteors, and meteorites?

Lab zone At-Home Activity

Observing Meteors Meteor showers occur regularly on specific dates. (The Perseid meteor shower, for example, occurs around August 12 each year.) Look in the newspaper, on the Internet, or in an almanac for information about the next meteor shower. With adult family members, go outside on that night and look for meteors. Explain to your family what causes the display.

Answers

✓ **Reading Checkpoint** Ceres, Pallas, and Vesta

✓ **Reading Checkpoint** A meteoroid that has passed through the atmosphere and hits Earth's surface

Assess

Reviewing Key Concepts

1. **a.** A loose collection of ice, dust, and small rocky particles **b.** Coma, nucleus, and tail **c.** The ice turns into gas, releasing gas and dust forming a coma and two tails; because of the energy in sunlight
2. **a.** A small, rocky space object **b.** In the asteroid belt that lies between Mars and Jupiter **c.** They are leftover pieces of the early solar system that never came together to form a planet.
3. **a.** A chunk of rock or dust in space **b.** Comets or asteroids **c.** A meteoroid is a chunk of rock or dust in space. A meteor is a meteoroid that enters Earth's atmosphere and burns up. A meteorite is a meteoroid that passes through the atmosphere and hits Earth's surface.

Reteach ⬛L1

Have students reexamine Figure 24 and discuss the structure of a comet.

Performance Assessment ⬛L2

Oral Presentation Have students write, then present the life story of a meteoroid whose orbit occasionally approaches Earth and eventually strikes Earth's surface.

All in One Teaching Resources

- Section Summary: *Comets, Asteroids, and Meteors*
- Review and Reinforce: *Comets, Asteroids, and Meteors*
- Enrich: *Comets, Asteroids, and Meteors*

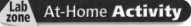

Observing Meteors ⬛L2 Because students will be outdoors after dark, caution them to view a meteor shower only with an adult. Meteor showers are more easily seen outside cities, in areas where bright lights do not block the glow from the meteors. The glow is caused by friction that occurs when Earth's atmosphere heats the rock as it falls.

Objectives

After this lesson, students will be able to
J.3.6.1 List the conditions living things need to exist on Earth.
J.3.6.2 Recognize why scientists think Mars and Europa are good places to look for signs of life.

Target Reading Skill

Asking Questions Explain that changing a head into a question helps students anticipate the ideas, facts, and events they are about to read.

Answers

Possible questions and answers include the following:

What are the "Goldilocks" conditions? *The favorable conditions on Earth that allow life to exist.* **Is there life on Mars?** *Scientists have not yet found evidence for life on Mars.* **Why do scientists think Europa might have life?** *Europa has an ice crust that could have a liquid water ocean underneath.*

All in One Teaching Resources

• Transparency J33

Preteach

Build Background Knowledge   L2

Characteristics of Living Things

Show students a potted plant and a goldfish in a bowl. Ask: **What is the same about these two things?** *(Both are alive.)* **How do we know these things are alive?** *(They grow, reproduce, and excrete wastes.)* **What do these things both need to stay alive?** *(Water, space, and energy)*

Is There Life Beyond Earth?

Reading Preview

Key Concepts

• What conditions do living things need to exist on Earth?
• Why do scientists think Mars and Europa are good places to look for signs of life?

Key Term

• extraterrestrial life

Target Reading Skill

Asking Questions Before you read, preview the red headings. In a graphic organizer like the one below, ask a question for each heading. As you read, write the answers to your questions.

Is There Life Beyond Earth?

Question	Answer
What are the "Goldilocks" conditions?	The "Goldilocks" conditions are . . .

Lab zone **Discover Activity**

Is Yeast Alive or Not?

1. Open a package of yeast and pour it into a bowl.
2. Look at the yeast carefully. Make a list of your observations.
3. Fill the bowl about halfway with warm water (about 20°C). Add a spoonful of sugar. Stir the mixture with the spoon. Wait 5 minutes.
4. Now look at the yeast again and make a list of your observations.

Think It Over
Forming Operational Definitions Which of your observations suggest that yeast is not alive? Which observations suggest that yeast is alive? How can you tell if something is alive?

Most of Antarctica is covered with snow and ice. You would not expect to see rocks lying on top of the whiteness. But surprisingly, people have found rocks lying on Antarctica's ice. When scientists examined the rocks, they found that many were meteorites. A few of these meteorites came from Mars. Astronomers think that meteoroids hitting the surface of Mars blasted chunks of rock into space. Some of these rocks eventually entered Earth's atmosphere and landed on its surface.

In 1996, a team of scientists announced that a meteorite from Mars found in Antarctica has tiny shapes that look like fossils—the remains of ancient life preserved in rock—though much smaller. Most scientists doubt that the shapes really are fossils. But if they are, it would be a sign that microscopic life-forms similar to bacteria once existed on Mars. Life other than that on Earth would be called **extraterrestrial life.**

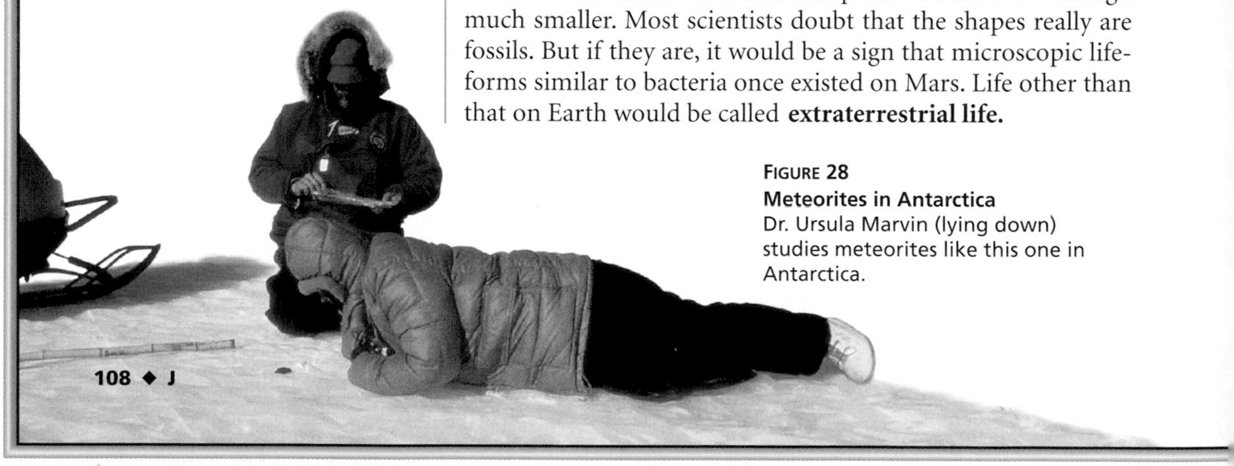

FIGURE 28
Meteorites in Antarctica
Dr. Ursula Marvin (lying down) studies meteorites like this one in Antarctica.

Lab zone **Discover Activity**

Skills Focus forming operational definitions

Materials yeast, warm water, bowl, thermometer, spoon, sugar, clock

Time 15 minutes

Tips You may wish to buy yeast in bulk rather than in packets. A packet of yeast contains about one tablespoon.

L2 **Expected Outcome** Before adding water, the yeast will appear dry, brown, grainy, and immobile. After adding water, the yeast will bubble and give off a distinct odor.

Think It Over The first set of observations suggests that yeast is not alive. The second set of observations suggests that yeast is alive. Something is alive if it eats, breathes, or grows.

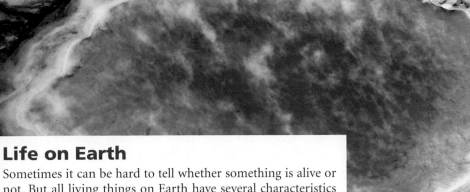

Life on Earth

Sometimes it can be hard to tell whether something is alive or not. But all living things on Earth have several characteristics in common. Living things are made up of one or more cells. Living things take in energy and use it to grow and develop. They reproduce, producing new living things of the same type. Living things also give off waste.

The "Goldilocks" Conditions No one knows whether life exists anywhere other than Earth. Scientists often talk about the conditions needed by "life as we know it." **Earth has liquid water and a suitable temperature range and atmosphere for living things to survive.** Scientists sometimes call these favorable conditions the "Goldilocks" conditions. That is, the temperature is not too hot and not too cold. It is just right. If Earth were much hotter, water would always be a gas—water vapor. If Earth were much colder, water would always be solid ice.

Are these the conditions necessary for life? Or are they just the conditions that Earth's living things happen to need? Scientists have only one example to study: life on Earth. Unless scientists find evidence of life somewhere else, there is no way to answer these questions for certain.

Extreme Conditions Recently, scientists have discovered living things in places where it was once believed that life could not exist. Giant tubeworms have been found under the extremely high pressures at the bottom of the ocean. Single-celled organisms have been found in the near-boiling temperatures of hot springs. Tiny life-forms have been discovered deep inside solid rock. Scientists have even found animals that do not require the energy of sunlight, but instead get their energy from chemicals.

These astounding discoveries show that the range of conditions in which life can exist is much greater than scientists once thought. Could there be life-forms in the solar system that do not need the "Goldilocks" conditions?

 Reading Checkpoint What are some characteristics of all living things?

FIGURE 29
Hot Spring
Bacteria that thrive in near-boiling water help to produce the striking colors of Grand Prismatic Spring in Wyoming. **Inferring** *How does studying unusual organisms on Earth help scientists predict what extraterrestrial life might be like?*

 **Skills Activity**

Communicating You are writing a letter to a friend who lives on another planet. Your friend has never been to Earth and has no idea what the planet is like. Explain in your letter why the conditions on Earth make it an ideal place for living things.

Chapter 3 J ◆ 109

Life Elsewhere in the Solar System?

Teach Key Concepts L2

Viking Missions

Focus Remind students that both *Viking* landers were programmed to search for signs of life on Mars.

Teach Ask: **What hypothesis were scientists testing when they sent the *Viking* spacecraft to Mars?** *(One hypothesis was that Mars may once have had life.)* **What kinds of samples did the *Viking* examine?** *(Air and soil)*

Apply Ask: **How were these samples useful to scientists?** *(Scientists found no evidence of life on Mars.)* **learning modality: logical/mathematical**

Lab zone **Build Inquiry** L2

Making Judgments

Materials none

Time 30 minutes

Focus Point out that some topics in science are hotly debated. One such topic is the possibility of life on Mars.

Teach Divide the class into two teams. Have one team make a list of arguments against the existence of life on Mars. Have the other team make a list of arguments supporting the existence of life on Mars.

Apply Have the pro and con teams present their arguments to each other and discuss the evidence on both sides. **learning modality: verbal**

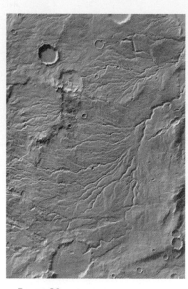

FIGURE 30
Liquid Water on Mars
The river-like patterns on the surface of Mars indicate that liquid water once flowed there.
Applying Concepts *Why does this evidence make it more likely that there may once have been life on Mars?*

Life Elsewhere in the Solar System?

Recall that Mars is the planet most similar to Earth. That makes Mars the most obvious place to look for living things.

Life on Mars? Spacecraft have found regions on the surface of Mars that look like streambeds with crisscrossing paths of water. Shapes like those shown in the left photo of Figure 30 were almost certainly formed by flowing water. **Since life as we know it requires water, scientists hypothesize that Mars may have once had the conditions needed for life to exist.**

In 1976 twin *Viking* spacecraft reached Mars. Each of the *Viking* landers carried a small laboratory meant to search for life forms. These laboratories tested Mars's air and soil for signs of life. None of these tests showed evidence of life.

More recently, the *Spirit* and *Opportunity* rovers found rocks and other surface features on Mars that were certainly formed by liquid water. However, the rovers were not equipped to search for past or present life.

Interest in life on Mars was increased by a report in 1996 about a meteorite from Mars that may contain fossils. The scientists' report started a huge debate. What were the tube-shaped things in the meteorite? Some scientists have suggested that the tiny shapes found in the meteorite are too small to be the remains of life forms. The shapes may have come from natural processes on Mars.

The most effective way to answer these questions is to send more probes to Mars. Future Mars missions should be able to bring samples of rocks and soil back to Earth for detailed analysis. Scientists may not yet have evidence of life on Mars, but hope is growing that we can soon learn the truth.

Reading Checkpoint What did the *Spirit* and *Opportunity* rovers discover on Mars?

FIGURE 31
Martian Fossils?
This false-color electron microscope image shows tiny fossil-like shapes found in a meteorite from Mars. These structures are less than one-hundredth the width of a human hair.

Life on Europa? Many scientists think that Europa, one of Jupiter's moons, may have the conditions necessary for life to develop. Europa has a smooth, icy crust with giant cracks. Close-up views from the *Galileo* space probe show that Europa's ice has broken up and re-formed, resulting in large twisted blocks of ice. Similar patterns occur in the ice crust over Earth's Arctic Ocean. Scientists hypothesize that there is a liquid ocean under Europa's ice. The water in the ocean could be kept liquid by heat coming from inside Europa. **If there is liquid water on Europa, there might also be life.**

How could scientists study conditions under Europa's ice sheet? Perhaps a future space probe might be able to use radar to "see" through Europa's icy crust. After that, robotic probes could be sent to drill through the ice to search for life in the water below.

FIGURE 32
Exploring Europa
Scientists have discussed sending a robotic probe to search for life in the ocean below Europa's icy crust.

Section 6 Assessment

Target Reading Skills Asking Questions Use the answers to the questions you wrote about the section headings to help answer the questions.

Reviewing Key Concepts

1. **a. Relating Cause and Effect** What conditions does life on Earth need to survive?
   b. Summarizing Why is Earth said to have the "Goldilocks" conditions?
   c. Applying Concepts Do you think there could be life as we know it on Neptune? Explain. (*Hint*: Review Section 4.)

2. **a. Explaining** Why do astronomers think there could be life on Europa?
   b. Identifying Scientists think that in the past Mars may have had the conditions needed for life to exist. What are these conditions? Do they still exist?

   c. Making Generalizations What characteristic do Mars and Europa share with Earth that makes them candidates to support extraterrestrial life?

Lab zone At-Home Activity

Making a Message Imagine that scientists have found intelligent extraterrestrial life. With family members, make up a message to send to the extraterrestrials. Remember that they will not understand English, so you should use only symbols and drawings in your message.

Lab zone At-Home Activity

Making a Message L1 Encourage students to consider what information about Earth and its inhabitants would be most important for extraterrestrials to know. Suggest that students ask each family member to contribute one piece of the message. Have students include a key to the symbols used in their message.

Use Visuals: Figure 32 L2
Life Under the Ice

Focus Point out that a variety of organisms live under Earth's Arctic ice.

Teach Encourage students to speculate on what kinds of life forms could exist beneath Europa's icy crust. Ask: **What sort of adaptations might these life-forms need?** (*Sample answers: Blubber to keep warm, ability to swim or float*)

Apply Have students design and sketch a life-form that has adapted to living on Europa. **learning modality: visual**

Monitor Progress L2

Answers
Figure 30 Because life as we know it requires water, evidence of liquid water flowing on Mars makes it more likely that there may once have been life there.

Reading Checkpoint The two rovers found rocks and other surface features on Mars that were formed by liquid water.

Assess

Reviewing Key Concepts

1. **a.** Liquid water, suitable temperature range and atmosphere, and source of energy **b.** Earth's water, temperature, and atmosphere are just right for living things to survive. **c.** No; Neptune is extremely cold and there is no liquid water.
2. **a.** Europa is covered by a layer of ice like Earth's Arctic Ocean; there may be liquid water beneath the ice. **b.** Flowing water; no **c.** They once had or may now have liquid water.

Reteach L1
Have students list the evidence for life on Mars and Europa and what other conditions need to exist.

Performance Assessment L2
Writing Have students explain which of the planets and their moons in our solar system would be good places to search for signs of life and which would not.

All in One Teaching Resources
- Section Summary: *Is There Life Beyond Earth?*
- Review and Reinforce: *Is There Life Beyond Earth?*
- Enrich: *Is There Life Beyond Earth?*

J ● 111

Study Guide

Study Guide

i nteractive Textbook

- Complete student edition
- Section and chapter self-assessments
- Assessment reports for teachers

Help Students Read

Building Vocabulary

Using Context Clues As students read "Observing the Solar System," have them look for unfamiliar words. For example, students may not know definitions for the words *constellations, heliocentric, geocentric,* or *ellipse.* Encourage them to use surrounding sentences and figures to help them understand the words. Demonstrate this procedure with the word *geocentric.*

Latin Plural Forms Explain that the word *nucleus* comes from a Latin word meaning "kernel." Explain that a kernel is a grain or seed. Ask students how the definition of the term *nucleus* relates to its Latin origin. *(Like the kernel of a nut, the nucleus is the small, solid center of a comet.)* Remind students that the plural of the word *nucleus* is *nuclei.*

Connecting Concepts

Concept Maps Help students develop one way to show how the information in this chapter is related. The solar system includes the sun; inner and outer planets; and comets, meteoroids, and asteroids. Have students brainstorm to identify the key concepts, key terms, details, and examples and then write each one on a sticky note and attach it at random on chart paper or on the board.

Tell students that this concept map will be organized in hierarchical order and will begin at the top with the key concepts. Ask students these questions to guide them to categorize the information on the sticky notes: **What is at the center of the solar system? Which planets are closest to the sun? What are some of the smaller bodies in the solar system called?** Prompt students by using connecting words or phrases, such as "includes" and "are part of" to indicate the

1 Observing the Solar System

Key Concepts

- In a geocentric system, Earth is perceived to be at the center of the revolving planets and stars. In a heliocentric system, Earth and the other planets revolve around the sun.
- Galileo's discoveries supported the heliocentric model. Kepler found that the orbit of each planet is an ellipse.
- The solar system consists of the sun, nine planets and their moons, and a series of smaller objects that revolve around the sun.

Key Terms

• geocentric • heliocentric • ellipse

2 The Sun

Key Concepts

- The sun's interior consists of the core, radiation zone, and convection zone. The sun's atmosphere consists of the photosphere, chromosphere, and corona.
- Features on or just above the sun's surface include sunspots, prominences, and solar flares.

Key Terms

• core • nuclear fusion • radiation zone
• convection zone • photosphere
• chromosphere • corona • solar wind
• sunspot • prominence • solar flare

3 The Inner Planets

Key Concepts

- The four inner planets are small and dense and have rocky surfaces.
- Earth is unique in our solar system in having liquid water at its surface.
- Mercury is the smallest terrestrial planet.
- Venus's internal structure is similar to Earth's.
- Scientists think that a large amount of liquid water flowed on Mars's surface in the distant past.

Key Terms

• terrestrial planets • greenhouse effect

4 The Outer Planets

Key Concepts

- Jupiter, Saturn, Uranus, and Neptune are much larger and more massive than Earth, and they do not have solid surfaces.
- Jupiter is the largest and most massive planet in the solar system.
- Saturn has the most spectacular rings of any planet.
- Uranus's axis of rotation is tilted at an angle of about 90 degrees from the vertical.
- Neptune is a cold, blue planet. Its atmosphere contains visible clouds.
- Pluto has a solid surface and is much smaller and denser than the other outer planets.

Key Terms

• gas giant • ring

5 Comets, Asteroids, and Meteors

Key Concepts

- Comets are loose collections of ice, dust, and small rocky particles whose orbits are usually very long, narrow ellipses.
- Most asteroids revolve around the sun between the orbits of Mars and Jupiter.
- Meteoroids come from comets or asteroids.

Key Terms

• comet • coma • nucleus • Kuiper belt
• Oort cloud • asteroid • asteroid belt
• meteoroid • meteor • meteorite

6 Is There Life Beyond Earth?

Key Concepts

- Earth has liquid water and a suitable temperature range and atmosphere for life.
- Scientists hypothesize that Mars may have once had the conditions for life to exist.
- If there is liquid water on Europa, there might also be life.

Key Term

• extraterrestrial life

basis for the organization of the concept map. The phrases should form a sentence between or among a set of concepts.

Answer Accept logical presentations by students.

All in One Teaching Resources

- Key Terms Review: *The Solar System*

Organizing Information

Comparing and Contrasting Fill in the graphic organizer to compare and contrast the geocentric system and the heliocentric system. (For more on Comparing and Contrasting, see the Skills Handbook.)

Feature	Geocentric System	Heliocentric System
Object at center	Earth	a. ____?____
Objects that move around center	Planets and sun	b. ____?____
Proposed by	c. ____?____	Copernicus
Supporters	Ptolemy	d. ____?____

Reviewing Key Terms

Choose the letter of the best answer.

1. Copernicus thought that the solar system was
   a. an ellipse.
   b. a constellation.
   c. geocentric.
   d. heliocentric.

2. The part of the sun where nuclear fusion occurs is the
   a. photosphere.
   b. core.
   c. chromosphere.
   d. corona.

3. Pluto is a(n)
   a. inner planet.
   b. terrestrial planet.
   c. outer planet.
   d. gas giant.

4. The region between Mars and Jupiter where many rocky objects are found is the
   a. asteroid belt.
   b. Oort cloud.
   c. convection zone.
   d. Kuiper belt.

5. A meteoroid that reaches Earth's surface is called a(n)
   a. comet.
   b. meteorite.
   c. meteor.
   d. asteroid.

If the statement is true, write _true_. If it is false, change the underlined word or words to make the statement true.

6. The shape of the orbit of each planet is a(n) <u>ellipse</u>.

7. <u>Prominences</u> are regions of cooler gases on the sun.

8. The trapping of heat by a planet's atmosphere is called <u>nuclear fusion</u>.

9. All the <u>terrestrial planets</u> are surrounded by rings.

10. The solid inner core of a comet is its <u>coma</u>.

Writing in Science

News Report Imagine you are on a mission to explore the solar system. Write a brief news report telling the story of your trip from Earth to another terrestrial planet and to a gas giant. Include a description of each planet.

Discovery CHANNEL SCHOOL

The Solar System
Video Preview
Video Field Trip
▶ Video Assessment

All in One Teaching Resources
- Transparency J34
- Chapter Test
- Performance Assessment Teacher Notes
- Performance Assessment Teacher Worksheet
- Performance Assessment Scoring Rubric

ExamView® Computer Test Bank CD-ROM

Organizing Information

a. Sun **b.** Planets **c.** Early Greek astronomers **d.** Brahe, Kepler, Galileo

Reviewing Key Terms

1. d 2. b 3. c 4. a 5. b
6. true
7. Sunspots
8. the greenhouse effect
9. gas giants
10. nucleus

Writing in Science

Writing Skill Description
Scoring Rubric
4 Exceeds criteria by including an accurate description of a gas giant, a terrestrial planet, and the trip in a lively, informative, and interesting manner
3 Meets all criteria by including required descriptions, but is not interesting
2 Includes accurate description of either a gas giant or a terrestrial planet and of the trip
1 Includes inaccurate information or is incomplete

Discovery CHANNEL SCHOOL Video Assessment

The Solar System

Show the Video Assessment to review chapter content and as a prompt for the writing assignment. Discussion question: **What makes Earth unique among the other planets in our solar system?** (*Earth is the only planet that supports life as we know it.*)

Checking Concepts

11. Tycho observed the planets and recorded planetary data over a period of 20 years. Kepler used Tycho's data to determine the true shape of planetary orbits.

12. The solar wind is a stream of electrically charged particles that emanate from the sun.

13. Mercury is so hot that the gases in its atmosphere easily escape from its weak gravity.

14. Mars's atmosphere is thin. However, Venus is entirely covered by thick clouds.

15. There are regions on the surface that look as if they had been formed by ancient streams, lakes, or floods. There are also huge canyons and features that look like the remains of ancient coastlines. Also, the *Spirit* and *Opportunity* rovers found rocks and surface features that were clearly formed by liquid water.

Math Practice

16. about 21,330 km

17. about 71,500 km

Review and Assessment

Checking Concepts

11. Describe the contributions Tycho Brahe and Johannes Kepler made to modern astronomy.

12. What is the solar wind?

13. Why does Mercury have very little atmosphere?

14. Why can astronomers see the surface of Mars clearly but not the surface of Venus?

15. What evidence do astronomers have that water once flowed on Mars?

Math Practice

16. Circumference Mars has a radius of 3,397 km at its equator. Find its circumference.

17. Circumference Jupiter has a circumference of about 449,000 km at its equator. Calculate its radius.

Thinking Critically

18. Applying Concepts Explain why Venus is hotter than it would be if it had no atmosphere.

19. Predicting Do you think astronomers have found all of the moons of the outer planets? Explain.

20. Comparing and Contrasting Compare and contrast comets, asteroids, and meteoroids.

21. Classifying Look at the diagram below. Do you think it represents the structure of a terrestrial planet or a gas giant? Explain.

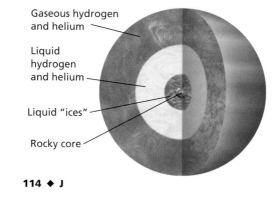

Gaseous hydrogen and helium

Liquid hydrogen and helium

Liquid "ices"

Rocky core

114 ◆ J

22. Making Generalizations Why would the discovery of liquid water on another planet be important?

Applying Skills

Use the diagram of an imaginary, newly discovered planetary system around Star X to answer Questions 23–25.

The periods of revolution of planets A, B, and C are 75 Earth days, 200 Earth days, and 300 Earth days.

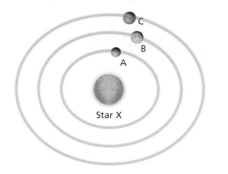

Star X

23. Interpreting Data Which planet in this new planetary system revolves around Star X in the shortest amount of time?

24. Making Models In 150 days, how far will each planet have revolved around Star X? Copy the diagram and sketch the positions of the three planets to find out. How far will each planet have revolved around Star X in 400 days? Sketch their positions.

25. Drawing Conclusions Can Planet C ever be closer to Planet A than to Planet B? Study your drawings to figure this out.

Performance Assessment Present your scale models of the solar system. Display your data tables showing how you did the calculations and how you checked them for accuracy.

Lab zone Chapter Project

Project Wrap Up All distances in the models should have been scaled by a constant amount to make them manageable. Students could have checked their numbers by multiplying the scaled numbers by the reciprocal of their scaling factor to see whether they obtained the correct planet sizes.

Reflect and Record Students might change the scale and present the model in a very large area in order to make the smallest planets visible. Students will reflect that it was difficult to find a scale to compare both the sizes of the planets and the sun and the distances between the planets and the sun.

Standardized Test Prep

Choose the letter of the best answer.

1. What characteristic do all of the inner planets share?

   A They are larger and more massive than the sun.

   B They have thick atmospheres of hydrogen and helium.

   C They have rocky surfaces.

   D They each have many moons.

2. Mercury has a daytime temperature of about 430° C and a nighttime temperature below −170° C. What is the best explanation?

   F Mercury has a greenhouse effect.

   G Global warming is occurring on Mercury.

   H Mercury is the closest planet to the sun.

   J Mercury has no real atmosphere.

The table below shows data for five planets in our solar system. Use the table and your knowledge of science to answer Questions 3–5.

Planet	Period of Rotation (Earth days)	Period of Revolution (Earth years)	Average Distance From the Sun (million km)
Mars	1.03	1.9	228
Jupiter	0.41	12	779
Saturn	0.45	29	1,434
Uranus	0.72	84	2,873
Neptune	0.67	164	4,495

3. Which of these planet's orbits is farthest from Earth's orbit?

   A Mars **B** Jupiter

   C Uranus **D** Neptune

4. Which planet has a "day" that is most similar in length to a day on Earth?

   F Mars **G** Jupiter

   H Uranus **J** Neptune

5. Light takes about 8 minutes and 20 seconds to travel from the sun to Earth, 150 million kilometers away. About how long does it take light to travel from the sun to Jupiter?

   A 10 minutes **B** 25 minutes

   C 43 minutes **D** 112 minutes

Constructed Response

6. Describe three major differences between the terrestrial planets and the gas giants.

Thinking Critically

18. Venus's atmosphere creates a greenhouse effect that traps heat energy from the sun.

19. No; many new moons have been discovered in recent years through improved technology. Many additional small moons are likely to be discovered.

20. Comets are loose collections of ice, dust, and small rocky particles. They usually have long, narrow elliptical orbits. Asteroids are small, rocky space objects often found in orbit between Mars and Jupiter. Meteoroids are chunks of rock or dust in space.

21. It represents a gas giant. Its overall structure and composition resemble those of Jupiter. (It is actually Saturn.)

22. Because water is essential to life on Earth, the presence of water on another planet increases the possibility that life may be found there.

Applying Skills

23. Planet A revolves around Star X in the shortest amount of time.

24. In 150 days, Planet A will have revolved around Star X twice. Planet B will have completed three quarters of one revolution. Planet C will have completed only one half of one revolution. In 400 days, Planet A will have completed five and one-third revolutions. Planet B will have completed two revolutions. Planet C will have completed one and one-third revolutions.

25. Yes, Planets A and C could be on one side of the star and B on the other. After 300 days, Planets A and C are where they began, on the same side of Star X, but Planet B is on the opposite side of the star.

Standardized Test Prep

1. C **2.** J **3.** D **4.** F **5.** C

6. The gas giants are much larger and more massive than the terrestrial planets. The gas giants are much farther from the sun and thus typically have lower temperatures. The terrestrial planets have rocky surfaces while the gas giants are composed mainly of hydrogen and helium. Also, each of the gas giants is surrounded by rings and have many moons. None of the terrestrial planets have rings and none have more than two moons.

Chapter at a Glance

PRENTICE HALL

Teacher EXPRESS™

Plan • Teach • Assess

Lab zone Chapter **Project** *Star Stories*

Technology

Local Standards

All in One Teaching Resources

- Chapter Project Teacher Notes, pp. 242–243
- Chapter Project Student Overview, pp. 244–245
- Chapter Project Student Worksheets, pp. 246–247
- Chapter Project Scoring Rubric, p. 248

DISCOVERY CHANNEL SCHOOL
Video Preview

Section 1

Telescopes

3 periods
1 1/2 blocks

J.4.1.1 State the regions of the electromagnetic spectrum.

J.4.1.2 Explain what telescopes are and how they work.

J.4.1.3 Identify where most large telescopes are located.

Go Online
SciLINKS NSTA

Section 2

Characteristics of Stars

2 periods
1 block

J.4.2.1 Explain how stars are classified.

J.4.2.2 Describe how astronomers measure distances to the stars.

J.4.2.3 Describe the H-R diagram, and explain how astronomers use it.

Go Online
PHSchool.com

Section 3

Lives of Stars

1 period
1/2 block

J.4.3.1 Explain how a star forms.

J.4.3.2 Identify what determines how long a star will live.

J.4.3.3 Describe what happens to a star when it runs out of fuel.

Go Online
active art

DISCOVERY CHANNEL SCHOOL
Video Field Trip

Section 4

Star Systems and Galaxies

2 periods
1 block

J.4.4.1 Define a star system.

J.4.4.2 Identify the major types of galaxies.

J.4.4.3 Explain how astronomers describe the scale of the universe.

Go Online
SciLINKS NSTA

Section 5

The Expanding Universe

1 period
1/2 block

J.4.5.1 State the big bang theory.

J.4.5.2 Explain how the solar system formed.

J.4.5.3 Describe what astronomers predict about the future of the universe.

Go Online
SciLINKS NSTA

Review and Assessment

Test Preparation

All in One Teaching Resources

- Key Terms Review, p. 290
- Transparency J48
- Performance Assessment Teacher Notes, p. 298
- Performance Assessment Scoring Rubric, p. 299
- Performance Assessment Student Worksheet, p. 300
- Chapter Test, pp. 301–304

DISCOVERY CHANNEL SCHOOL
Video Assessment

Go Online
PHSchool.com

Test Preparation Blackline Masters

 # Chapter Activities Planner

For more activities

LAB ZONE
Easy Planner
CD-ROM

Student Edition	Inquiry	Time	Materials	Skills	Resources
Chapter Project, p. 117	Open-Ended	Ongoing (3 to 4 weeks)	**All in One** Teaching Resources See p. 242	Interpreting diagrams, observing	**Lab zone Easy Planner** **All in One** Teaching Resources Support pp. 242–243
Section 1					
Discover Activity, p. 118	Guided	10 minutes	Plastic hand lens	Observing	**Lab zone Easy Planner**
Try This Activity, p. 121	Guided	30 minutes	Umbrella, small radio, aluminum foil, masking tape	Inferring	**Lab zone Easy Planner**
Technology Lab, p. 125	Guided	80 minutes	2 paper towel tubes of slightly different diameters, several plastic objective lenses, several plastic eyepiece lenses, foam holder for eyepiece, transparent tape, meter stick	Evaluating the design, redesigning	**Lab zone Easy Planner** **Lab Activity Video** Technology Lab: *Design and Build a Telescope*, pp. 256 257
Section 2					
Discover Activity, p. 126	Guided	10 minutes	None	Observing	**Lab zone Easy Planner**
Skills Activity, p. 128	Guided	10 minutes	None	Inferring	**Lab zone Easy Planner**
Try This Activity, p. 129	Guided	20 minutes	3 flashlights (2 with equal brightness and 1 brighter than the others)	Making models	**Lab zone Easy Planner**
Skills Lab, pp. 134–135	Guided	Prep 10 minutes; Class 40 minutes	Masking tape, paper clips, pen, black and red pencils, metric ruler, paper, meter stick, calculator, lamp without a shade (with 100-watt light bulb), copier paper box (without the lid), flat rectangular table (about 1 m wide)	Inferring, calculating, predicting	**Lab zone Easy Planner** **Lab Activity Video** **All in One** Teaching Resources Skills Lab: *How Far Is That Star?*, pp. 267–269
Section 3					
Discover Activity, p. 136	Directed	10 minutes	None	Drawing conclusions	**Lab zone Easy Planner**
Skills Activity, p. 138	Directed	10 minutes	None	Predicting	**Lab zone Easy Planner**
Section 4					
Discover Activity, p. 141	Guided	15 minutes	Pencil, paper, tape	Making models	**Lab zone Easy Planner**
Try This Activity, p. 145	Guided	20 minutes	Pipe cleaners	Observing	**Lab zone Easy Planner**
Section 5					
Discover Activity, p. 148	Guided	10 minutes	Balloon, felt-tip marker	Inferring	**Lab zone Easy Planner**

Section 1 Telescopes

⏱ 3 periods, 1 1/2 blocks

Objectives

J.4.1.1 State the regions of the electromagnetic spectrum.

J.4.1.2 Explain what telescopes are and how they work.

J.4.1.3 Identify where most large telescopes are located.

Local Standards

Key Terms

- telescope • electromagnetic radiation • visible light • wavelength
- spectrum • optical telescope • refracting telescope • convex lens
- reflecting telescope • radio telescope • observatory

Preteach

Build Background Knowledge

Have students describe how a telescope or binoculars change images.

Lab zone Discover Activity *How Does Distance Affect an Image?* **L2**

Targeted Print and Technology Resources

All in One Teaching Resources

L2 Reading Strategy: Building Vocabulary

⊙ **Presentation-Pro CD-ROM**

Instruct

Electromagnetic Radiation Use a diagram to identify the regions of the electromagnetic spectrum.

Types of Telescopes Discuss different types of telescopes, and compare and contrast how they work.

Observatories Describe and apply factors that affect locations of telescopes.

Lab zone Technology Lab *Design and Build a Telescope* **L2**

Targeted Print and Technology Resources

All in One Teaching Resources

L2 Guided Reading, pp. 251–253

L2 Transparencies J35, J36

L2 Technology Lab: *Design and Build a Telescope,* pp. 256–257

📼 **Lab Activity Video/DVD**
Technology Lab: *Design and Build a Telescope*

www.SciLinks.org Web Code: scn-0641

⊙ **Student Edition on Audio CD**

Assess

Section Assessment Questions

◎ Have students use their graphic organizers with their definitions of key terms to answer the questions.

Reteach

Use a diagram to review different types of telescopes and their locations.

Targeted Print and Technology Resources

All in One Teaching Resources

- Section Summary, p. 250

L1 Review and Reinforce, p. 254

L3 Enrich, p. 255

Section 2 Characteristics of Stars

🕐 *2 periods, 1 block*

Objectives

J.4.2.1 Explain how stars are classified.

J.4.2.2 Describe how astronomers measure distances to the stars.

J.4.2.3 Describe the H-R diagram, and explain how astronomers use it.

Key Terms

- constellation • spectrograph • apparent brightness • absolute brightness
- light-year • parallax • Hertzsprung-Russell diagram • main sequence

Local Standards

Preteach

Build Background Knowledge

Invite students to describe their experiences visiting a planetarium.

Lab zone Discover Activity *How Does Your Thumb Move?* **L2**

Targeted Print and Technology Resources

All in One Teaching Resources

L2 Reading Strategy Transparency J37: Using Prior Knowledge

L2 Transparencies J49, J50, J51, J52

💿 **Presentation-Pro CD-ROM**

Instruct

Classifying Stars Classify stars according to their physical characteristics.

Brightness of Stars Use an analogy to distinguish apparent and absolute brightness.

Measuring Distances to Stars Examine the relationship between light-years and parallax to explain how astronomers measure distance.

The Hertzsprung-Russell Diagram Use the H-R diagram to describe the information it provides and how astronomers use it.

Lab zone Skills Lab *How Far Is That Star?* **L3**

Targeted Print and Technology Resources

All in One Teaching Resources

L2 Guided Reading, pp. 260–264

L2 Transparencies J38, J39, J40, J41

L2 Skills Lab: *How Far Is That Star?* pp. 267–269

📼 **Lab Activity Video/DVD**
Skills Lab: *How Far Is That Star?*

PHSchool.com Web Code: cfd-5042

💿 **Student Edition on Audio CD**

Assess

Section Assessment Questions

↻ Have students use the questions and answers they developed by using prior knowledge to answer the questions.

Reteach

Have students list characteristics used to classify stars and provide examples.

Targeted Print and Technology Resources

All in One Teaching Resources

- Section Summary, p. 259
- **L1** Review and Reinforce, p. 265
- **L3** Enrich, p. 266

Section 3 Lives of Stars

⏰ *1 period, 1/2 block*

ABILITY LEVELS
L1 Basic to Average
L2 For All Students
L3 Average to Advanced

Objectives

J.4.3.1 Explain how a star forms.
J.4.3.2 Identify what determines how long a star will live.
J.4.3.3 Describe what happens to a star when it runs out of fuel.

Local Standards

Key Terms

• nebula • protostar • white dwarf • supernova • neutron star • pulsar
• black hole

Preteach

Build Background Knowledge

Relate how a campfire burns and burns out to how stars fade.

Lab zone **Discover Activity** *What Determines How Long Stars Live?*
L1

Targeted Print and Technology Resources

All in One Teaching Resources
L2 Reading Strategy Transparency
J42: Sequencing

⊙ **Presentation-Pro CD-ROM**

Instruct

The Lives of Stars Use photos to help students explain how a star forms. Identify the factor that determines a star's life.

Deaths of Stars Ask leading questions for a discussion on the evolution of dying stars.

Targeted Print and Technology Resources

All in One Teaching Resources
L2 Guided Reading, pp. 272–274
L2 Transparency J43

PHSchool.com Web Code: cfp-5043

⊙ **Student Edition on Audio CD**

Assess

Section Assessment Questions

Have students use their flowcharts showing the sequence of events in the life of a star to answer the questions.

Reteach

Use a diagram to summarize the life cycles of stars with different masses.

Targeted Print and Technology Resources

All in One Teaching Resources
• Section Summary, p. 271
L1 Review and Reinforce, p. 275
L3 Enrich, p. 276

Section 4 Star Systems and Galaxies

ABILITY LEVELS
L1 Basic to Average
L2 For All Students
L3 Average to Advanced

🕐 *2 periods, 1 block*

Objectives

J.4.4.1 Define a star system.
J.4.4.2 Identify the major types of galaxies.
J.4.4.3 Explain how astronomers describe the scale of the universe.

Key Terms

- binary star • eclipsing binary • open cluster • globular cluster • galaxy
- spiral galaxy • elliptical galaxy • irregular galaxy • quasar • universe
- scientific notation

Local Standards

Preteach

Build Background Knowledge

Connect students' experiences with optical illusions to the appearance of constellations.

Lab zone **Discover Activity** *Why Does the Milky Way Look Hazy?* **L1**

Targeted Print and Technology Resources

All in One Teaching Resources

L2 Reading Strategy: Building Vocabulary

⊙ **Presentation-Pro CD-ROM**

Instruct

Star Systems and Clusters Use a diagram to define a star system, and demonstrate an example of an eclipsing binary system.

Galaxies Classify the major types of galaxies.

The Milky Way Use math to illustrate the enormity of the galaxy.

The Scale of the Universe Use math examples to demonstrate how astronomers use scientific notation.

Targeted Print and Technology Resources

All in One Teaching Resources

L2 Guided Reading, pp. 279–281
L2 Transparency J44

www.SciLinks.org Web Code: scn-0644

⊙ **Student Edition on Audio CD**

Assess

Section Assessment Questions

🔄 Have students use their definitions of key terms to answer the questions.

Reteach

Use diagrams to review the concepts in this section, and have students classify clusters and galaxies.

Targeted Print and Technology Resources

All in One Teaching Resources

- Section Summary, p. 278
L1 Review and Reinforce, p. 282
L3 Enrich, p. 283

Section 5 The Expanding Universe

⏱ *1 period, 1/2 block*

Objectives

J.4.5.1 State the big bang theory.

J.4.5.2 Explain how the solar system formed.

J.4.5.3 Describe what astronomers predict about the future of the universe.

Key Terms

• big bang • Hubble's law • cosmic background radiation • solar nebula
• planetesimal • dark matter • dark energy

Local Standards

Preteach

Build Background Knowledge

Predict what might happen to particles from fireworks if they did not burn out.

Lab zone Discover Activity *How Does the Universe Expand?* **L1**

Targeted Print and Technology Resources

All in One Teaching Resources

L2 Reading Strategy Transparency J45: Identifying Supporting Evidence

💿 **Presentation-Pro CD-ROM**

Instruct

How the Universe Formed Define the big bang theory and identify supporting evidence.

Formation of the Solar System Use illustrations to describe how the solar system formed.

The Future of the Universe Discuss the possibility of the universe's expanding forever and the evidence that supports this view.

Targeted Print and Technology Resources

All in One Teaching Resources

L2 Guided Reading, pp. 286–287
L2 Transparencies J46, J47

www.SciLinks.org Web Code: scn-0645

💿 **Student Edition on Audio CD**

Assess

Section Assessment Questions

🎯 Have students use the supporting evidence they identified for the big bang theory to answer the questions.

Reteach

Summarize the evidence for the big bang theory and the theory that the universe will continue to expand.

Targeted Print and Technology Resources

All in One Teaching Resources

• Section Summary, p. 285
L1 Review and Reinforce, p. 288
L3 Enrich, p. 289

Chapter 4 **Content Refresher**

Go Online

NSTA-PD LINKS

For: Professional development support
Visit: www.SciLinks.org/PDLinks
Web Code: scf-0640

Professional Development

Section 1 **Telescopes**

Light Pollution and Telescopes America glows in the dark as light from sources such as street lamps, stores, houses, schools, and airports streams upward into the sky. Scattered by air and dust particles, this light becomes a murky haze that washes out much of the night sky. Where our ancestors saw meteors, constellations, and millions of stars, most Americans today see only a few of the very brightest stars. The growing problem of light pollution also makes it increasingly difficult to use a telescope in populated areas. But backyard astronomers are not the only ones who contend with this problem. Some of our biggest telescopes, built when skies were darker, must now deal with light from communities growing up around them. For example, in 1894 the Lowell Observatory was built on a mountain overlooking Flagstaff, Arizona. Flagstaff grew, and by the 1950s, light pollution threatened the usefulness of the observatory. Flagstaff eventually recognized the problem and passed legislation requiring low-pressure sodium (LPS) fixtures for most outdoor lighting. Light from LPS can be filtered out of astronomical measurements, and LPS is also an energy-efficient light source. One solution to two problems gave Lowell Observatory darker skies.

⚑ Address Misconceptions

Some students may think that stars are present at nighttime only. However, stars are always in the sky, even during the day. For a strategy for overcoming this misconception, see **Address Misconceptions** in "Telescopes."

Image of Earth at night

Section 2 **Characteristics of Stars**

Parsecs Distances between objects in space can be incredibly vast. Often, light-years are not adequate units of measurement for professional astronomers; so a unit called a parsec may be used. The parsec is related to parallax—a star at a distance of one parsec from Earth has a parallax of one second of arc (1/3600 of a degree). One parsec equals 3.26 light-years.

Astronomers often measure distance to stars in the Milky Way in kiloparsecs (1 kiloparsec = 1,000 parsecs). For example, the sun is 8.5 kiloparsecs from the center of the Milky Way. To measure distances to other galaxies or clusters of galaxies, astronomers use megaparsecs (1 megaparsec = 1 million parsecs). Some galaxies are 3,000 to 4,000 megaparsecs from Earth—9 to 13 billion light-years away.

Development of the H-R Diagram The realization that the color of stars could be related to their brightness came independently to Hertzsprung and Russell. The result, the Hertzsprung-Russell diagram, was published in 1914. Russell eventually became the director of the observatory at Princeton University. Hertzsprung had no formal training in astronomy—his background was chemical engineering. However, his interest in the chemistry of photography led to work in small observatories, where he applied photography to the measurement of starlight. Like Russell, Hertzsprung later became the director of a university observatory.

Magnitudes The modern system of stellar magnitudes comes from a system developed in ancient Greece and Rome. Hipparchus, a Greek astronomer who lived during the second century B.C., compiled a catalog of about 850 stars. He assigned the brightest stars a magnitude of 1, the next brightest a magnitude of 2, and so on in equal steps down to 6, the dimmest star that could be seen with the unaided eye. Seventeenth-century astronomers added classes below 6 to describe dim stars they could now see with the newly developed telescope.

In 1850 English astronomer Norman Robert Pogson proposed the system used by modern astronomers. Pogson used mathematical ratios to define the difference in absolute brightness between magnitudes. In his system, a star of magnitude 1 is about 2.5 times as bright as a star with magnitude 2. As astronomers used this new scale they found that it still wasn't perfect. Some stars with a magnitude of 1 were brighter than others. So astronomers extended the scale to zero and beyond, giving Rigel and Arcturus a magnitude of 0 and Sirius a −1.5. The brightest object in the sky, the sun, has a magnitude of −26.7.

Section 3 Lives of Stars

Supernovas Supernovas that are visible from Earth without a telescope are very rare. Only seven supernovas were recorded before the seventeenth century. They were seen in 185, 393, 1006, 1054, 1181, 1572, and 1604. The supernova of 1054 was so bright that it was visible even in the daytime, and it remained bright for several weeks. Rock paintings discovered in Arizona and New Mexico suggest that this supernova may have been seen and recorded by Native Americans. The supernova of 1572 was observed by Tycho Brahe and is now called Tycho's Supernova. It became as bright as Venus, and could also be seen during the day. The supernova of 1604, now called Kepler's Supernova, was first observed by Kepler's assistant. Kepler watched it until 1606, when it could no longer be seen with the unaided eye. At its brightest, Kepler's Supernova was brighter than Jupiter.

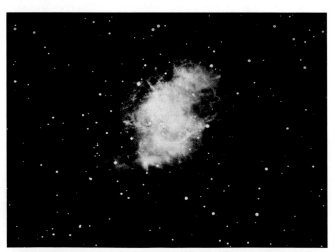

The Crab Nebula is the remains of the 1054 supernova.

Section 4 Star Systems and Galaxies

Search for Extraterrestrial Life Astronomers first started monitoring radio waves for signs of extraterrestrial life in 1960. In 1977, researchers at the Ohio State Radio Observatory picked up an unusual signal, known as the "Wow" signal for a researcher's comment on the computer printout. This signal was never detected again.

Scientists at the SETI (Search for Extraterrestrial Intelligence) Institute are using radio telescopes all over the world to search areas near sunlike stars for artificially produced signals. Because of interference from radio sources on Earth, SETI scientists use computers to screen out Earth-based signals. So far, no artificial extraterrestrial signals have been detected.

Section 5 The Expanding Universe

Measuring Distances to Galaxies Without the work of Henrietta Swan Leavitt (1868–1921), another American astronomer, Edwin Hubble, would not have discovered that the farther a galaxy is from Earth, the faster it is moving away. Leavitt found a method of measuring distances to galaxies by studying a certain type of variable star, called a Cepheid, within the galaxies. Variable stars vary in luminosity, or absolute brightness. Cepheids vary in regular, measurable periods of luminosity. Leavitt discovered that brighter Cepheids had longer periods. A Cepheid's absolute brightness can be found by measuring its period. Distance can be determined by comparing a star's absolute brightness with its apparent brightness. For example, a dim Cepheid with a long period is far away.

Cepheid variable stars can be studied in this Hubble photo of galaxy NGC 3370.

Dark Matter Observations of the movement of stars and galaxies and theoretical considerations about how the universe formed indicate that more mass exists in the universe than can be seen with the technology that is available today. This missing mass is called dark matter. Although little is known about this mysterious missing mass, it is possible that dark matter consists of some combination of normal matter and as yet unknown types of subatomic particles.

The normal matter might include nonluminous objects such as brown dwarfs (failed stars that are not massive enough to produce nuclear fusion, which causes stars to shine), neutron stars, black holes, and cooled white dwarfs. Such objects often are called MACHOS, massive compact halo objects. Most dark matter may consist of exotic, unknown particles, such as types of neutrinos or a group of particles called WIMPS (weakly interacting massive particles). Other hypotheses about the nature of dark matter also have been proposed. Because much new experimental evidence is being acquired, additional insights about dark matter should be forthcoming during the next decade.

Help Students Read

Anticipation Guide

Stimulating Interest in a Topic

Strategy Encourage students' active engagement with a selection by activating prior knowledge and helping establish purposes for reading. Generate a series of statements related to the topic of the passage, and ask students to respond to and discuss these before they begin reading. Choose the passage and prepare the statements before class.

Example

1. Before class, read through the passage and identify major concepts and details.

2. Construct an anticipation guide:
- Write 5–10 short, thought-provoking, declarative statements about the most important concepts featured in the section.
- If students are likely to have misconceptions about the topic, be sure to include statements that address those misconceptions.
- The statements may be in either a true-false or an agree-disagree format.
- To the left of each statement, allow space for student responses.

3. Before assigning the section to be read, display the guide on the board or on an overhead, or distribute individual worksheets.

4. Discuss students' responses, asking students to support their answers with examples from past experience or prior reading.

5. Then, have students read the section, evaluating the statements from the anticipation guide as they read.

6. When students have finished reading, revisit the guide, encouraging students to compare and contrast their prereading responses with their current ideas. Have students quote information from the passage to support their decisions.

Interactive Textbook
- Complete student edition
- Video and audio
- Simulations and activities
- Section and chapter activities

Chapter 4

Stars, Galaxies, and the Universe

Chapter Preview

Interactive Textbook

The dark Horsehead Nebula is visible against red-glowing hydrogen gas. ▶

Lab zone ▲ **Chapter Project** `L3`

Objectives

In this project, students will research stories that various cultures have developed to explain the constellations. Students will create their own name for the star pattern they see in a constellation of their choice and write a story to support it. Students will also use star charts to locate constellations in the night sky. After this Chapter Project, students will be able to

- interpret star charts
- observe and identify constellations
- research the myth of one constellation
- write and present an original star myth to the class

Skills Focus

Interpreting diagrams, observing, communicating

Project Time Line 3 to 4 weeks

All in One Teaching Resources
- Chapter Project Teacher Notes
- Chapter Project Worksheet 1
- Chapter Project Worksheet 2
- Chapter Project Worksheet 3
- Chapter Project Scoring Rubric

Developing a Plan

Students will need one to two clear nights at the beginning of the project to observe constellations by using the star charts. During the first week or two, advise students to do research. Have them use the third week for drafting the original myth and another week for editing and presenting the final project.

Possible Materials

The project requires reference sources such as encyclopedias, books on mythology, and the Internet. Advise students to use the star charts in Appendix B to help them identify the constellations. Students may need art supplies to make posters for their final presentations.

Lab zone™ Chapter Project

Star Stories

Many years ago, people created stories to explain the patterns of stars they saw in the sky. In your project, you'll learn how the names of these constellations reflect the cultures of the people who named them.

Your Goal To complete the project you will

- learn the star patterns of at least three constellations
- research the myths that gave one constellation its name
- create your own star myth

Plan It! Begin by making a list of constellations that you have heard about. Then use the star charts in Appendix B to locate constellations in the night sky. Make a sketch of the constellations that you locate. Choose one constellation and research the myths that gave it its name. Draw a new picture for the star pattern in your constellation and choose a name for it. Finally, write a story about your constellation. At the end of the chapter, you will present your constellation and a story that explains its name.

Possible Shortcuts

Have students work in groups to complete the project. Assign each group a constellation to research. Compile a list of reference materials for students to access.

Launching the Project

Ask students to name some constellations. Ask: **Do you know how those constellations were named?** (Possible answer: Most are named for characters from Greek or Roman myths. For example, Orion was the son of the god Neptune. Some stars have Arabic origins; for example, Deneb, part of the swan's tail in the constellation Cygnus, is derived from the Arabic word for "tail.")

DISCOVERY CHANNEL SCHOOL Video Preview

Stars, Galaxies, and the Universe

Show the Video Preview to introduce the Chapter Project and present an overview of the chapter content. Discussion question: **How do black holes form?** (Most form when massive stars—much larger than our sun—use up their fuel, stop burning, and die, collapsing into a sphere. As the core collapses and layers of the star fall in, the star is torn apart and explodes into space. A black hole is formed when the material left from the explosion collapses upon itself. The gravitational pull is so great that not even light can escape.)

Performance Assessment

The Chapter Project Scoring Rubric will help you evaluate how well students complete the Chapter Project. Share the scoring rubric with students at the beginning of the project so that they will know what is expected of them. Students will be assessed on

- how familiar they are with the star patterns of their chosen constellation
- how thoroughly they researched the myths involving their chosen constellation
- how clear and well-written the final draft of their star myth is
- how well their presentation explains or illustrates the new name and story for their star patterns

Portfolio

Objectives

After this lesson, students will be able to
J.4.1.1 State the regions of the electromagnetic spectrum.
J.4.1.2 Explain what telescopes are and how they work.
J.4.1.3 Identify where most large telescopes are located.

Target Reading Skill

Building Vocabulary Explain that knowing the definitions of key-concept words helps students understand what they read.

Answers

Have students write what they know about each key term before they read the definitions in the section. Explain that connecting what they already know about key terms helps them remember the terms. As students read each passage that contains key terms, remind them to write the definitions in their own words.

All in One Teaching Resources

• Guided Reading Study Worksheet: *Telescopes, Use Target Reading Skills*

Preteach

Build Background Knowledge L2

Telescopes

Ask students whether they have ever looked through a telescope or a pair of binoculars. Have them describe how these instruments affected their view of objects. *(Possible answer: Telescopes and binoculars make distant objects appear closer and larger than they actually are.)* Tell students that in this section, they will learn how telescopes work.

Reading Preview

Key Concepts
• What are the regions of the electromagnetic spectrum?
• What are telescopes and how do they work?
• Where are most large telescopes located?

Key Terms
• telescope
• electromagnetic radiation
• visible light
• wavelength
• spectrum
• optical telescope
• refracting telescope
• convex lens
• reflecting telescope
• radio telescope
• observatory

Target Reading Skill

Building Vocabulary Carefully read the definition of each key term. Also read the neighboring sentences. Then write a definition of each key term in your own words.

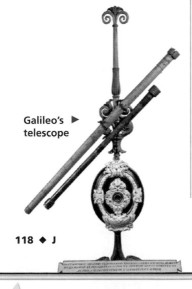

◄ Galileo's telescope

118 ◆ J

Lab zone Discover **Activity**

How Does Distance Affect an Image?

1. Hold a plastic hand lens about 7 cm away from your eye and about 5 cm away from a printed letter on a page. Move the lens slowly back and forth until the letter is in clear focus.
2. Keep the letter about 5 cm from the lens as you move your eye back to about 20 cm from the lens. Then, keeping the distance between your eye and the lens constant, slowly move the object away from the lens.

Think It Over
Observing What did the letter look like through the lens in Step 1 compared with how it looked without the lens? How did the image change in Step 2?

Ancient peoples often gazed up in wonder at the many points of light in the night sky. But they could see few details with their eyes alone. It was not until the invention of the telescope in 1608 that people could observe objects in the sky more closely. Recall that a **telescope** is a device that makes distant objects appear to be closer. The telescope revolutionized astronomy. Scientists now had a tool that allowed them to see many objects in space for the first time.

Although Galileo was not the first to use a telescope, he soon made it famous as he turned his homemade instrument to the sky. With his telescope, Galileo saw things that no one had even dreamed of. He was the first to see sunspots, Saturn's rings, and the four large moons of Jupiter. Galileo could see fine details, such as mountains on the moon, which cannot be seen clearly by the unaided eye.

Since Galileo's time, astronomers have built ever larger and more powerful telescopes. These telescopes have opened up a whole universe of wonders that would have amazed even Galileo.

Lab zone Discover **Activity**

Skills Focus Observing

Materials plastic hand lens

Time 10 minutes

Tips Start with the distances mentioned in the instructions, but have the students slowly move the lens back and forth until the image in the lens is in focus (sharp and clear).

L2 **Expected Outcome** 1. It looks larger. 2. The image will invert as the object is moved away from the lens.

Think It Over The image of the letter in the lens will look larger than that observed by the unaided eye. In Step 2, as the object is moved farther from the lens, it becomes blurry and then inverts (appears to be upside down).

Electromagnetic Radiation

To understand how telescopes work, it's useful to understand the nature of electromagnetic radiation. Light is a form of **electromagnetic radiation** (ih lek troh mag NET ik), or energy that can travel through space in the form of waves. You can see stars when the light that they produce reaches your eyes.

Forms of Radiation Scientists call the light you can see **visible light.** Visible light is just one of many types of electromagnetic radiation. Many objects give off radiation that you can't see. For example, in addition to their reddish light, the glowing coils of an electric heater give off infrared radiation, which you feel as heat. Radio transmitters produce radio waves that carry signals to radios and televisions. Objects in space give off all types of electromagnetic radiation.

The Electromagnetic Spectrum As shown in Figure 1, the distance between the crest of one wave and the crest of the next wave is called **wavelength.** Visible light has very short wavelengths, less than one millionth of a meter. Some electromagnetic waves have even shorter wavelengths. Other waves have much longer wavelengths, even several meters long.

If you shine white light through a prism, the light spreads out to make a range of different colors with different wavelengths, called a **spectrum.** The spectrum of visible light is made of the colors red, orange, yellow, green, blue, and violet. **The electromagnetic spectrum includes the entire range of radio waves, infrared radiation, visible light, ultraviolet radiation, X-rays, and gamma rays.**

 Reading Checkpoint What are two kinds of electromagnetic waves that you might experience every day?

Go Online
SCI LINKS NSTA

For: Links on telescopes
Visit: www.SciLinks.org
Web Code: scn-0641

FIGURE 1
The Electromagnetic Spectrum
The electromagnetic spectrum ranges from long-wavelength radio waves through short-wavelength gamma rays.
Interpreting Diagrams *Are infrared waves longer or shorter than ultraviolet waves?*

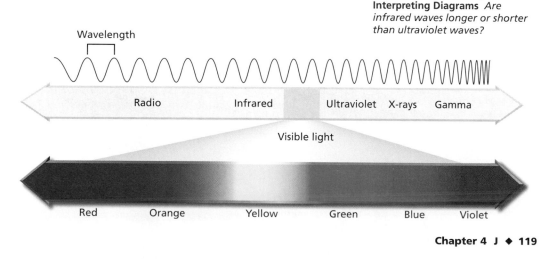

Wavelength

Radio Infrared Ultraviolet X-rays Gamma

Visible light

Red Orange Yellow Green Blue Violet

Chapter 4 J ◆ 119

Instruct

Electromagnetic Radiation

 **Go Online**
SCI LINKS NSTA

For: Links on telescopes
Visit: www.SciLinks.org
Web Code: scn-0641

Download a worksheet that will guide students' review of Internet resources on telescopes.

Teach Key Concepts [L1]

Regions of the Electromagnetic (EM) Spectrum

Focus Refer students to Figure 1.

Teach Point out that the spectrum of visible light is part of the spectrum of EM radiation and is shown below it to make it larger to see. Ask: **Which part of the EM spectrum can you see?** *(Visible light)* **Which parts are not visible?** *(Radio waves, infrared radiation, ultraviolet radiation, X-rays, gamma rays)*

Apply Ask students whether they have ever seen a rainbow. Point out that in doing so, they have observed the different colors that make up the spectrum of visible light.
learning modality: visual

All in One Teaching Resources
• Transparency J35

Independent Practice [L2]

All in One Teaching Resources
• Guided Reading and Study Worksheet: *Telescopes*

⊙ **Student Edition on Audio CD**

Differentiated Instruction

Gifted and Talented [L3]
Communicating How Telescopes Work Organize students in pairs. Tell one student in each pair that he or she will play the role of Galileo. The other student will pretend to be Isaac Newton. Each "Galileo" will sketch a refracting telescope, and each "Newton" will sketch a reflecting telescope.

Have each pair write a script explaining how the two telescopes work. Then ask selected pairs to present their work to the class in the form of a skit. Encourage the "Galileos" and "Newtons" to debate the advantages and disadvantages of each design. **learning modality: verbal**

Monitor Progress [L1]

Writing Have students compile a list of sources of various types of radiation.

Answers
Figure 1 Longer

 Reading Checkpoint Possible answer: Radio waves carry signals to radios and televisions. Infrared rays from the sun feel warm on your skin.

Types of Telescopes

Teach Key Concepts
How Telescopes Work

Focus Tell students that refraction is the bending of light rays that occurs when light moves from one material into another material. Reflection occurs when light waves bounce off of a surface.

Teach Ask: **What is used in refracting telescopes to collect light and magnify images?** (*Lenses*) **Where in these telescopes does refraction occur?** (*Where the light passes through the lenses*) **What is used in reflecting telescopes to collect and focus light?** (*a mirror*)

Extend Ask: **Can telescopes collect EM waves other than visible light?** (*Yes*) **What are some examples?** (*Radio telescopes, infrared telescopes, X-ray telescopes*) Tell students that special telescopes are built to collect these types of EM radiation.
learning modality: verbal

All in One Teaching Resources

• Transparency J36

Lab zone Build **Inquiry** 	**L2**

Observing a Continuous Spectrum

Materials white light source, poster board with a slit 2 cm × 2 mm, prism, colored pencils, white paper, tape

Time 30 minutes

Focus Explain that a prism bends, or refracts, white light.

Teach Have students work in small groups to position the slit over the white light source and tape the poster board to the light source. Darken the room, and tell students to shine light from the slit through the prism and onto a sheet of paper. Students can use colored pencils to record their observations.

Apply Ask: **What characteristic determines each color?** (*Wavelength*) Have groups compare the order of the colors they have seen. (*It is the same for all groups.*) **What can you infer about how wavelengths bend?** (*Wavelengths of each color bend differently.*)
learning modality: kinesthetic

Types of Telescopes

On a clear night, your eyes can see at most a few thousand stars. But with a telescope, you can see many millions. Why? The light from stars spreads out as it moves through space, and your eyes are too small to gather much light.

Telescopes are instruments that collect and focus light and other forms of electromagnetic radiation. Telescopes make distant objects appear larger and brighter. A telescope that uses lenses or mirrors to collect and focus visible light is called an **optical telescope.** The two major types of optical telescope are refracting telescopes and reflecting telescopes.

Modern astronomy is based on the detection of many forms of electromagnetic radiation besides visible light. Non-optical telescopes collect and focus different types of electromagnetic radiation, just as optical telescopes collect visible light.

Refracting Telescopes A **refracting telescope** uses convex lenses to gather and focus light. A **convex lens** is a piece of transparent glass, curved so that the middle is thicker than the edges.

Figure 2 shows a simple refracting telescope. This telescope has two convex lenses, one at each end of a long tube. Light enters the telescope through the large objective lens at the top. The objective lens focuses the light at a certain distance from the lens. This distance is the focal length of the lens. The larger the objective lens, the more light the telescope can collect. This makes it easier for astronomers to see faint objects.

The smaller lens at the lower end of a refracting telescope is the eyepiece lens. The eyepiece lens magnifies the image produced by the objective lens.

FIGURE 2
Refracting and Reflecting Telescopes
A refracting telescope uses convex lenses to focus light. A reflecting telescope has a curved mirror in place of an objective lens.

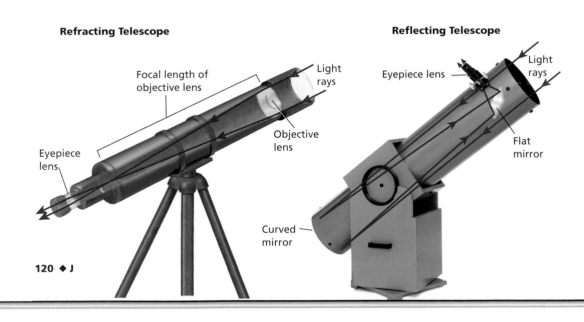

Refracting Telescope

Focal length of objective lens

Light rays

Objective lens

Eyepiece lens

Reflecting Telescope

Light rays

Eyepiece lens

Flat mirror

Curved mirror

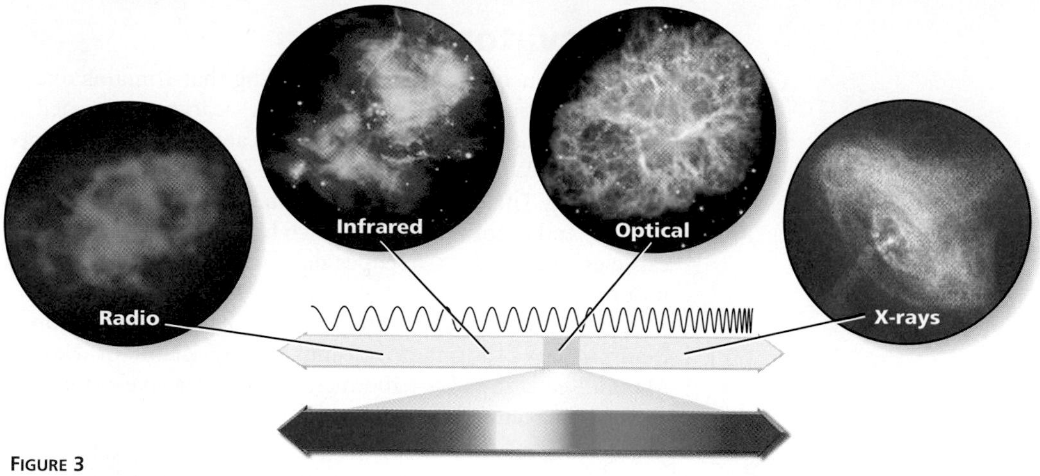

FIGURE 3
Four Views of the Crab Nebula
Different types of telescopes collect
electromagnetic radiation at different
wavelengths. Astronomers are able to
learn a great deal about the Crab Nebula
by examining these different images. The
images are shown at different scales.

Reflecting Telescopes

Reflecting Telescopes In 1668, Isaac Newton built the first reflecting telescope. A **reflecting telescope** uses a curved mirror to collect and focus light. Like the objective lens in a refracting telescope, the curved mirror in a reflecting telescope focuses a large amount of light onto a small area. The larger the mirror, the more light the telescope can collect. The largest optical telescopes today are all reflecting telescopes.

Radio Telescopes Devices used to detect radio waves from objects in space are called **radio telescopes.** Most radio telescopes have curved, reflecting surfaces—up to 305 meters in diameter. These surfaces focus radio waves the way the mirror in a reflecting telescope focuses light waves. The surfaces concentrate the faint radio waves from space onto small antennas like those on radios. As with optical telescopes, the larger a radio telescope is, the more radio waves it can collect.

Other Telescopes Some telescopes detect infrared radiation, which has longer wavelengths than visible light but shorter wavelengths than radio waves. There are also telescopes that detect the shortest wavelengths—ultraviolet radiation, X-rays, and gamma rays.

> **Reading Checkpoint** Who built the first reflecting telescope?

Lab zone Try This Activity

Locating Radio Waves
You can use an umbrella to focus radio waves.

1. Line the inside of an open umbrella with aluminum foil.
2. Turn on a small radio and tune it to a station.
3. Move the radio up and down along the umbrella handle. Find the position where the station is clearest. Radio waves reflecting off the foil focus at this point. Tape the radio to the handle.
4. Hold the umbrella at different angles. At which angle is the station the clearest?

Inferring In which direction do you think the radio station's transmitter is located? Explain.

Lab zone Try This Activity

Skills Focus Inferring
Materials umbrella, small radio, aluminum foil, masking tape
Time 30 minutes
Tips Have students use masking tape to attach the foil to the umbrella and to attach the radio to the handle.
Expected Outcome Reception is best with the handle held parallel to the floor.

L2 The best position of the radio is at the focal point of the umbrella. The handle points to the transmitter. The waves are reflected by the foil and directed to a focal point on the handle.

Extend Challenge students to select another radio station and predict where the reception will be best. **learning modality: kinesthetic**

Use Visuals: Figure 3   L2
Images from Different Telescopes

Focus Explain that different types of telescopes collect different types of radiation.

Teach Have students take turns describing each image. Ask: **If you were in space near this nebula, which image shows what you would see with the naked eye?** *(The one taken by an optical telescope)* **What does the infrared image show?** *(Differences in temperature in different areas)*

Apply Ask: **How have radio, X-ray, and infrared telescopes helped astronomers expand their exploration of space?** *(These nonoptical telescopes gather information that cannot be obtained visually.)* **learning modality: visual**

🚩 Address Misconceptions   L1
Sunlight's Effect on Telescopes

Focus Some students may think that stars are present at nighttime only.

Teach Point out that stars are always in the sky, even during the day. They are not visible, however, because our eyes are not able to distinguish them because of the brightness of the sun. For this reason, optical telescopes cannot be used during daytime. Visible light from the sun, on the other hand, does not interfere with radio waves. Therefore, radio telescopes can be used both night and day.

Apply Have students brainstorm other examples of how the sun's brightness "overpowers" other forms of visible light. *(Possible answer: In the daytime, it can be hard to tell whether a car's headlights are on. A flashlight's beam cannot be seen in bright sunlight.)* **learning modality: logical/ mathematical**

Monitor Progress _____   L2

Skills Check Ask students to compare and contrast refracting, reflecting, and nonoptical telescopes.

Answer

> **Reading Checkpoint** Isaac Newton

Observatories

Teach Key Concepts　L2

Location of Telescopes

Focus Review the definition of an observatory.

Teach Ask: **Why are many large optical telescopes located on mountaintops?** *(Earth's atmosphere makes objects in space look blurry. The sky is clearer at higher elevations and there is less interference from city lights.)* **What type of telescope does not have to be located on a mountaintop?** *(Radio)* **What is an advantage of placing telescopes in space instead of on Earth?** *(Space telescopes can detect wavelengths that are blocked or interfered with by Earth's atmosphere.)*

Apply Tell students that the reflecting mirrors on the telescopes on Mauna Kea are much larger than the mirrors on Hubble. Ask: **Why are the images taken by Hubble clearer?** *(Earth's atmosphere does not interfere with Hubble images.)* **learning modality: verbal**

Lab zone　Teacher **Demo**　L1

Modeling Light Pollution

Materials large poster board, adhesive, glow-in-the-dark decals of stars and planets, several small penlights

Time 20 minutes

Focus Tell students that light from streetlights, businesses, and signs makes it difficult to view objects in the night sky. This is known as light pollution.

Teach Place decals of different sizes on a large poster board. Then place the poster board under a light to "charge" the decals. Place the poster board in a prominent position, close the shades, and turn off the room lights. Give students a few moments to observe the brightness of the decals. Ask a volunteer to help you shine penlights on the poster board. Tell students to note the difference in the brightness of the decals. Ask: **What does this model represent?** *(Light pollution, or the effect of lights on the brightness of stars and planets)*

Apply Tell students that some communities have placed specially made shields over streetlights to reduce light pollution. **learning modality: visual**

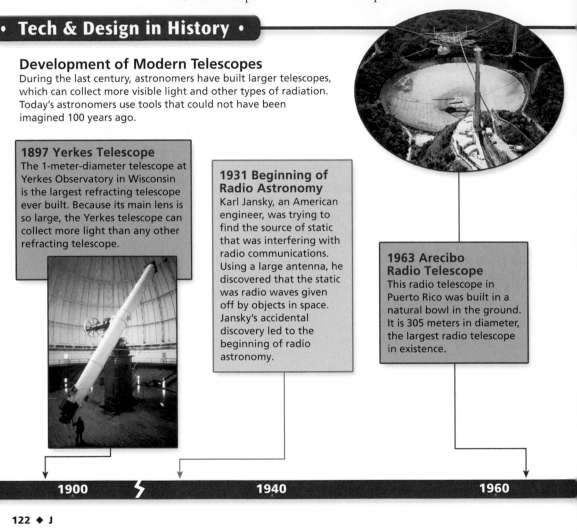

Observatories

In general, an **observatory** is a building that contains one or more telescopes. However, some observatories are located in space. **Many large observatories are located on mountaintops or in space.** Why? Earth's atmosphere makes objects in space look blurry. The sky on some mountaintops is clearer than at sea level and is not brightened much by city lights. Unlike optical telescopes, radio telescopes do not need to be located on mountaintops.

One of the best observatory sites on Earth is on the top of Mauna Kea, a dormant volcano on the island of Hawaii. Mauna Kea is so tall—4,200 meters above sea level—that it is above 40 percent of Earth's atmosphere.

• Tech & Design in History •

Development of Modern Telescopes
During the last century, astronomers have built larger telescopes, which can collect more visible light and other types of radiation. Today's astronomers use tools that could not have been imagined 100 years ago.

1897 Yerkes Telescope
The 1-meter-diameter telescope at Yerkes Observatory in Wisconsin is the largest refracting telescope ever built. Because its main lens is so large, the Yerkes telescope can collect more light than any other refracting telescope.

1931 Beginning of Radio Astronomy
Karl Jansky, an American engineer, was trying to find the source of static that was interfering with radio communications. Using a large antenna, he discovered that the static was radio waves given off by objects in space. Jansky's accidental discovery led to the beginning of radio astronomy.

1963 Arecibo Radio Telescope
This radio telescope in Puerto Rico was built in a natural bowl in the ground. It is 305 meters in diameter, the largest radio telescope in existence.

1900　1940　1960

Advanced Telescopes Today, many large optical telescopes are equipped with systems that significantly improve the quality of their images. Optical telescopes on Earth equipped with such systems are able to produce images of small regions of the sky that rival those of optical telescopes based in space.

Some new telescopes are equipped with computer systems that correct images for problems such as telescope movement and changes in air temperature or mirror shape. Other advanced telescopes use lasers to monitor conditions in the atmosphere. The shape of the telescope's mirror is automatically adjusted thousands of times each second in response to changes in the atmosphere.

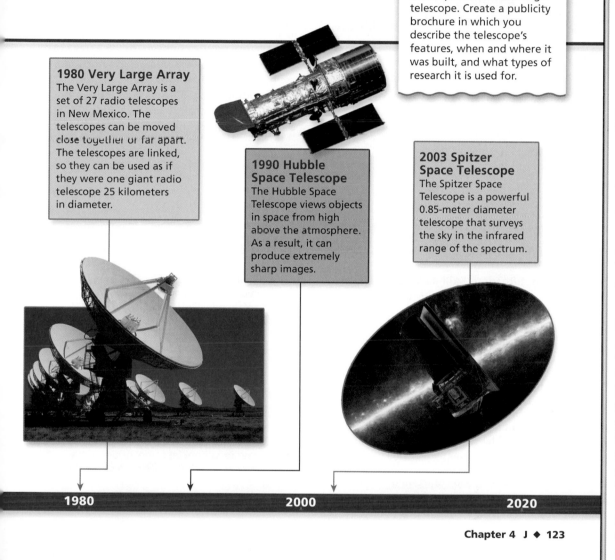

Writing in Science

Research and Write
Research one of these telescopes or another large telescope. Create a publicity brochure in which you describe the telescope's features, when and where it was built, and what types of research it is used for.

1980 Very Large Array
The Very Large Array is a set of 27 radio telescopes in New Mexico. The telescopes can be moved close together or far apart. The telescopes are linked, so they can be used as if they were one giant radio telescope 25 kilometers in diameter.

1990 Hubble Space Telescope
The Hubble Space Telescope views objects in space from high above the atmosphere. As a result, it can produce extremely sharp images.

2003 Spitzer Space Telescope
The Spitzer Space Telescope is a powerful 0.85-meter diameter telescope that surveys the sky in the infrared range of the spectrum.

1980　　2000　　2020

Science and **History**

Focus Tell students that the first telescopes were used in the 1600s.

Teach Have students take turns reading aloud the annotations to the timeline. Have a world map available that students can use to locate the various telescopes. Help students visualize how large the telescopes are by comparing them to objects students know. Ask students to estimate the sizes of the telescopes in terms of the sizes of familiar objects, such as the length of a school bus or football field. (*Possible answer: The diameter of the Arecibo Radio Telescope is about the length of three football fields.*)

Writing in Science

Writing Mode Research
Scoring Rubric
4 Exceeds criteria, includes a full description of the telescope's features, history, and uses; written in the lively style of a brochure
3 Meets all criteria, but description is uninteresting
2 Meets only two criteria
1 Is incomplete and inaccurate

Help Students Read　L1
Active Comprehension Read aloud the introductory paragraph under Observatories. Ask: **What more would you like to know about the locations of large telescopes? What about telescopes interests you?** Make connections for students between telescopes and their lives. For example, students are likely to have observed the moon and stars and wished for a closer view. Write down several responses. Tell students to read the text and to consider the questions raised earlier as they read. Then, discuss the content, making sure that each question is answered or that students know where to look for the answer.

Differentiated Instruction

Less Proficient Readers　L1
Interpreting Data Help students better interpret the timeline by asking questions that encourage critical thinking. For example, ask: **What time span does the timeline cover?** (*1897 to 2003*) **How does this time span compare to that of other timelines you have seen, such as a** geologic timeline? (*This timeline covers a relatively short amount of time.*) **Are there any large gaps in the timeline?** (*No.*) **What does that tell you about the development of modern telescopes?** (*The development of this technology has occurred at a steady pace over the last century or so.*) **learning modality: verbal**

Monitor Progress　L2

Skills Check Have students classify several different types of telescopes by their optimal locations and explain why those locations are suitable.

Monitor Progress

Answer

✓ **Reading Checkpoint** A building that contains one or more telescopes

Assess

Reviewing Key Concepts

1. a. Radio, infrared, visible light, ultraviolet, X-rays, and gamma rays **b.** The Hubble is above Earth's atmosphere; the atmosphere blurs the transmission of visible light.

2. a. Refracting and reflecting **b.** A refracting telescope uses two convex lenses. The objective lens gathers and focuses the light. The eyepiece lens magnifies the image produced by the objective lens. **c.** A reflecting telescope uses a curved mirror to collect and focus light; a refracting telescope uses convex lenses to do the same.

3. a. The atmosphere makes objects in space look blurry because it interferes with the transmission of visible light. The atmosphere also blocks X-rays, gamma rays, and most ultraviolet radiation. **b.** There is less atmosphere above mountaintops to interfere with the transmission of electromagnetic waves. Also the sky is not brightened much by city lights. **c.** No. X-rays and gamma rays are blocked by Earth's atmosphere, so telescopes to detect these waves must be placed in space.

Reteach
L1

Use Figure 1 to review the types of telescopes that detect different forms of electromagnetic radiation and their locations.

Performance Assessment
L2

Skills Check Have students diagram the path of light as it moves through a refracting telescope.

All in One Teaching Resources

- Section Summary: *Telescopes*
- Review and Reinforce: *Telescopes*
- Enrich: *Telescopes*

FIGURE 4
Repairing Hubble
Astronauts have repaired and upgraded the Hubble Space Telescope on several occasions.

Telescopes in Space X-rays, gamma rays, and most ultraviolet radiation are blocked by Earth's atmosphere. To detect these wavelengths, astronomers have placed telescopes in space. Some space telescopes are designed to detect visible light or infrared radiation, since Earth's atmosphere interferes with the transmission of these forms of radiation.

The Hubble Space Telescope is a reflecting telescope with a mirror 2.4 meters in diameter. Because the Hubble telescope orbits Earth above the atmosphere, it can produce very detailed images in visible light. It also collects ultraviolet and infrared radiation. The spectacular Hubble telescope images have changed how astronomers view the universe.

The hottest objects in space give off X-rays. The Chandra X-ray Observatory produces images in the X-ray portion of the spectrum. Chandra's X-ray images are much more detailed than those of earlier X-ray telescopes.

The most recent addition to NASA's lineup of telescopes in space is the Spitzer Space Telescope. Launched in 2003, the Spitzer telescope produces images in the infrared portion of the spectrum.

✓ **Reading Checkpoint** What is an observatory?

Section 1 Assessment

🎯 **Target Reading Skill** Building Vocabulary
Use your definitions to help answer the questions below.

Reviewing Key Concepts

1. a. Sequencing List the main types of electromagnetic waves, from longest wavelength to shortest.
   b. Applying Concepts Why are images from the Hubble Space Telescope clearer than images from telescopes on Earth?
2. a. Identifying What are the two major types of optical telescope?
   b. Explaining How does a refracting telescope work?
   c. Comparing and Contrasting Use Figure 2 to explain the major differences between reflecting and refracting telescopes.

3. a. Summarizing How does the atmosphere affect electromagnetic radiation?
   b. Explaining Why are many large optical telescopes located on mountaintops?
   c. Applying Concepts Would it make sense to place an X-ray or gamma ray telescope on a mountaintop? Explain why or why not.

Writing in Science

Writing Instructions Write a short explanation of how to build a reflecting telescope for a booklet to be included in a model telescope kit. Be sure to describe the shape and position of each of the lenses or mirrors. You may include drawings.

Lab zone Chapter **Project**

Keep Students on Track Confirm that students have located and sketched their constellations. Encourage students to compare their sketches. Research on the myths should be underway. Advise each student to find as many stories as possible about the chosen constellation and to take notes on these stories.

Writing in Science

Writing Mode Exposition How-to
Scoring Rubric
4 Exceeds criteria, includes accurate, detailed instructions and a labeled drawing
3 Includes instructions only
2 Includes unclear instructions
1 Includes only some of the steps

Design and Build a Telescope

Foam holder

Objective lens (tape to the end of tube)

Eyepiece

Paper towel tubes

Problem

Can you design and build a telescope?

Skills Focus

evaluating the design, redesigning

Materials

- 2 paper towel tubes of slightly different diameters • several plastic objective lenses
- several plastic eyepiece lenses • meter stick
- foam holder for eyepiece • transparent tape

Procedure

1. Fit one of the paper towel tubes inside the other. Make sure you can move the tubes but that they will not slide on their own.

2. Place the large objective lens flat against the end of the outer tube. Tape the lens in place.

3. Insert the small eyepiece lens into the opening in the foam holder.

4. Place the foam eyepiece lens holder into the inner tube at the end of the telescope opposite to the objective lens.

5. Tape a meter stick to the wall. Look through the eyepiece at the meter stick from 5 m away. Slide the tubes in and out to focus your telescope so that you can clearly read the numbers on the meter stick. Draw your telescope. On the drawing, mark the tube position that allows you to read the numbers most clearly.

6. Use your telescope to look at other objects at different distances, both in your classroom and through the window. For each object you view, draw your telescope, marking the tube position at which you see the object most clearly. **CAUTION:** *Do not look at the sun. You will damage your eyes.*

7. Design and build a better telescope. Your new telescope should make objects appear larger than your first model from the same observing distance. It should have markings on the inner tube to enable you to pre-focus the telescope for a given observing distance.

8. Draw a design for your new telescope. List the materials you'll need. Obtain your teacher's approval. Then build your new model.

Analyze and Conclude

1. **Inferring** Why do you need two tubes?

2. **Observing** If you focus on a nearby object and then focus on something farther away, do you have to move the tubes together or apart?

3. **Evaluating the Design** How could you improve on the design of your new telescope? What effects would different lenses or tubes have on its performance?

4. **Redesigning** Describe the most important factors in redesigning your telescope.

Communicate

Write a product brochure for your new telescope. Be sure to describe in detail why your new telescope is better than the first telescope.

Design and Build a Telescope   L2

Prepare for Inquiry

Key Concept

Students will construct and use a simple refracting telescope.

Skills Objectives

After this lab, students will be able to
- evaluate the design of their telescopes
- redesign their telescopes to improve performance

⏱ Class Time 80 minutes

Advance Planning

Use kits or collect paper towel tubes for the telescopes. Tubes from different brands can be used for the inner and outer tubes. Various combinations of lenses are possible. For example, a 43-mm diameter 400-mm focal length objective lens paired with a 25-mm focal length eyepiece would produce a magnification of 16×.

All in One Teaching Resources

- Lab Worksheet: *Design and Build a Telescope*

Guide Inquiry

Introduce the Procedure

Have students examine the text drawing to give them an idea of what they are building.

Troubleshooting the Experiment

- Suggest that students rest their telescopes on a stable surface.
- Make sure that lenses are perpendicular to tube walls and parallel to each other.

Expected Outcome

Objects will be magnified and inverted when viewed through the telescopes.

Analyze and Conclude

1. To focus on objects at different distances
2. You must move the tubes together.
3. Answers will vary. A wider tube and wider lenses would collect more light.
4. The size and magnification of the objective and the eyepiece lenses are likely to be the most important factors.

Extend Inquiry

Communicate The brochure should include all of the features of the new telescope and a comparison of the magnification capabilities of the original and redesigned telescopes.

Characteristics of Stars

Objectives

After this lesson, students will be able to

J.4.2.1 Explain how stars are classified.

J.4.2.2 Describe how astronomers measure distances to the stars.

J.4.2.3 Describe the H-R diagram and explain how astronomers use it.

Target Reading Skill

Using Prior Knowledge Explain that using prior knowledge helps students connect what they already know to what they are about to read.

Answers

Possible answers:

What You Know

1. Stars are bright and hot.
2. Distances between stars are measured in light-years.
3. The sun is a yellow star.

What You Learned

1. Stars are classified by color, temperature, size, composition, and brightness.
2. Light travels 9.5 million million kilometers in one year.
3. The sun has a surface temperature of about 5,800°C.

All in One Teaching Resources

• Transparencies J37, J49, J50, J51, J52

Preteach

Build Background Knowledge   L1

Star Charts and the Night Sky

Invite students who have visited a planetarium to describe their experiences. Display the transparency from J49–J52 that shows the night sky for the current season. Ask: **How do the star chart and the night sky compare?** *(Possible answer: You can't see all the stars shown in the chart when you look at the night sky.)* Invite students to discuss how they could use star charts to locate objects in the sky.

Section 2 — Characteristics of Stars

Reading Preview

Key Concepts

• How are stars classified?
• How do astronomers measure distances to the stars?
• What is an H-R diagram and how do astronomers use it?

Key Terms

• constellation
• spectrograph
• apparent brightness
• absolute brightness
• light-year
• parallax
• Hertzsprung-Russell diagram
• main sequence

Target Reading Skill

Using Prior Knowledge Before you read, write what you know about the characteristics of stars in a graphic organizer like the one below. As you read, write what you learn.

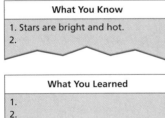

What You Know
1. Stars are bright and hot.
2.

What You Learned
1.
2.

Discover Activity

How Does Your Thumb Move?

1. Stand facing a wall, at least an arm's length away. Stretch your arm out with your thumb up and your fingers curled.
2. Close your right eye and look at your thumb with your left eye. Line your thumb up with something on the wall.
3. Now close your left eye and open your right eye. How does your thumb appear to move along the wall?
4. Bring your thumb closer to your eye, about half the distance as before. Repeat Steps 2 and 3.

Think It Over

Observing How does your thumb appear to move in Step 4 compared to Step 3? How are these observations related to how far away your thumb is at each step? How could you use this method to estimate distances?

When ancient observers around the world looked up at the night sky, they imagined that groups of stars formed pictures of people or animals. Today, we call these imaginary patterns of stars **constellations.**

Different cultures gave different names to the constellations. For example, a large constellation in the winter sky is named Orion, the Hunter, after a Greek myth. In this constellation, Orion is seen with a sword in his belt and an upraised arm. The ancient Sumerians thought that the stars in Orion formed the outline of a sheep. In ancient China, this group of stars was called "three," probably because of the three bright stars in Orion's belt.

Astronomers use the patterns of the constellations to locate objects in the night sky. But although the stars in a constellation look as if they are close to one another, they generally are not. They just happen to lie in the same part of the sky as seen from Earth.

Illustration of Orion ▼

Discover Activity

Skills Focus Observing

Materials none

Time 10 minutes

Tip Encourage students to focus on their thumbs, not on the wall. Guide students to choose a wall that has features such as mortar grooves or attached posters.

L2 **Expected Outcome** The thumb seems to move more in Step 4, when it is closer to the student.

Think It Over You could use this method to estimate distances by comparing how much an object appears to move against a background.

Classifying Stars

Like the sun, all stars are huge spheres of glowing gas. They are made up mostly of hydrogen, and they produce energy through the process of nuclear fusion. This energy makes stars shine brightly. Astronomers classify stars according to their physical characteristics. **Characteristics used to classify stars include color, temperature, size, composition, and brightness.**

Color and Temperature If you look at the night sky, you can see slight differences in the colors of the stars. For example, Betelgeuse (BAY tul jooz), the bright star in Orion's shoulder, looks reddish. Rigel, the star in Orion's heel, is blue-white.

Like hot objects on Earth, a star's color reveals its temperature. If you watch a toaster heat up, you can see the wires glow red-hot. The wires inside a light bulb are even hotter and glow white. Similarly, the coolest stars—with a surface temperature of about 3,200 degrees Celsius—appear reddish in the sky. With a surface temperature of about 5,800 degrees Celsius, the sun appears yellow. The hottest stars in the sky, which are over 20,000 degrees Celsius, appear bluish.

Size When you look at stars in the sky, they all appear to be points of light of the same size. Many stars are actually about the size of the sun, which is a medium-sized star. However, some stars are much larger than the sun. Very large stars are called giant stars or supergiant stars. If the supergiant star Betelgeuse were located where our sun is, it would be large enough to fill the solar system as far out as Jupiter.

Most stars are much smaller than the sun. White dwarf stars are about the size of Earth. Neutron stars are even smaller, only about 20 kilometers in diameter.

Go Online
PHSchool.com
For: More on types of stars
Visit: PHSchool.com
Web Code: cfd-5042

FIGURE 5
Star Size
Stars vary greatly in size. Giant stars are typically 10 to 100 times larger than the sun and more than 1,000 times the size of a white dwarf. **Calculating** Betelgeuse has a diameter of 420 million kilometers. How many times larger is this than the sun, which has a diameter of 1.4 million kilometers?

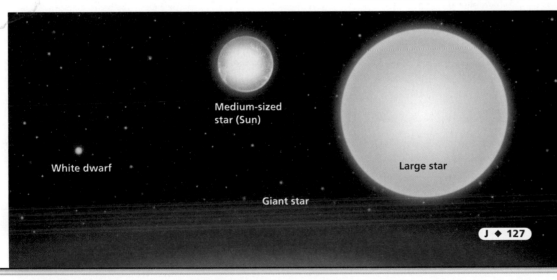

White dwarf

Medium-sized star (Sun)

Giant star

Large star

J ◆ 127

Go Online
PHSchool.com
For: More on types of stars
Visit: PHSchool.com
Web Code: cfd-5042
Students can review types of stars in an online activity.

Classifying Stars

Teach Key Concepts **L2**
Physical Characteristics of Stars

Focus Tell students that just as physical characteristics are used to classify plants or rocks, astronomers use characteristics to classify stars.

Teach Explain to students that the most important characteristics for classifying stars are color, temperature, size, composition, and brightness and that these characteristics are often related. Ask: **Which star is hotter—a red star or a blue star?** *(A blue star)* **Which star is brighter—a supergiant or the sun?** *(A supergiant)*

Apply Tell students that they will learn in this section how to classify stars according to these properties.

All in One Teaching Resources
• Transparencies J38, J39

Independent Practice **L2**
All in One Teaching Resources
• Guided Reading and Study Worksheet: *Characteristics of Stars*

◉ **Student Edition on Audio CD**

Monitor Progress **L1**

Oral Presentation Invite students to name and describe the characteristics astronomers use to classify stars.

Answer
Figure 5 300 times

Modeling Color Separation

Materials projector; prism; red, green, and blue cellophane

Time 15 minutes

Focus Review how a spectrograph classifies stars.

Teach Darken the room, and shine the light from the projector through the prism so that the spectrum is visible on a white surface. Use a double thickness of red cellophane to reduce the occurence of light leaks. Ask students to predict what will happen when red cellophane is held between the prism and the spectrum. Students will observe that only the red part of the spectrum remains visible. Ask: **Why did the other colors disappear?** *(The cellophane allowed only the red light to pass through.)* Repeat this process with a double thickness of green cellophane and then a double thickness of blue cellophane. Ask students to predict what will happen when both red and blue cellophane are held between the prism and the spectrum. *(No light will pass through.)* Allow students to observe whether their predictions were correct. Then ask: **Why did no light pass through the cellophane?** *(If the blue cellophane is held closer to the prism, the blue light passes through and is then blocked by the red cellophane. If the red cellophane is held closer to the prism, the red light passes through and is then blocked by the blue cellophane.)*

Apply Ask: **How does this demonstration relate to a spectrograph?** *(Like a spectrograph, the prism breaks light into a spectrum and certain wavelengths are absorbed by the cellophane.)* **learning modality: visual**

Help Students Read L1

Monitor Your Understanding Have students read Brightness of Stars and write down the main ideas. Tell students to ask themselves, "Did I have any trouble reading this passage? If so, why?" Then, have them devise their own strategies to improve their understanding. Encourage them to use these strategies as they continue reading.

FIGURE 6
Spectrums of Four Stars
Astronomers can use line spectrums to identify the chemical elements in a star. Each element produces a characteristic pattern of spectral lines.

Hydrogen

Helium

Sodium

Calcium

Chemical Composition Stars vary in their chemical composition. The chemical composition of most stars is about 73 percent hydrogen, 25 percent helium, and 2 percent other elements by mass. This is similar to the composition of the sun.

Astronomers use spectrographs to determine the elements found in stars. A **spectrograph** (SPEK truh graf) is a device that breaks light into colors and produces an image of the resulting spectrum. Most large telescopes have spectrographs.

The gases in a star's atmosphere absorb some wavelengths of light produced within the star. When the star's light is seen through a spectrograph, each absorbed wavelength is shown as a dark line on a spectrum. Each chemical element absorbs light at particular wavelengths. Just as each person has a unique set of fingerprints, each element has a unique set of lines for a given temperature. Figure 6 shows the spectral lines of four elements. By comparing a star's spectrum with the spectrums of known elements, astronomers can infer how much of each element is found in the star.

✓ **Reading Checkpoint** What is a spectrograph?

Brightness of Stars

Stars also differ in brightness, the amount of light they give off. **The brightness of a star depends upon both its size and temperature.** Recall that the photosphere is the layer of a star that gives off light. Betelgeuse is fairly cool, so a square meter of its photosphere doesn't give off much light. But Betelgeuse is very large, so it shines brightly.

Rigel, on the other hand, is very hot, so each square meter of Rigel's photosphere gives off a lot of light. Even though it is smaller than Betelgeuse, Rigel shines more brightly.

Lab
zone **Skills Activity**

Inferring

The lines on the spectrums below are from three different stars. Each of these star spectrums is made up of an overlap of spectrums from the individual elements shown in Figure 6. In star A, which elements have the strongest lines? Which are the strongest in star B? In star C?

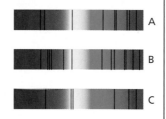

A

B

C

Lab
zone **Skills Activity**

Skills Focus Inferring

Materials Figure 6

Time 10 minutes

Tips Encourage students to compare the element spectrums to the star spectrums individually, rather than all at once.

L3 **Expected Outcome** Star A: hydrogen and helium; star B: helium and calcium; star C: hydrogen and sodium

Extend Challenge students to draw the spectrum for a star that has strong lines for hydrogen and calcium. **learning modality: visual**

How bright a star looks from Earth depends on both its distance from Earth and how bright the star truly is. Because of these two factors, the brightness of a star can be described in two ways: apparent brightness and absolute brightness.

Apparent Brightness A star's **apparent brightness** is its brightness as seen from Earth. Astronomers can measure apparent brightness fairly easily using electronic devices. However, astronomers can't tell how much light a star gives off just from the star's apparent brightness. Just as a flashlight looks brighter the closer it is to you, a star looks brighter the closer it is to Earth. For example, the sun looks very bright. This does not mean that the sun gives off more light than all other stars. The sun looks so bright simply because it is so close. In reality, the sun is a star of only average brightness.

Absolute Brightness A star's **absolute brightness** is the brightness the star would have if it were at a standard distance from Earth. Finding a star's absolute brightness is more complex than finding its apparent brightness. An astronomer must first find out both the star's apparent brightness and its distance from Earth. The astronomer can then calculate the star's absolute brightness

Astronomers have found that the absolute brightness of stars can vary tremendously. The brightest stars are more than a billion times brighter than the dimmest stars!

Reading Checkpoint What is a star's absolute brightness?

FIGURE 7
Absolute Brightness
The streetlights in this photo all give off about the same amount of light, and so have about the same absolute brightness.
Applying Concepts Why do the closer streetlights appear brighter than the more distant lights?

Chapter 4 J ◆ 129

Brightness of Stars

Teach Key Concepts **L1**

Differences in Brightness

Focus Tell students to imagine that they are riding in a car at night, and two cars are approaching from the opposite direction. Ask: **Which car appears to have brighter headlights?** *(The one closer to you)* **Does this mean that its headlights are actually brighter?** *(Not necessarily; the headlights on the other car may be the same brightness but appear dimmer because of distance.)*

Teach Explain that a star may appear to be brighter than another star because it is closer to Earth, when in fact the brightness of the two stars is the same. Ask: **What do we call a star's brightness as seen from Earth?** *(Apparent brightness)* **At a standard distance from Earth?** *(Absolute brightness; astronomers generally use the term luminosity)* **What must astronomers know to calculate a star's absolute brightness?** *(The star's apparent brightness and its distance from Earth)*

Apply Ask: **Why does the sun appear to be the brightest star we see?** *(It is the closest star to Earth.)* **learning modality: verbal**

Monitor Progress _____ **L2**

Oral Presentation Have students explain how to find the composition of a star.

Answers

Figure 7 Lights that are close appear brighter than lights with the same absolute brightness that are farther away.

Reading Checkpoint A device that breaks light into colors and produces an image of the resulting spectrum

Reading Checkpoint The brightness a star would have if it were at a standard distance from Earth

---

Measuring Distances to Stars

Teach Key Concepts $L2$

Light-Years and Parallax

Focus Remind students that a light-year is not a measure of time.

Teach Ask: **Why do astronomers use light-years?** *(Kilometers or miles are not practical units for measuring the large distances in space.)* **What is parallax?** *(The apparent change in position of an object when you look at it from different places)* **How do astronomers use parallax to calculate distance?** *(They measure how much a nearby star appears to move against a background of stars that are farther away.)*

Apply Have students calculate the distance in kilometers of a star two light-years from Earth. *(About 19 million million kilometers)* **learning modality: logical/ mathematical**

All in One Teaching Resources

• Transparency J40

Lab zone Build Inquiry $L3$

Measuring Distances

Materials two protractors, two cardboard shoe boxes, measuring tape

Time 30 minutes

Focus Review how astronomers use parallax to calculate distances.

Teach Provide the following instructions: Tape the straight side of a protractor to the top of the short side of each box. Position the boxes at least 2 m apart. Face the boxes toward a vertical object in the distance, such as a tree. Sight over the protractor, with one eye lined up at the center of the base of the protractor. Move a sharp pencil down along the curved edge of the protractor until the pencil point appears to be lined up with the distant object. Hold the pencil at this spot and read the number of degrees on the protractor. Measure the distance between the two protractors. Make a scale drawing of the triangle formed by the two protractors and the object. From that drawing, measure the scaled distance to the tree and calculate the actual distance.

Apply Ask students to explain how this procedure uses parallax. **learning modality: kinesthetic**

FIGURE 8
Parallax at the Movies
You and your friend are sitting behind a woman with a large hat. **Applying Concepts** *Why is your view of the screen different from your friend's view?*

Your view

Your friend's view

Measuring Distances to Stars

Imagine that you could travel to the stars at the speed of light. To travel from Earth to the sun would take about 8 minutes, not very much time for such a long trip. The next nearest star, Proxima Centauri, is much farther away. A trip to Proxima Centauri at the speed of light would take 4.2 years!

The Light-Year Distances on Earth's surface are often measured in kilometers. However, distances to the stars are so large that kilometers are not very practical units. **Astronomers use a unit called the light-year to measure distances between the stars.** In space, light travels at a speed of about 300,000 kilometers per second. A **light-year** is the distance that light travels in one year, about 9.5 million million kilometers.

Note that the light-year is a unit of distance, not time. To help you understand this, consider an everyday example. If you bicycle at 10 kilometers per hour, it would take you 1 hour to go to a mall 10 kilometers away. You could say that the mall is "1 bicycle-hour" away.

Parallax Standing on Earth looking up at the sky, it may seem as if there is no way to tell how far away the stars are. However, astronomers have found ways to measure those distances. **Astronomers often use parallax to measure distances to nearby stars.**

Parallax is the apparent change in position of an object when you look at it from different places. For example, imagine that you and a friend have gone to a movie. A woman with a large hat sits down in front of you, as shown in Figure 8. Because you and your friend are sitting in different places, the woman's hat blocks different parts of the screen. If you are sitting on her left, the woman's hat appears to be in front of the large dinosaur. But to your friend on the right, she appears to be in front of the bird.

Have the woman and her hat moved? No. But because you changed your position, she appears to have moved. This apparent movement when you look from two different directions is parallax.

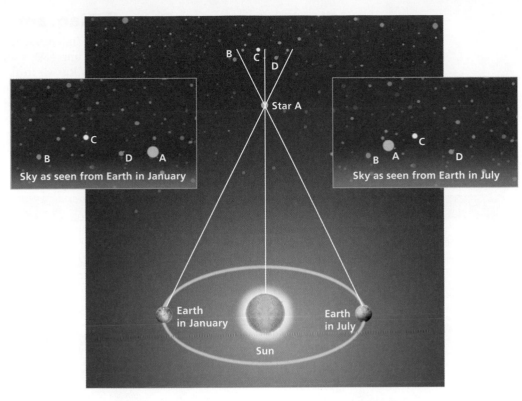

Sky as seen from Earth in January

Sky as seen from Earth in July

Earth in January

Earth in July

Sun

FIGURE 9
Parallax of Stars
The apparent movement of a star when seen from a different position is called parallax. Astronomers use parallax to calculate the distance to nearby stars. Note that the diagram is not to scale.
Interpreting Diagrams *Why do nearby stars appear to change position between January and July?*

Parallax in Astronomy Astronomers are able to measure the parallax of nearby stars to determine their distances. As shown in Figure 9, astronomers look at a nearby star when Earth is on one side of the sun. Then they look at the same star again six months later, when Earth is on the opposite side of the sun. Astronomers measure how much the nearby star appears to move against a background of stars that are much farther away. They can then use this measurement to calculate the distance to the nearby star. The less the nearby star appears to move, the farther away it is.

Astronomers can use parallax to measure distances up to a few hundred light-years from Earth. The parallax of any star that is farther away is too small to measure accurately.

Reading Checkpoint How is parallax useful in astronomy?

Use Visuals: Figure 9
Parallax

Focus Review the definition of parallax.

Teach Have students carefully study the images of the sky as seen in January and in July and describe differences between the two images. (*Star A appears in the right portion of the image taken in January and in the left portion of the image taken in July.*) Have students trace the lines in the diagram with their fingers. Ask: **Why does star A seem to change positions relative to the more distant stars?** (*In July, the star is seen along the straight line that falls between stars B and C. But in January, the star is seen along the straight line that falls to the right of star D.*)

Apply Ask: **What is one limitation of using parallax to measure distances to stars?** (*Parallax cannot be used to measure distances to stars that are more than a few hundred light-years from Earth.*) **learning modality: visual**

Monitor Progress

Drawing Ask each student to think of an example of parallax that he or she can observe in the classroom and draw a diagram to illustrate it. Students can save their drawings in their portfolios.

Portfolio

Answers
Figure 8 Each person is looking at the screen from a different position.
Figure 9 Earth moves, so the nearby stars appear against a different part of the distant background.

Reading Checkpoint Astronomers can use parallax to calculate the distances to nearby stars.

Differentiated Instruction

English Learners/Beginning Comprehension: Modified Cloze L1

Distribute a simplified paragraph about light-years, but leave some strategic words blank. For example, "We measure _____(distance) on Earth in miles and kilometers. But the large distances between stars are measured in units called _____(light-years). This unit is the distance that _____(light) travels in a _____(year). Provide students with a list of the correct answers, and have them fill in each blank with one of those terms. **learning modality: verbal**

English Learners/Intermediate Comprehension: Modified Cloze Have student pairs write simple cloze sentences about measuring distances in space. L2

Students then can trade and complete the sentences. **learning modality: logical/mathematical**

The Hertzsprung-Russell Diagram

Teach Key Concepts L2

Using H-R Diagrams to Classify Stars

Focus Ask students to recall the colors of stars from coolest to hottest.

Teach Refer students to Figure 10. Point out that the H-R diagram is a graph, not a chart. It does not show positions of stars in the sky. Ask: **What is the relationship between surface temperature and brightness for main sequence stars?** (*Surface temperature increases as absolute brightness increases.*) **How do astronomers use the H-R diagram?** (*To classify stars and to understand how stars change over time*)

Apply Ask: **Are the brightest stars always the hottest stars? Explain.** (*No; giants and red supergiants are very bright, but not very hot.*) **learning modality: visual**

All in One Teaching Resources

• Transparency J41

Lab zone Build Inquiry L2

Interpreting the H-R Diagram

Focus Remind students that the surface temperature on the H-R diagram increases from right to left.

Teach Make enlarged copies of the H-R diagram, and distribute them to students. Write the following information on the board, indicating the surface temperature and relative absolute brightness of stars: Star A: 18,000°C, low; Star B: 3,500°C, high; Star C: 5,800°C, middle range. Have students use their copies of the H-R diagram to identify each of these stars. (*Star A: Sirius B; Star B: Betelgeuse; Star C: the sun or Alpha Centauri A*)

Apply Ask students to infer whether a star's placement on the H-R diagram ever changes. (*Yes; it may change as the star's brightness and temperature change.*) **learning modality: visual**

The Hertzsprung-Russell Diagram

About 100 years ago, two scientists working independently made the same discovery. Both Ejnar Hertzsprung (EYE nahr HURT sprung) in Denmark and Henry Norris Russell in the United States made graphs to find out if the temperature and the absolute brightness of stars are related. They plotted the surface temperatures of stars on the *x*-axis and their absolute brightness on the *y*-axis. The points formed a pattern. The graph they made is still used by astronomers today. It is called the **Hertzsprung-Russell diagram,** or H-R diagram.

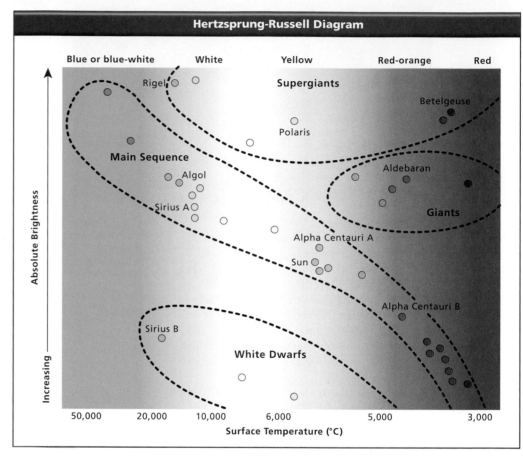

FIGURE 10
The Hertzsprung-Russell diagram shows the relationship between the surface temperature and absolute brightness of stars.
Interpreting Diagrams *Which star has a hotter surface: Rigel or Aldebaran?*

Astronomers use H-R diagrams to classify stars and to understand how stars change over time. As you can see in Figure 10, most of the stars in the H-R diagram form a diagonal area called the **main sequence.** More than 90 percent of all stars, including the sun, are main-sequence stars. Within the main sequence, surface temperature increases as absolute brightness increases. Thus, hot bluish stars are located at the left of an H-R diagram and cooler reddish stars are located at the right of the diagram.

The brightest stars are located near the top of an H-R diagram, while the dimmest stars are located at the bottom. Giant and supergiant stars are very bright. They can be found near the top center and right of the diagram. White dwarfs are hot, but not very bright, so they appear at the bottom left or bottom center of the diagram.

Reading Checkpoint What is the main sequence?

FIGURE 11
Orion
Orion includes the red supergiant Betelgeuse, the blue supergiant Rigel, and many other main sequence and giant stars.

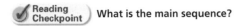

Section 2 Assessment

Target Reading Skill Using Prior Knowledge Review your graphic organizer and revise it based on what you just learned in the section.

Reviewing Key Concepts

1. a. Listing Name three characteristics used to classify stars.
 b. Comparing and Contrasting What is the difference between apparent brightness and absolute brightness?
 c. Applying Concepts Stars A and B have about the same apparent brightness, but Star A is about twice as far from Earth as Star B. Which star has the greater absolute brightness? Explain your answer.
2. a. Measuring What is a light-year?
 b. Defining What is parallax?
 c. Predicting Vega is 25.3 light-years from Earth and Arcturus is 36.7 light-years away. Which star would have a greater parallax? Explain.

3. a. Summarizing What two characteristics of stars are shown in an H-R diagram?
 b. Identifying Identify two ways in which astronomers can use an H-R diagram.
 c. Classifying The star Procyon B has a surface temperature of 6,600° Celsius and an absolute brightness that is much less than the sun's. What type of star is Procyon B? (*Hint:* Refer to the H-R diagram.)

Lab zone At-Home Activity

Observing Orion With adult family members, go outside on a clear, dark night. Determine which way is south. Using the star charts in Appendix B, look for the constellation Orion, which is visible in the evening during winter and spring. Find the stars Betelgeuse and Rigel in Orion and explain to your family why they are different colors.

Lab zone At-Home Activity

Observing Orion L1 Ask students to make sketches of and take notes on their observations. Allow class time for students to share their observations. Encourage students to name and describe any other constellations they have seen. Make sure that students can explain that red stars such as Betelgeuse are cooler than blue stars such as Rigel.

Monitor Progress L2
Answers
Figure 10 Rigel

Reading Checkpoint A diagonal area in an H-R diagram where most stars can be found

Assess

Reviewing Key Concepts
1. a. Any three: Color, temperature, size, mass, composition, and absolute brightness
b. Apparent brightness is the brightness of a star as seen from Earth. Absolute brightness is the brightness a star would have if it were at a standard distance from Earth. **c.** Star A has the greater absolute brightness because it is farther away, yet still appears as bright as Star B.
2. a. The distance that light travels through space in one year **b.** The apparent change in position of an object when viewed from different places **c.** Vega would have a greater parallax because the closer a star is to Earth, the more it appears to move.
3. a. Surface temperature and absolute brightness **b.** Astronomers can use the H-R diagram to classify stars and to understand how stars change over time. **c.** White dwarf

Reteach L1
As a class, list the characteristics used to classify stars. Have students provide examples of how stars are classified according to each factor.

Performance Assessment L2
Oral Presentation Tell students to imagine that they are astronomers studying a recently discovered star. Have them prepare a presentation in which they define the characteristics of the star, compare the star to our sun, and show the placement of the star on the H-R diagram.

All in One Teaching Resources
• Section Summary: *Characteristics of Stars*
• Review and Reinforce: *Characteristics of Stars*
• Enrich: *Characteristics of Stars*

How Far Is That Star? L3

Prepare for Inquiry

Key Concept
Parallax is used to determine the distance to nearby stars. Parallax is an apparent motion resulting from a change in viewing position. The accuracy of the parallax method of measuring star distances decreases as the distance to the star increases.

Skills Objectives
After this lab, students will be able to
- infer the apparent change in position of the dots of light for each star
- calculate the distance to an object by using ratios of measured values
- predict the parallax of an object at different distances

Prep Time 10 minutes
Class Time 40 minutes

Advance Planning
Review ratio calculation before performing the lab. Set up two or three stations.

Safety
⚠ Caution students to be careful when walking around the room so that they do not knock over the lamp or trip on a power cord. Caution them not to look directly into the lamp. Review the safety guidelines in Appendix A.

All in One Teaching Resources
- Lab Worksheet: *How Far Is That Star?*

How Far Is That Star?

Problem
How can parallax be used to determine distances?

Skills Focus
inferring, calculating, predicting

Materials
- masking tape • paper clips • pen
- black and red pencils • metric ruler • paper
- meter stick • calculator
- lamp without a shade, with 100-watt light bulb
- copier paper box (without the lid)
- flat rectangular table, about 1 m wide

Procedure

PART 1 Telescope Model
1. Place the lamp on a table in the middle of the classroom.
2. Carefully use the tip of the pen to make a small hole in the middle of one end of the box. The box represents a telescope.

3. At the front of the classroom, place the box on a flat table so the hole points toward the lamp. Line the left side of the box up with the left edge of the table.
4. Put a small piece of tape on the table below the hole. Use the pen to make a mark on the tape directly below the hole. The mark represents the position of the telescope when Earth is on one side of its orbit.

PART 2 Star 1
5. Label a sheet of paper Star 1 and place it inside the box as shown in the drawing. Hold the paper in place with two paper clips. The paper represents the film in a telescope.
6. Darken the room. Turn on the light to represent the star.
7. With the red pencil, mark the paper where you see a dot of light. Label this dot A. Dot A represents the image of the star on the film.
8. Move the box so the right edge of the box lines up with the right edge of the table. Repeat Step 4. The mark on the tape represents the position of the telescope six months later, when Earth is on the other side of its orbit.

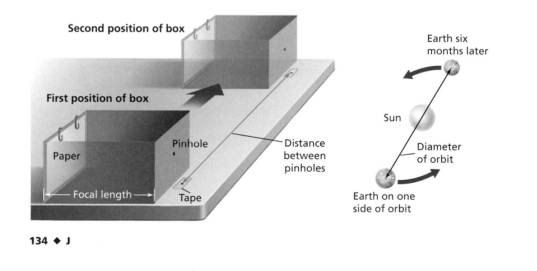

134 ◆ J

Guide Inquiry

Invitation
Ask students to compare the apparent movement of close and distant objects when these are viewed from the window of a moving car. Ask: **Which appears to move faster?** (*Objects close to the car appear to move very fast; objects farther away do not seem to move much at all.*)

Introduce the Procedure
- Demonstrate the measurements students will make, and show them how to mark the star on their "film."
- Set up several stations around the sides of the room. Arrange the tables so that the positions of the box can be as far apart as possible.

Data Table

Star	Parallax Shift (mm)	Focal Length (mm)	Diameter of Orbit (mm)	Calculated Distance to Star (mm)	Calculated Distance to Star (m)	Actual Distance to Star (m)

9. Repeat Step 7, using a black pencil to mark the second dot B. Dot B represents the image of the star as seen 6 months later from the other side of Earth's orbit.

10. Remove the paper. Before you continue, copy the data table into your notebook.

11. Measure and record the distance in millimeters between dots A and B. This distance represents the parallax shift for Star 1.

12. Measure and record the distance from the hole in the box to the lamp. This distance represents the actual distance to the star.

13. Measure and record the distance from the hole (lens) to the back of the box in millimeters. This distance represents the focal length of your telescope.

14. Measure and record the distance in millimeters between the marks on the two pieces of masking tape. This distance represents the diameter of Earth's orbit.

PART 3 Stars 2 and 3

15. Move the lamp away from the table—about half the distance to the back of the room. The bulb now represents Star 2. Predict what you think will happen to the light images on your paper.

16. Repeat Steps 6–12 with a new sheet of paper to find the parallax shift for Star 2.

17. Move the lamp to the back of the classroom. The bulb now represents Star 3. Repeat Steps 6–12 with a new sheet of paper to find the parallax shift for Star 3.

Analyze and Conclude

1. **Inferring** What caused the apparent change in position of the dots of light for each star? Explain.

2. **Calculating** Use the following formula to calculate the distance from the telescope to Star 1.

$$\text{Distance} = \frac{\text{Diameter} \times \text{Focal length}}{\text{Parallax shift}}$$

3. **Calculating** Divide your result from Question 2 by 1,000 to get the distance to the light bulb in meters.

4. **Calculating** Repeat Questions 2 and 3 for Stars 2 and 3.

5. **Predicting** Was your prediction in Step 15 correct? Why or why not?

6. **Interpreting Data** How did your calculation for Star 3 compare with the actual distance? What could you do to improve your results?

7. **Communicating** Write a paragraph that explains how parallax shift varies with distance. Relate each star's parallax shift to its distance from Earth.

Design an Experiment

What would happen if you kept moving the lamp away from the box? Is there a distance at which you can no longer find the distance to the star? Design an experiment to find out.

Make sure that students understand that the length of the box represents the telescope's focal length, the paper represents photographic film, and the marks on the table represent different positions of Earth in its orbit. The light bulb represents the distant star. The distances from the box to the lamp represent distances to the stars. The change in position of the dot images represents the parallax shift.

Expected Outcome
Students will see the dot of light move from one side of the film to the other when they move the box. The dot of light will move a shorter distance when the lamp is farther from the box.

Analyze and Conclude

1. The viewing position changed.

2. The distance to Star 1 is 2,530 mm, according to sample data.

3. 2.53 m

4. Sample data: Star 2—5,060 mm, 5.06 m; Star 3— 10,120 mm, 10.12 m

5. Students who predicted that the dot would move less are correct.

6. See the sample Data Table. The difference was large for Star 3 (10 cm). Possible ways to improve results include repeating the measurements and calculations, making sure that the box does not shift in position, and making sure that the exact images are marked.

7. The parallax shift is smaller for stars that are farther away. The closest star, Star 1, had the greatest shift; and the farthest star, Star 3, had the smallest shift.

Extend Inquiry

Design an Experiment The greater the distance to a star, the smaller the shift in parallax. An experimental design might duplicate the Skills Lab in a gym or hallway, taking measurements at increasing distances until parallax is no longer observable.

Sample Data Table

Star	Parallax Shift (mm)	Focal Length (mm)	Diam. Orbit (mm)	Calc. Dist. Star (mm)	Calc. Dist. Star (m)	Actual Dist. Star (m)
1	80	440	460	2, 530	2.53	2.52
2	40	440	460	5, 060	5.06	5.09
3	20	440	460	10, 120	10.12	10.22

Objectives

After this lesson, students will be able to

J.4.3.1 Explain how a star forms.

J.4.3.2 Identify what determines how long a star will live.

J.4.3.3 Describe what happens to a star when it runs out of fuel.

Target Reading Skill

Sequencing Explain that organizing information from beginning to end helps students understand a step-by-step process.

Answers

This is one possible way to organize the flowchart:

Life Cycle of a Sun-like Star

Protostar forms from a nebula.

↓

A star is born as fusion begins.

↓

The star stays on the main sequence for billions of years.

↓

The star begins to run out of fuel.

↓

The star becomes a red giant, then a white dwarf, then a black dwarf.

All in One Teaching Resources

• Transparency J42

Preteach

Build Background Knowledge L1

How a Campfire Burns

Have volunteers describe the stages of the burning campfire. (*Possible answer: The fire starts with a blaze, then the flames become smaller. Gradually, the fire is reduced to glowing embers.*) Point out that wood is the fuel that feeds the flame. When all of the fuel has been consumed, the flame goes out. In a similar manner, a star goes through a life cycle, during which it produces energy by using up its fuel. A typical star's fuel is hydrogen, which it consumes during the process of nuclear fusion by changing it to helium. Unlike a campfire, however, a star does not simply fade out when it uses up all of its fuel. Instead, a star goes through a series of changes, which students will learn about in this section.

Reading Preview

Key Concepts

• How does a star form?

• What determines how long a star will exist?

• What happens to a star when it runs out of fuel?

Key Terms

• nebula • protostar
• white dwarf • supernova
• neutron star • pulsar
• black hole

Target Reading Skill

Sequencing As you read, make a flowchart like the one below that shows the stages in the life of a star like the sun. Write each step of the process in a separate box in the flowchart in the order that it occurs.

Life Cycle of a Sun-like Star

| Protostar forms from a nebula. |

↓

| A star is born as fusion begins. |

↓

| ⌄⌄⌄ |

Lab zone Discover Activity

What Determines How Long Stars Live?

1. This graph shows how the mass of a star is related to its lifetime—how long the star lives before it runs out of fuel.

2. How long does a star with 0.75 times the mass of the sun live? How long does a star with 3 times the mass of the sun live?

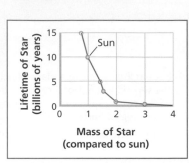

Think It Over

Drawing Conclusions Describe the general relationship between a star's mass and its lifetime.

Imagine that you want to study how people age. You wish you could watch a few people for 50 years, but your project is due next week! You have to study a lot of people for a short time, and classify the people into different age groups. You may come up with groups like *babies, young adults,* and *elderly people.* You don't have time to see a single person go through all these stages, but you know the stages exist.

Astronomers have a similar problem in trying to understand how stars age. They can't watch a single star for billions of years. Instead, they study many stars and other objects in space. Over time, astronomers have figured out that these objects represent different stages in the lives of stars.

◀ Three generations

136 ◆ J

Lab zone Discover Activity

Skills Focus Drawing conclusions L1

Materials none

Time 10 minutes

Tips Point out that a star with 0.75 times the mass of the sun has 75 percent of the sun's mass.

Expected Outcome The star with 0.75 times the sun's mass lives about 15 billion years. The star with 3 times the sun's mass lives less than a billion years.

Think It Over Less massive stars live longer than do more massive stars.

The Lives of Stars

Stars do not last forever. Each star is born, goes through its life cycle, and eventually dies. (Of course, stars are not really alive. The words *born*, *live*, and *die* are just helpful comparisons.)

A Star Is Born All stars begin their lives as parts of nebulas. A **nebula** is a large cloud of gas and dust spread out in an immense volume. A star, on the other hand, is made up of a large amount of gas in a relatively small volume.

In the densest part of a nebula, gravity pulls gas and dust together. A contracting cloud of gas and dust with enough mass to form a star is called a **protostar.** *Proto* means "earliest" in Greek, so a protostar is the earliest stage of a star's life.

A star is born when the contracting gas and dust from a nebula become so dense and hot that nuclear fusion starts. Recall that nuclear fusion is the process by which atoms combine to form heavier atoms. In the sun, for example, hydrogen atoms combine to form helium. During nuclear fusion, enormous amounts of energy are released.

Lifetimes of Stars **How long a star lives depends on its mass.** You might think that stars with more mass would last longer than stars with less mass. But instead, the reverse is true. You can think of stars as being like cars. A small car has a small gas tank, but it also has a small engine that burns gas slowly. A large car has a larger gas tank, but it also has a larger engine that burns gas rapidly. So the small car might be able to travel farther on a tank of gas than the larger car. Small-mass stars use up their fuel more slowly than large-mass stars, so they have much longer lives.

Generally, stars that have less mass than the sun use their fuel slowly, and can live for up to 200 billion years. Medium-mass stars like the sun live for about 10 billion years. Astronomers think the sun is about 4.6 billion years old, so it is almost halfway through its lifetime.

Stars that have more mass than the sun have shorter lifetimes. A star that is 15 times as massive as the sun may live only about ten million years. That may seem like a long time, but it is only one tenth of one percent of the lifetime of the sun.

 Reading Checkpoint How long will a star that is the mass of the sun live?

FIGURE 12
Young Stars
New stars are forming in the nebula on top. The bottom photo shows a protostar in the Orion Nebula. **Applying Concepts** *How do some of the gas and dust in a nebula become a protostar?*

Stars, Galaxies, and the Universe
Video Preview
▶ Video Field Trip
Video Assessment

The Lives of Stars

Video Field Trip

Stars, Galaxies, and the Universe

Show the Video Field Trip to let students experience views of outer space through the Hubble Telescope and understand the fate of dying stars. Discussion question: **What is a pulsar?** *(A pulsar is a spinning neutron star that appears to emit regular pulses of radio waves that can be detected on Earth.)*

Teach Key Concepts ▢L2
Star Life Cycles

Focus Refer students to Figure 12.

Teach Ask students to use the photos to explain how a protostar forms. *(Some of the gas and dust in a nebula, shown on top, contract to form a protostar, shown on the bottom.)* **When is a star born?** *(The contracting gas and dust become so dense and hot that nuclear fusion starts.)* **What determines how long a star lives?** *(Mass; stars with less mass live longer.)*

Apply Ask: **If a star has half the mass of the sun, will it have a shorter or a longer life than the sun?** *(longer)* **learning modality: logical/mathematical**

Independent Practice ▢L2

All in One Teaching Resources

• Guided Reading and Study Worksheet: *Lives of Stars*

◉ **Student Edition on Audio CD**

Monitor Progress ▢L2

Writing Have students describe in their own words how a star is born.

Answers
Figure 12 Gravity causes the gas and dust to contract into a protostar.

 Reading Checkpoint About 10 billion years

Differentiated Instruction

Less Proficient Readers ▢L1
Sequencing the Life Cycles of Stars
Provide students with the Student Edition on Audio CD, and have them listen to the passages The Lives of Stars and Deaths of Stars. Provide photocopies of these passages, and have students follow along as they listen. Ask them to identify steps in the life cycles of stars as they read and mark these steps with a highlighter. Students can use their work to help them complete the flowchart for the section's Target Reading Skill activity. **learning modality: verbal**

Deaths of Stars

Teach Key Concepts L2
Running Out of Fuel

Focus Remind students that stars last millions to billions of years.

Teach Ask: **What happens when a star runs out of fuel?** *(It becomes a white dwarf, a neutron star, or a black hole.)* **What determines which of these three the star becomes?** *(The star's mass)* **How does the life cycle of a high-mass star differ from that of a low-mass star?** *(When a high-mass star runs out of fuel, it explodes. A low-mass star becomes a red giant, forms a planetary nebula, and then becomes a white dwarf.)* **Which stars become black holes?** *(Those that are most massive)*

Apply Tell students that pulsars have been discovered in the remains of supernova explosions. Ask them to explain such observations. *(A massive star went supernova and the core collapsed into a rotating neutron star.)* **learning modality: logical/ mathematical**

Modeling Matter and Empty Space

Materials plastic cup, marbles, sand

Time 5 minutes

Focus Remind students that all matter is primarily empty space.

Teach Fill a plastic cup with marbles, and determine its total weight. Empty the cup, and refill it with sand. Determine its weight again. Ask: **If it is true that glass and sand have nearly the same density, why does the cup weigh more when filled with sand than it does when filled with marbles?** *(There is less empty space between the particles of sand than between the marbles.)*

Apply Explain that when empty space is squeezed out, as in a white dwarf or neutron star, the matter occupies a much smaller area. **learning modality: visual**

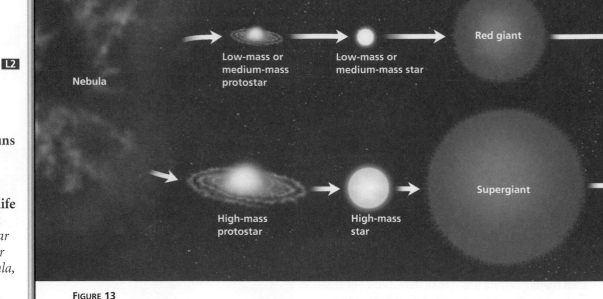

FIGURE 13
The Lives of Stars

A star's life history depends on its mass. A low-mass main-sequence star uses up its fuel slowly and eventually becomes a white dwarf. A high-mass star uses up its fuel quickly. After its supergiant stage, it will explode as a supernova, producing a neutron star or a black hole.
Interpreting Diagrams *What type of star produces a planetary nebula?*

Skills Activity

Predicting
Find Algol, Sirius B, and Polaris in the H-R diagram on page 132. What type of star is each of these now? Predict what the next stage in each star's life will be.

138 ◆ J

Deaths of Stars

When a star begins to run out of fuel, its core shrinks and its outer portion expands. Depending on its mass, the star becomes either a red giant or a supergiant. All main-sequence stars eventually become red giants or supergiants. As shown in Figure 13, red giants and supergiants evolve in very different ways. **After a star runs out of fuel, it becomes a white dwarf, a neutron star, or a black hole.**

White Dwarfs Low-mass stars and medium-mass stars like the sun take billions of years to use up their nuclear fuel. As they start to run out of fuel, their outer layers expand, and they become red giants. Eventually, the outer parts grow larger still and drift out into space, forming a glowing cloud of gas called a planetary nebula. The blue-white core of the star that is left behind cools and becomes a **white dwarf.**

White dwarfs are only about the size of Earth, but they have about as much mass as the sun. Since a white dwarf has the same mass as the sun but only one millionth the volume, it is one million times as dense as the sun. A spoonful of material from a white dwarf has as much mass as a large truck. White dwarfs have no fuel, but they glow faintly from leftover energy. After billions of years, a white dwarf eventually stops glowing. Then it is called a black dwarf.

Reading Checkpoint What is a white dwarf?

Skills Activity

Skills Focus Predicting

Materials none

Time 10 minutes

Tips Have students use Figure 13 to find the next stage. Tell students that a main sequence star may become a red giant or a supergiant.

L2 **Expected Outcome** Algol: main sequence, supergiant; Sirius B: white dwarf, black dwarf; Polaris: supergiant, supernova

Extend Have students identify the next stage for other stars labeled in the H-R diagram. **learning modality: logical/ mathematical**

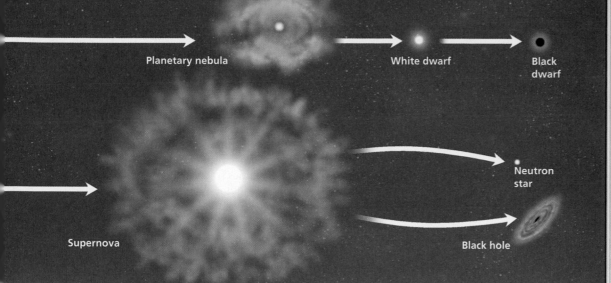

Planetary nebula → White dwarf → Black dwarf

Supernova → Neutron star

→ Black hole

Supernovas The life cycle of a high-mass star is quite different from the life cycle of a low-mass or medium-mass star. High-mass stars quickly evolve into brilliant supergiants. When a supergiant runs out of fuel, it can explode suddenly. Within hours, the star blazes millions of times brighter. The explosion is called a **supernova.** After a supernova, some of the material from the star expands into space. This material may become part of a nebula. This nebula can then contract to form a new, partly recycled star. Astronomers think the sun began as a nebula that contained material from a supernova.

Neutron Stars After a supergiant explodes, some of the material from the star is left behind. This material may form a neutron star. **Neutron stars** are the remains of high-mass stars. They are even smaller and denser than white dwarfs. A neutron star may contain as much as three times the mass of the sun but be only about 25 kilometers in diameter, the size of a city.

In 1967, Jocelyn Bell, a British astronomy student, detected an object in space that appeared to give off regular pulses of radio waves. Some astronomers hypothesized that the pulses might be a signal from an extraterrestrial civilization. At first, astronomers even named the source LGM, for the "Little Green Men" in early science-fiction stories. Soon, however, astronomers concluded that the source of the radio waves was really a rapidly spinning neutron star. Spinning neutron stars are called **pulsars,** short for pulsating radio sources. Some pulsars spin hundreds of times per second!

Go Online
active art

For: The Lives of Stars activity
Visit: PHSchool.com
Web Code: cfp-5043

Chapter 4 J ◆ 139

Differentiated Instruction

Special Needs L1
Demonstrating Stages of a Star's Life
Explain the steps indicated by each arrow in Figure 13. Use movements to represent each stage. For example, you might use the following: Spread your arms quickly and wide for an explosion, extend your arms horizontally to represent expansion, wrap your arms around yourself to indicate condensing or shrinking, and kneel close to the ground to signify running out of fuel. Have students use these movements to compare and contrast the different stages of giant stars and medium-sized stars. **learning modality: kinesthetic**

Go Online
active art

For: The Lives of Stars activity
Visit: PHSchool.com
Web Code: cfp-5043

Students can interact with online art of evolving stars.

Use Visuals: Figure 13 L2
The Lives of Stars

Focus Ask: **What stages, regardless of mass, do all stars have in common?** (*Nebula, protostar, main sequence star*)

Teach Have students read aloud the descriptions of the stages of the life cycle of stars.

Apply Have students use the diagram to complete their flowcharts for the section Target Reading Skill activity. **learning modality: visual**

All in One Teaching Resources
• Transparency J43

Address Misconceptions L2
Pulsars

Focus Many students may think that pulsars actually give off pulses of radio waves.

Teach Explain that neutron stars emit steady beams of radio waves in narrow cones. As the neutron star spins, these beams of radiation appear to turn on and off at regular intervals, like the spinning beacon of a lighthouse. Ask: **Do pulsars really pulse on and off?** (*No, they just appear to pulse as their beam of radio waves sweeps across Earth*)

Apply Have students research the speeds at which pulsars rotate. (*Some can rotate hundreds of times per second, although periods of about 1 second are more common.*) **learning modality: verbal**

Monitor Progress L2

Drawing Have students compare and contrast white dwarfs, neutron stars, and black holes by drawing sketches with labels that indicate size and other characteristics. Students can save their drawings in their portfolios.

Portfolio

Answer
Figure 13 A low-mass or medium-mass star that has evolved into a red giant

Reading Checkpoint The remaining core of a low- or medium-mass star

Monitor Progress

L2

Answers

Figure 14 They can use X-ray telescopes to detect X-rays coming from hot gas near the black hole and infer that a black hole is present. They can also detect a black hole by observing its gravitational effect on a nearby star.

Reading Checkpoint An object with gravity so strong that nothing, not even light, can escape

Assess

Reviewing Key Concepts

1. a. A large cloud of gas and dust spread out in an immense volume **b.** Gravity pulls some of the gas and dust in the densest part of a nebula together, eventually forming a protostar. When the contracting gas and dust become very dense and hot, nuclear fusion begins and a star is born. **c.** A protostar is contracting cloud of gas and dust with enough mass to form a star; nuclear fusion does not yet take place in a protostar.

2. a. Its mass **b.** Shorter

3. a. A white dwarf is the blue-white core of a star that was once a red giant. It differs from a neutron star in that it evolves from low-mass stars or medium-mass stars, whereas neutron stars evolve from high-mass stars. **b.** The mass of the original star determines whether it becomes a white dwarf, a neutron star, or a black hole. **c.** When the sun runs out of fuel, its outer layers will expand and it will become a red giant. Eventually, the outer layers of the red giant will drift into space and the remaining hot core will be a white dwarf.

Reteach

L1

Use Figure 13 to summarize the life cycles of stars with different masses.

Performance Assessment

L2

Writing Have students write short biographies that detail the life cycle of a medium-mass star. Encourage students to focus on details to make the story interesting.

All in One Teaching Resources
- Section Summary: *Lives of Stars*
- Review and Reinforce: *Lives of Stars*
- Enrich: *Lives of Stars*

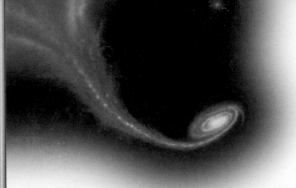

FIGURE 14
Black Holes
The remains of the most massive stars collapse into black holes. This artist's impression shows a black hole pulling matter from a companion star. The material glows as it is pulled into the black hole. **Applying Concepts** *If it is impossible to detect a black hole directly, how do astronomers find them?*

Black Holes The most massive stars—those having more than 40 times the mass of the sun—may become black holes when they die. A **black hole** is an object with gravity so strong that nothing, not even light, can escape. After a very massive star dies in a supernova explosion, more than five times the mass of the sun may be left. The gravity of this mass is so strong that the gas is pulled inward, packing the gas into a smaller and smaller space. The gas becomes so densely packed that its intense gravity will not allow even light to escape. The remains of the star have become a black hole.

No light, radio waves, or any other form of radiation can ever get out of a black hole, so it is not possible to detect a black hole directly. But astronomers can detect black holes indirectly. For example, gas near a black hole is pulled so strongly that it revolves faster and faster around the black hole. Friction heats the gas up. Astronomers can detect X-rays coming from the hot gas and infer that a black hole is present. Similarly, if another star is near a black hole, astronomers can calculate the mass of the black hole from the effect of its gravity on the star. Scientists have detected dozens of star-size black holes with the Chandra X-ray Observatory. They have also detected huge black holes that are millions or billions of times the sun's mass.

Reading Checkpoint What is a black hole?

Section 3 Assessment

Target Reading Skill **Sequencing** Refer to your flowchart as you answer the questions.

Reviewing Key Concepts

1. a. Defining What is a nebula?
   b. Explaining How does a star form from a nebula?
   c. Comparing and Contrasting How is a protostar different from a star?
2. a. Identifying What factor determines how long a star lives?
   b. Applying Concepts A star is twice as massive as the sun. Will its lifespan be longer, shorter, or the same as that of the sun?
3. a. Comparing and Contrasting What is a white dwarf? How is it different from a neutron star?

b. Relating Cause and Effect Why do some stars become white dwarfs and others become neutron stars or black holes?
c. Predicting What will happen to the sun when it runs out of fuel? Explain.

Writing in Science

Descriptive Paragraph Write a description of one of the stages in the life of a star, such as a nebula, red giant, supernova, or white dwarf. Include information on how it formed and what will happen next in the star's evolution.

Lab zone Chapter Project

Keep Students on Track Confirm that students are in the process of sketching their own constellations. Suggest that they come up with several ideas before deciding on one pattern and name. Allow students to work in small groups to brainstorm ideas. Have them explain how they chose the names for their constellations.

Writing in Science

Writing Mode Description
Scoring Rubric
4 Exceeds criteria, including a vivid and detailed description of the stage, its formation, and its future stages
3 Meets all criteria, but details are sparse or uninteresting
2 Includes only one stage
1 Is inaccurate and incomplete

Reading Preview

Key Concepts
- What is a star system?
- What are the major types of galaxies?
- How do astronomers describe the scale of the universe?

Key Terms
- binary star
- eclipsing binary • open cluster
- globular cluster • galaxy
- spiral galaxy • elliptical galaxy
- irregular galaxy • quasar
- universe • scientific notation

Target Reading Skill
Building Vocabulary Carefully read the definition of each key term. Also read the neighboring sentences. Then write a definition of each key term in your own words.

Lab zone Discover Activity

Why Does the Milky Way Look Hazy?

1. Using a pencil, carefully poke at least 20 holes close together in a sheet of white paper.
2. Tape the paper to a chalkboard or dark-colored wall.
3. Go to the other side of the room and look at the paper. From the far side of the room, what do the dots look like? Can you see individual dots?

Think It Over
Making Models How is looking at the paper from the far side of the room like trying to see many very distant stars that are close together? How does your model compare to the photograph of the Milky Way below?

On a clear, dark night in the country, you can see a hazy band of light stretched across the sky. This band of stars is called the Milky Way. It looks as if the Milky Way is very far away. Actually, though, Earth is inside the Milky Way! The Milky Way looks milky or hazy from Earth because the stars are too close together for your eyes to see them individually. The dark blotches in the Milky Way are clouds of dust that block light from stars behind them.

The Milky Way

J ◆ 141

Section 4
Star Systems and Galaxies

Objectives
After this lesson, students will be able to
J.4.4.1 Define a star system.
J.4.4.2 Identify the major types of galaxies.
J.4.4.3 Explain how astronomers describe the scale of the universe.

Target Reading Skill

Building Vocabulary Explain that knowing the definitions of key-concept words helps students understand what they read.

Answers
When students write the definitions, ask them to underline the most important features. Example: An eclipsing binary is a two-star system in which <u>one star cannot be seen</u> at times because the other star <u>blocks the light</u>.

All in One Teaching Resources
- Guided Reading Study Worksheet: *Star Systems and Galaxies, Use Target Reading Skills*

Preteach

Build Background Knowledge L2
Optical Illusions
Invite students to share their experiences with optical illusions. Point out that an optical illusion tricks the eye; the object appears to be different than it actually is. Ask students to recall that stars in constellations are optical illusions because they appear to be next to one another, but they are actually at widely different distances from Earth.

Lab zone Discover Activity

Skills Focus Making models

Materials pencil, paper, tape

Time 15 minutes

Tips Have students predict what the holes will look like when observed from the other side of the room.

Expected Outcome Students will not be able to see the individual dots from the far side of the room.

L1 **Think It Over** Looking at the holes on the paper from a distance is like looking at stars because they blur together, just as the stars do. Like the stars that are close together in the photograph of the Milky Way, the model is hazy when viewed from far away.

Star Systems and Clusters

Teach Key Concepts   L2
Eclipsing Binary

Focus Remind students that an eclipse occurs when one body in space blocks light from another.

Teach As students examine Figure 15, ask: **What is a group of two or more stars called?** *(A star system)* **What are double stars often called?** *(Binary stars)* Ask: **What would be the positions of the bright star in Algol, its dim companion star, and Earth when Algol appears less bright?** *(The companion star would be passing between the bright star and Earth.)*

Apply Ask: **How might life on Earth be different if our sun were part of a binary system?** *(Possible answers: there would be two suns in the sky at times; the other sun might be farther away, for example near Jupiter's orbit, so that sometimes Earth would be in sunlight both day and "night." Accept all reasonable responses.)* **learning modality: logical/ mathematical**

Help Students Read   L1
Anticipation Guide Refer to the Content Refresher for guidance on this reading skill. Before students read this section and the next, write these statements on the board:
- **Planets exist around many stars.**
- **The inner planets have compositions that are much different from those of the outer planets.**

Ask students whether they agree with the statements. Discuss their responses, and then have students read the sections and evaluate their initial answers.

Independent Practice   L2
All in One Teaching Resources
- Guided Reading and Study Worksheet: *Star Systems and Galaxies*

⊙ **Student Edition on Audio CD**

FIGURE 15
Invisible Partners
If you saw someone dancing but couldn't see a partner, you could infer that the partner was there by watching the dancer you could see. Astronomers use a similar method to detect faint stars in star systems.

FIGURE 16
Eclipsing Binary
Algol is an eclipsing binary star system consisting of a bright star and a dim companion. Each time the dimmer star passes in front of the brighter one, Algol appears less bright.
Interpreting Diagrams *When does Algol appear brighter?*

142 ◆ J

Star Systems and Clusters

Our solar system has only one star, the sun. But this is not the most common situation for stars. **Most stars are members of groups of two or more stars, called star systems.** If you were on a planet in one of these star systems, at times you might see two or more suns in the sky! At other times, one or more of these suns would be below the horizon.

Multiple Star Systems Star systems that have two stars are called double stars or **binary stars.** (The prefix *bi* means "two.") Those with three stars are called triple stars. The nearby star Proxima Centauri may be part of a triple star system. The other two stars in the system, Alpha Centauri A and Alpha Centauri B, form a double star. Scientists are not sure whether Proxima Centauri is really part of the system or is just passing close to the other two stars temporarily.

Often one star in a binary star is much brighter and more massive than the other. Astronomers can sometimes detect a binary star even if only one of the stars can be seen from Earth. Astronomers can often tell that there is a dim star in a binary system by observing the effects of its gravity. As the dim companion star revolves around a bright star, the dim star's gravity causes the bright star to wobble back and forth. Imagine watching a pair of dancers who are twirling each other around. Even if one dancer were invisible, you could tell that the invisible dancer was there from watching the motion of the visible dancer.

Eclipsing Binaries A wobble is not the only clue that a star has a dim companion. A dim star in a binary star may pass in front of a brighter star and eclipse it. From Earth, the binary star would suddenly look much dimmer. A system in which one star periodically blocks the light from another is called an **eclipsing binary.** As Figure 16 shows, the star Algol is actually an eclipsing binary star system.

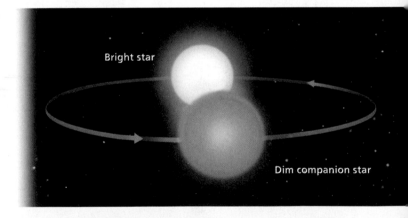

Bright star

Dim companion star

Planets Around Other Stars In 1995, astronomers first discovered a planet revolving around another ordinary star. They used a method similar to the one used in studying binary stars. The astronomers observed that a star was moving slightly toward and away from us. They knew that the invisible object causing the movement didn't have enough mass to be a star. They inferred that it must be a planet.

Since then, astronomers have discovered more than 100 planets around other stars, and new ones are being discovered all of the time. Most of these new planets are very large, with at least half of the mass of Jupiter. A small planet would be hard to detect because it would have little gravitational effect on the star it orbited.

Could there be life on planets in other solar systems? Some scientists think it is possible. A few astronomers are using radio telescopes to search for signals that could not have come from natural sources. Such a signal might be evidence that an extra-terrestrial civilization was sending out radio waves.

Star Clusters Many stars belong to larger groupings called star clusters. All of the stars in a particular cluster formed from the same nebula at about the same time and are about the same distance from Earth.

There are two major types of star clusters: open clusters and globular clusters. **Open clusters** have a loose, disorganized appearance and contain no more than a few thousand stars. They often contain many bright supergiants and much gas and dust. In contrast, **globular clusters** are large groupings of older stars. Globular clusters are round and densely packed with stars—some may contain more than a million stars.

✓ **Reading Checkpoint** What is a globular cluster?

FIGURE 17
Star Clusters
The stars in a globular cluster (above) are all about the same age and the same distance from Earth. The Pleiades (left), also called the *Seven Sisters*, is an open cluster.

Chapter 4 J ◆ 143

Lab zone Teacher **Demo** L1

Planets Around Other Stars

Materials lamp with incandescent bulb, light bulbs of various wattages, plastic foam balls of three sizes, wire coat hangers, metal snips, rulers, textbooks

Time 20 minutes

Focus Have students consider this statement: *Trying to observe a planet next to a distant star is like trying to spot a firefly next to a street light.*

Teach Before class, remove the lampshade from a lamp. Straighten a wire hanger, leaving the crook at one end. Snip the wire to a length of 12 cm, measuring from the crook. Discard the remaining straight section. Do the same for three other wire hangers, snipping them to lengths of 24 cm, 36 cm, and 48 cm. Insert the unbent end of each hanger in a foam ball—all of the balls should be the same size. To perform the demonstration, place the lamp in front of the classroom so that all of the students can see it. Twist all of the hangers around the neck of the lamp, and tell students to observe the balls. Ask: **Which "planet" is easiest to see?** (*The one farthest from the light*) **Which planet is hardest to see?** (*The one closest to the light*) Have students hold up a book or another object to block the light. Discuss how this affects what they can see. Using other ball sizes, repeat the demonstration and compare the results.

Apply Try the demonstration with different bulb wattages. Have students relate their observations to the brightness of stars.
learning modality: visual

Differentiated Instruction

Less Proficient Readers L1
Identifying Main Ideas Have students each write a sentence that describes the main idea for each subheading in "Star Systems and Clusters." Encourage students to write the sentences in their own words and illustrate their main ideas. **learning modality: verbal**

Special Needs L1
Inferring To help students understand why scientists are looking for radio signals from space, ask: **Why don't scientists use optical telescopes to look for intelligent life on other planets?** (*The planets are so far away that signs of life wouldn't be visible through an optical telescope.*) **learning modality: logical/mathematical**

Monitor Progress L2

Oral Presentation Ask students to explain why some scientists think life on planets outside our solar system is possible.

Answers
Figure 15 When the dim companion star no longer prevents the bright star's light from reaching Earth

✓ **Reading Checkpoint** A large grouping of older stars

J ● 143

Galaxies

Teach Key Concepts L2
Types of Galaxies

Focus Point out that classification systems help scientists organize and analyze events or objects so that these items are easier to study and discuss.

Teach Ask: **Which type of galaxy looks like a flattened or round ball?** *(Elliptical)* **Which type of galaxy has a bulge in the middle and arms that look like pinwheels?** *(Spiral)* **Which type of galaxy does not have a regular shape?** *(Irregular)* **Which type of galaxy is the Milky Way?** *(Spiral)*

Apply Tell students that just as Earth revolves around the sun, so the sun revolves around the Milky Way. It takes about 220 million years for our solar system to complete one revolution. **learning modality: verbal**

Help Students Read
Relate Cause and Effect Cause-and-effect relationships are the basis of scientific discovery. However, some students may not fully understand the nature of the cause-and-effect relationship. To reinforce the concept, ask: **What causes quasars to shine so brightly?** *(Quasars are active young galaxies with giant black holes at their centers. As enormous amounts of gas revolve around the black hole, the gas heats up and shines brightly.)*

FIGURE 18
Types of Galaxies
There are three major types of galaxies: spiral, elliptical, and irregular.

Galaxies

A **galaxy** is a huge group of single stars, star systems, star clusters, dust, and gas bound together by gravity. There are billions of galaxies in the universe. The largest galaxies have more than a trillion stars. **Astronomers classify most galaxies into the following types: spiral, elliptical, and irregular.** Figure 18 shows examples of these three.

Spiral Galaxies Some galaxies appear to have a bulge in the middle and arms that spiral outward, like pinwheels. Such galaxies are called **spiral galaxies.** The spiral arms contain many bright, young stars as well as gas and dust. Most new stars in spiral galaxies form in these spiral arms. Relatively few new stars are forming in the central bulge. Some spiral galaxies, called barred-spiral galaxies, have a huge bar-shaped region of stars and gas that passes through their center.

Elliptical Galaxies Not all galaxies have spiral arms. **Elliptical galaxies** look like round or flattened balls. These galaxies contain billions of stars but have little gas and dust between the stars. Because there is little gas or dust, stars are no longer forming. Most elliptical galaxies contain only old stars.

Irregular Galaxies Some galaxies do not have regular shapes. These are known as **irregular galaxies.** Irregular galaxies are typically smaller than other types of galaxies. They generally have many bright, young stars and lots of gas and dust to form new stars.

Quasars In the 1960s, astronomers discovered objects that are very bright, but also very far away. Many of these objects are 10 billion light-years or more away, making them among the most distant objects in the universe. These distant, enormously bright objects looked almost like stars. Since *quasi* means "something like" in Latin, these objects were given the name quasi-stellar objects, or **quasars.**

What could be so bright at such a great distance from Earth? Astronomers have concluded that quasars are active young galaxies with giant black holes at their centers. Each of these black holes has a mass a billion times or more as great as that of the sun. As enormous amounts of gas revolve around the black hole, the gas heats up and shines brightly.

 **Reading Checkpoint** What is a quasar?

Differentiated Instruction

Gifted and Talented L3
Interpreting Pictures Ask students to illustrate the three types of galaxies by accessing pictures on the NASA Web site. Have students use information from NASA to label the parts of the galaxies. **learning modality: visual**

Gifted and Talented L3
Researching *Voyager* Ask students to learn the history and mission of the *Voyager* space probes and to give a description of the messages that these vehicles are carrying into space to any form of life. Have students develop their own messages. Tell students that these probes are now the most distant human-made objects in the universe. **learning modality: verbal**

Side view

Sun's location

Top view

Sun's location

About 100,000 light-years

FIGURE 19
Structure of the Milky Way
From the side, the Milky Way appears to be a narrow disk with a bulge in the middle. The galaxy's spiral structure is visible only from above or below the galaxy.
Interpreting Diagrams *Where in the galaxy is the sun located?*

The Milky Way

Our solar system is located in a spiral galaxy called the Milky Way. As Figure 19 shows, the shape of the Milky Way varies depending on your vantage point. From the side, the Milky Way would look like a narrow disk with a large bulge in the middle. But from the top or bottom, the Milky Way would have a spiral, pinwheel shape. You can't see the spiral shape of the Milky Way from Earth because our solar system is inside the galaxy in one of the spiral arms.

The Milky Way is usually thought of as a standard spiral galaxy. However, some evidence suggests that the Milky Way may be a barred-spiral galaxy instead.

When you see the Milky Way at night during the summer, you are looking toward the center of our galaxy. The center of the galaxy is about 25,000 light-years away, but it is hidden from view by large clouds of dust and gas. However, astronomers can study the center using X-rays, infrared radiation, and radio waves.

Reading Checkpoint How far away is the center of the galaxy?

Lab zone **Try This Activity**

A Spiral Galaxy
You can make a model of our galaxy.

1. Using pipe cleaners, make a pinwheel with two spirals.
2. View the spirals along the surface of the table. Sketch what you see.
3. Next, view the spirals from above the table and sketch them.

Observing The sun is inside a flat spiral galaxy. From Earth's position on the flat surface, is it possible to get a good view of stars in the spiral arms? Why or why not?

Lab zone **Try This Activity**

Skills Focus Observing

Materials pipe cleaners

Time 20 minutes

Tip Suggest that students make their pinwheels as flat as possible.

L1

Expected Outcome You cannot get a good view of stars in the spiral arms of Earth's galaxy because you are inside this galaxy, looking at it edge-on.

Extend Invite students to make models of elliptical and irregular galaxies. Ask students to speculate what observers on planets within these galaxies would see. **learning modality: visual**

The Milky Way

Teach Key Concepts

The Enormous Number of Stars in the Milky Way   **L2**

Focus Tell students that the Milky Way Galaxy may contain up to 400 billion stars and that this number is sometimes hard for people to imagine.

Teach Ask: **How many zeros are in 400 billion?** *(Eleven)* If students have difficulty answering, ask them how many zeros are in one million. *(Six)* Ask: **When you add three zeros to that, what do you get?** *(One billion)* Tell students that 400 has two more zeros, so 400 billion has nine plus two, or eleven zeros.

Apply Give students an idea of the enormity of the above number. Ask: **How long would it take to count the stars in the Milky Way if you count at the rate of one star per second?** *(60 × 60 × 24 = 86,400 seconds in one day; 86,400 × 365 = 31,536,000 seconds in one year; 400,000,000,000 ÷ 31,536,000 = approx 12,684 years)* **learning modality: logical/ mathematical**

All in One **Teaching Resources**
• Transparency J44

Monitor Progress   **L2**

Skills Check Have students make tables comparing and contrasting different types of galaxies, including the shapes and the ages of stars found in each. Students can save their tables in their portfolios.

Portfolio

Answers
Figure 19 On a spiral arm, about 25,000 light-years out from the center of the galaxy

Reading Checkpoint A distant, enormously bright object in space that looks almost like a star

Reading Checkpoint 25,000 light-years

The Scale of the Universe

Teach Key Concepts L2

Scientific Notation

Focus Write a very large number on the board, such as 400,000,000,000.

Teach Point out that very large numbers are difficult to work with. Ask: **Why do scientists use scientific notation?** *(They often use very large or very small numbers; scientific notation makes it easier to work with such numbers.)* **How would you write the number on the board in scientific notation?** *(4×10^{11})*

Apply Ask students to infer how scientific notation is used for numbers that are very small. *(A number that is very small, such as 0.000013, would be written as 1.3×10^{-5}.)*
learning modality: logical/mathematical

Math Skill Decimals

Focus Remind students that because a light-year is a unit of measurement, it does not have to be converted to kilometers to express distance.

Teach Make sure that students place the decimal point after the last digit before moving it to the left. In the example, the decimal point would be placed after the zero before moving it three spaces. Advise students to check the answer by moving the decimal point to the right the number of spaces indicated by the superscript. The result should be the original number.

Answer
2.2×10^{8}

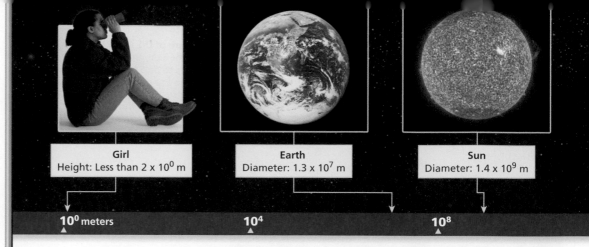

Girl
Height: Less than 2×10^0 m

Earth
Diameter: 1.3×10^7 m

Sun
Diameter: 1.4×10^9 m

10^0 meters 10^4 10^8

Scientific Notation

The bright star Deneb is about 3,230 light-years from Earth. To express this number in scientific notation, first insert a decimal point in the original number so that you have a number between one and ten. In this case, the number is 3.23.

To determine the power of 10, count the number of places that the decimal point moved. Here the decimal point moved three places.

3,230 light-years =
3.23×10^3 light-years

Practice Problem The sun takes about 220,000,000 years to revolve once around the center of the galaxy. Express this length of time in scientific notation.

The Scale of the Universe

Astronomers define the **universe** as all of space and everything in it. The universe is enormous, almost beyond imagination. Astronomers study objects as close as the moon and as far away as quasars. They study incredibly large objects, such as galaxies that are millions of light-years across. They also study the behavior of tiny particles, such as the atoms within stars. **Since the numbers astronomers use are often very large or very small, they frequently use scientific notation to describe sizes and distances in the universe.**

Scientific Notation Scientific notation uses powers of ten to write very large or very small numbers in shorter form. Each number is written as the product of a number between 1 and 10 and a power of 10. For example: 1,200 is written as 1.2×10^3. One light-year is about 9,500,000,000,000,000 meters. Since there are 15 digits after the first digit, in scientific notation this number is written as 9.5×10^{15} meters.

The Immensity of Space The structures in the universe vary greatly in scale. To understand the scale of these structures, imagine that you are going on a journey through the universe. Refer to Figure 20 as you take your imaginary trip. Start at the left with something familiar—a girl looking through binoculars. She is about 1.5 meters tall. Now shift to the right and change the scale by 10,000,000 or 10^7. You're now close to the diameter of Earth, 1.28×10^7 meters. As you move from left to right across Figure 20, the scale increases. The diameter of the sun is about 100 times that of Earth.

Cat's Eye Nebula
Diameter: 3×10^{16} m

Andromeda Galaxy
Diameter: 2×10^{21} m

Virgo Supercluster
Diameter: 9×10^{23} m

10^{16} 10^{20} 10^{24}

Beyond the solar system, the sizes of observable objects become much larger. For example, within our galaxy, the beautiful Cat's Eye Nebula is about 3×10^{16} meters across.

Beyond our galaxy are billions of other galaxies, many of which contain billions of stars. For example, the nearby spiral galaxy Andromeda is about 2×10^{21} meters across. The Milky Way is part of a cluster of 50 or so galaxies called the Local Group. The Local Group is part of the Virgo Supercluster, which contains hundreds of galaxies. The size of the observable universe is about 10^{10} light years, or 10^{26} meters.

FIGURE 20
Scientific Notation
Scientists often use scientific notation to help describe the vast sizes and distances in space.
Calculating About how many times larger is the Cat's Eye Nebula than Earth?

Section 4 Assessment

Target Reading Skill **Building Vocabulary** Use your definitions to help answer the questions.

Reviewing Key Concepts

1. a. **Defining** What is a binary star?
   b. **Classifying** Are all binary stars part of star systems? Explain.
   c. **Applying Concepts** Some binary stars are called eclipsing binaries. Explain why this term is appropriate. (*Hint:* Think about Algol as you write your answer.)
2. a. **Listing** Name the main types of galaxies.
   b. **Classifying** What type of galaxy is the Milky Way?
   c. **Classifying** Suppose astronomers discover a galaxy that contains only old stars. What type of galaxy is it likely to be?

3. a. **Reviewing** What is scientific notation?
   b. **Explaining** How is scientific notation useful to astronomers?
   c. **Calculating** How large is the Cat's Eye Nebula in light-years? (*Hint:* Refer to Figure 20.)

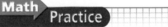

4. **Scientific Notation** The star Betelgeuse has a diameter of 940,000,000 km. Betelgeuse is 427 light-years from Earth. Write each of these figures in scientific notation.

Monitor Progress _____ L2

Answers
Figure 20 about 2.3×10^9 times larger

Assess

Reviewing Key Concepts

1. a. A star system with two stars **b.** Yes; any group of two or more stars makes up a star system. **c.** One of the stars in the eclipsing binary system periodically blocks light from—or eclipses—the other star.
2. a. Spiral, elliptical, and irregular **b.** Spiral or barred-spiral **c.** Elliptical
3. a. A system that uses powers of ten to write very large or very small numbers in shorter form **b.** Astronomers use scientific notation to help describe the vast distances and sizes found in space. **c.** About 3.2 light-years

4. **Math Practice** **a.** 9.4×10^8 km; 4.27×10^2 light-years

Reteach   L1
Write the words *star*, *star system*, *star cluster*, and *galaxy* on the board. Work with students to define and rank each according to size.

Performance Assessment   L2
Skills Check Ask students to work in pairs to model a binary star system. Have students use key terms to explain their models.

All in One Teaching Resources
- Section Summary: *Star Systems and Galaxies*
- Review and Reinforce: *Star Systems and Galaxies*
- Enrich: *Star Systems and Galaxies*

Lab zone   Chapter Project

Keep Students on Track Encourage students to complete their rough drafts and then exchange their stories for peer review before they start editing. Advise students to ask questions as they review the drafts, such as "Does the introduction grab the reader's interest? Does the story make sense? Are more details needed?"

Section 5 — The Expanding Universe

Objectives
After this lesson, students will be able to
J.4.5.1 State the big bang theory.
J.4.5.2 Explain how the solar system formed.
J.4.5.3 Describe what astronomers predict about the future of the universe.

Target Reading Skill

Identifying Supporting Evidence Explain that identifying supporting evidence helps students understand the relationship between the evidence and the theory.

Answer
One possible way to complete the graphic organizer:

Evidence:
Moving Galaxies: All galaxies are moving away from us and from one other.
Cosmic Background Radiation: This glow comes from thermal energy left over from the big bang explosion.

All in One Teaching Resources
• Transparency J45

Preteach

Build Background Knowledge   L2
Expanding Explosion
Ask students who have seen a fireworks display to describe a single rocket exploding in the sky. Ask: **After the rocket explodes, in what direction do the particles move?** Guide students to see that the particles move away from one another. Ask: **What do you think would happen if the particles from the explosion did not burn out and fade?** *(Possible answer: They would probably keep moving away from one another until they hit the ground or something on their way to the ground.)*

Reading Preview

Key Concepts
• What is the big bang theory?
• How did the solar system form?
• What do astronomers predict about the future of the universe?

Key Terms
• big bang • Hubble's law
• cosmic background radiation
• solar nebula • planetesimal
• dark matter • dark energy

Target Reading Skill
Identifying Supporting Evidence As you read, identify the evidence that supports the big bang theory. Write the evidence in a graphic organizer like the one below.

Theory — Big bang
Evidence — Moving galaxies

Lab zone Discover Activity

How Does the Universe Expand?
1. Use a marker to put 10 dots on an empty balloon. The dots represent galaxies.
2. Blow up the balloon. What happens to the distances between galaxies that are close together? Galaxies that are far apart?

Think It Over
Inferring If the universe is expanding, do galaxies that are close together move apart faster or slower than galaxies that are far apart? Explain.

The Andromeda Galaxy is the most distant object that the human eye can see. Light from this galaxy has traveled for about 3 million years before reaching Earth. When that light finally reaches your eye, you are seeing how the galaxy looked 3 million years ago. It is as though you are looking back in time.

Astronomers have photographed galaxies that are billions of light-years away. Light from these galaxies traveled for billions of years before it reached Earth. From these observations, astronomers are able to infer the age of the universe.

How the Universe Formed
Astronomers theorize that the universe began billions of years ago. At that time, the part of the universe we can now see was no larger than the period at the end of this sentence. This tiny universe was incredibly hot and dense. The universe then exploded in what astronomers call the **big bang.**

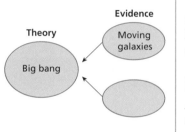

◄ Nearly every visible object in this image is a distant galaxy.

Lab zone Discover Activity

Skills Focus Inferring
Materials balloon, felt-tip marker
Time 10 minutes
Tips Make sure that students mark the balloon before inflating it. Advise students to mark some dots close together and some farther apart.

L1 Expected Outcome The dots on the balloon spread apart as the balloon expands.

Think It Over As the universe expands, galaxies that are closer together move apart more slowly than galaxies that are farther apart.

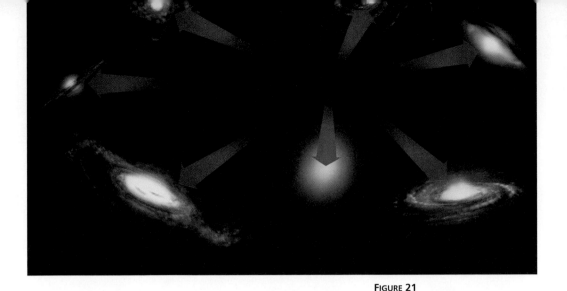

According to the big bang theory, the universe formed in an instant, billions of years ago, in an enormous explosion. Since the big bang, the size of the universe has been increasing rapidly. The universe is billions of times larger now than it was early in its history.

As the universe expanded, it gradually cooled. After a few hundred thousand years, atoms formed. About 200 million years after the big bang, the first stars and galaxies formed.

If the big bang theory is accurate, what evidence might you expect to find in today's universe? You might expect that the matter that had been hurled apart by the big bang would still be moving apart. You might also expect to find evidence of energy left over from the explosion.

Moving Galaxies An American astronomer, Edwin Hubble, discovered important evidence that later helped astronomers to develop the big bang theory. In the 1920s, Hubble studied the spectrums of many galaxies at various distances from Earth. By examining a galaxy's spectrum, Hubble could tell how fast the galaxy is moving and whether it is moving toward our galaxy or away from it.

Hubble discovered that, with the exception of a few nearby galaxies, all galaxies are moving away from us and from each other. Hubble found that there is a relationship between the distance to a galaxy and its speed. **Hubble's law** states that the farther away a galaxy is, the faster it is moving away from us. Hubble's law strongly supports the big bang theory.

Instruct

How the Universe Formed

Teach Key Concepts   L2
The Big Bang Theory

Focus Have students imagine that they can see ripples on a pond, moving out in rings from a center. Point out that they do not know what disturbed the pond to make the ring. Ask: **How do you know that a rock was thrown in or that a fish came up and touched the surface?** (*You can see the rings extending from a point of contact.*)

Teach Tell students that astronomers look for indirect evidence in the same way to support the big bang theory. Ask: **What theory describes the formation of the universe?** (*The big bang*) **What does this theory state?** (*The universe formed in an instant from an enormous explosion.*) **What evidence would support the big bang theory?** (*Matter that had been hurled apart by the big bang would still be moving apart, and energy produced by the explosion would be detectable.*)

Apply Remind students that scientific theories are hypotheses that have been supported by many independent observations or experiments. Emphasize that theories are subject to change as additional evidence becomes available. **learning modality: verbal**

All in One Teaching Resources
• Transparency J46

Independent Practice   L2

All in One Teaching Resources
• Guided Reading and Study Worksheet: *The Expanding Universe*

Student Edition on Audio CD

Differentiated Instruction

Special Needs   L1
Interpreting Light-Years Students may have difficulty with the concept that we see distant stars as they were in the past, not as they are in the present. Remind students that if a star is five light-years away, its light would take five years to reach Earth. Ask:

How long would it take light from a star that is 100 light-years from Earth to reach Earth? (*100 years*) When we look at this star, do we see it as it is now? (*No, we see it as it was 100 years ago.*) **learning modality: logical/mathematical**

Monitor Progress   L2

Drawing Have students draw their own versions of the big bang. Then give students reference materials that illustrate the big bang. Have students compare their drawings to the illustrations and revise their drawings if necessary.

Math Skill Making and interpreting graphs

Focus Remind students that graphs show a relationship between two or more factors.

Teach Advise students to use the lines across the graph to help them identify the x and y values for each point.

Answers
1. About 2.5 billion light-years; about 39,000 km/sec
2. Hydra; Virgo
3. The greater the distance from Earth, the greater the speed of the galaxy.
4. Its speed would be close to zero.

Lab zone Teacher **Demo** L2

Cosmic Background Radiation

Materials long, slender balloon, magic marker

Time 5 minutes

Focus Tell students that the universe was much hotter shortly after it formed. Remind them that very hot objects emit shorter wavelength radiation than cooler objects do.

Teach Partially inflate a long, slender balloon. Draw a waveform with short wavelength. Tell students that the background radiation had a short wavelength (probably similar to those of visible light) after the universe formed. Inflate the balloon more and show students how the wavelength increases.

Apply Ask: **What happened to the cosmic background radiation as the universe expanded?** (*Its wavelength increased.*) Tell them that the background radiation today consists of microwaves. **learning modality: visual**

Speeding Galaxies
Use the graph to answer the questions below about moving clusters of galaxies.

1. **Reading Graphs** How far away is the Bootes cluster? How fast is it moving?
2. **Reading Graphs** Which galaxy is moving away the fastest? Which galaxy is closest to Earth?
3. **Drawing Conclusions** How are the distance and speed of a galaxy related?
4. **Predicting** Predict the speed of a galaxy that is 80,000 light-years from Earth.

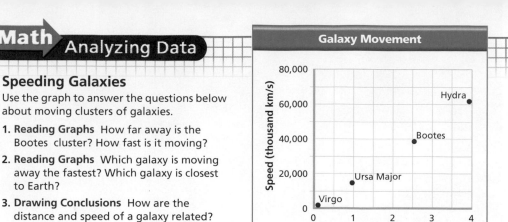

Galaxy Movement

FIGURE 22
Rising Dough
The galaxies in the universe are like the raisins in rising bread dough. **Making Models** *How does rising raisin bread dough resemble the expanding universe?*

To understand how the galaxies are moving, think of raisin bread dough that is rising. If you could shrink yourself to sit on a raisin, you would see all the other raisins moving away from you. The farther a raisin was from you, the faster it would move away, because there would be more bread dough to expand between you and the raisin. No matter which raisin you sat on, all the other raisins would seem to be moving away from you. You could tell that the bread dough was expanding by watching the other raisins.

The universe is like the bread dough. Like the raisins in the dough, the galaxies in the universe are moving away from each other. In the universe, it is space that is expanding, like the dough between the raisins.

Cosmic Background Radiation In 1965, two American physicists, Arno Penzias and Robert Wilson, accidentally detected faint radiation on their radio telescope. This mysterious glow was coming from all directions in space. Scientists later concluded that this glow, now called **cosmic background radiation,** is the leftover thermal energy from the big bang. This energy was distributed in every direction as the universe expanded.

Age of the Universe Since astronomers can measure approximately how fast the universe is expanding now, they can infer how long it has been expanding. Based on careful measurements of how fast distant galaxies are moving away from us and the cosmic background radiation, astronomers estimate that the universe is about 13.7 billion years old.

Formation of the Solar System

After the big bang, matter in the universe separated into galaxies. Gas and dust spread throughout space. Where the solar system is now, there was only cold, dark gas and dust. How did the solar system form? The leading hypothesis is explained below.

The Solar Nebula **About five billion years ago, a giant cloud of gas and dust collapsed to form our solar system.** A large cloud of gas and dust such as the one that formed our solar system is called a **solar nebula.** Slowly, gravity began to pull the solar nebula together. As the solar nebula shrank, it spun faster and faster. The solar nebula flattened, forming a rotating disk. Gravity pulled most of the gas into the center of the disk, where the gas eventually became hot and dense enough for nuclear fusion to begin. The sun was born.

Planetesimals Meanwhile, in the outer parts of the disk, gas and dust formed small asteroid-like bodies called **planetesimals.** These formed the building blocks of the planets. Planetesimals collided and grew larger by sticking together, eventually combining to form the planets.

The Inner Planets When the solar system formed, temperatures were very high. It was so hot close to the sun that most water and other ice-forming materials simply vaporized. Most gases escaped the gravity of the planets that were forming in this region. As a result, the inner planets, Mercury, Venus, Earth, and Mars, are relatively small and rocky.

The Outer Planets In contrast, farther from the sun it was much cooler. As the planets in this region grew, their gravity increased and they were able to capture much of the hydrogen and helium gas in the surrounding space. As a result, the planets Jupiter, Saturn, Uranus, and Neptune became very large. Beyond these gas giants, a huge disk of ice and other substances formed, with a cloud of such substances farther out. This disk and cloud are the main sources of comets. Pluto also formed in this region as part of the icy outer disk.

 Reading Checkpoint What is a solar nebula?

A cloud of gas and dust formed a spinning disk.

Gas in the center of the disk collapsed to form the sun.

The remaining gas and dust formed the planets.

The solar system includes the sun, planets, and belts of rock, ice, and dust.

FIGURE 23
How the Solar System Formed
The solar system formed from a collapsing cloud of gas and dust.

Teach Key Concepts [L2]

Solar System Formation

Focus Direct students' attention to Figure 23.

Teach Ask: **What was the first stage in the formation of the solar system?** *(A giant cloud of gas and dust collapsed to form a solar nebula.)* **What force pulled the solar nebula together?** *(Gravity)* **How did the planets form?** *(Dust and gas formed small asteroid-like bodies, called planetesimals. These planetesimals collided and grew larger, eventually forming the planets.)*

Apply Inform students that nonrigid round masses flatten into disks when they spin, which explains why the solar system has a flat shape. Challenge students to list other examples of round objects flattening into disks when they spin. *(Possible answer: When spun, pizza dough assumes a flattened shape.)*
learning modality: visual

All in One Teaching Resources

- Transparency J47

Monitor Progress _____ [L3]

Skills Check Have students make a timeline that shows the events from the moment of the big bang to the present, including the formation of the solar system.

Answers
Figure 22 As the dough expands, the raisins move farther apart. As the universe expands, its galaxies move farther apart.

Reading Checkpoint A large cloud of gas and dust in space such as the one that formed the solar system

---

Differentiated Instruction

English Learners/Beginning Comprehension: Modified Cloze [L1]
Students may need extra help to understand such analogies as the "bread dough model." Ask students to complete the following analogies and describe their relationships. **Hat is to head as glove is to _____.** *(Hand; something worn on part of the body)* **Moon is to Earth as Earth is to _____.** *(Sun; in orbit around another body)*

Raisins are to dough as galaxies are to _____. *(Universe; separate as expansion occurs)* **learning modality: verbal**

English Learners/Intermediate Comprehension: Modified Cloze [L2] Have students complete the *Beginning* activity and then create a different analogy that describes the expanding universe.
learning modality: verbal

The Future of
the Universe

Teach Key Concepts L2
Predicting the Future of the Universe

Focus Remind students that scientific
knowledge is not static; theories are often
revised as new evidence becomes available.
This is particularly true in the field of
astronomy, where new discoveries are
occurring constantly.

Teach Ask: **If the universe continues to
expand, what might happen to galaxies?**
*(Possible answer: They will spread farther and
farther apart.)* **What evidence supports the
theory that the universe might expand
forever?** *(Galaxies appear to be moving apart
faster now than they were in the past)*

Apply Tell students that the idea that
galaxies will continue to move apart at an
accelerating rate is sometimes called the *Big
Rip.* Remind them that the fate of the
universe is not completely understood.
Astronomers estimate that the universe is
composed of 73 percent dark energy, 23
percent dark matter, and 4 percent "normal
matter." **learning modality: verbal**

FIGURE 24
Vera Rubin
Astronomer Vera Rubin's
observations proved the
existence of dark matter.

152 ◆ J

The Future of the Universe

What will happen to the universe in the future? One possibility
is that the universe will continue to expand, as it is doing now.
All of the stars will eventually run out of fuel and burn out, and
the universe will be cold and dark. Another possibility is that
the force of gravity will begin to pull the galaxies back together.
The result would be a reverse big bang, or "big crunch." All of
the matter in the universe would be crushed into an enormous
black hole.

Which of these possibilities is more likely? Recent discoveries
have produced a surprising new view of the universe that is still
not well understood. **New observations lead many astronomers to conclude that the universe will likely expand forever.**

Dark Matter Until fairly recently, astronomers assumed that
the universe consisted solely of the matter they could observe
directly. But this idea was disproved by the American astronomer Vera Rubin. Rubin made detailed observations of the rotation of spiral galaxies. She discovered that the matter that
astronomers can see, such as stars and nebulas, makes up as
little as ten percent of the mass in galaxies. The remaining mass
exists in the form of dark matter.

Dark matter is matter that does not give off electromagnetic radiation. Dark matter cannot be seen directly. However,
its presence can be inferred by observing the effect of its gravity
on visible objects, such as stars, or on light.

Astronomers still don't know much about dark matter—
what it is made of or all of the places where it is found. But
astronomers estimate that about 23 percent of the universe's
mass is made of dark matter.

An Accelerating Expansion In the late 1990s, astronomers observed that the expansion of the universe appears be
accelerating. That is, galaxies seem to be moving apart at a
faster rate now than in the past. This observation was puzzling,
as no known force could account for it. Astronomers infer that
a mysterious new force, which they call **dark energy,** is causing
the expansion of the universe to accelerate. Current estimates
indicate that most of the universe is made of dark energy and
dark matter.

Astronomy is one of the oldest sciences, but there are still
many discoveries to be made and puzzles to be solved about this
universe of ours!

✓ **Reading
Checkpoint** **What is the effect of dark energy?**

FIGURE 25
Dark Matter
Astronomers measured the effect of gravity on light to produce this computer image of how dark matter (in blue) is distributed across a cluster of galaxies.

Section 5 Assessment

Target Reading Skill Identifying Supporting Evidence Refer to your graphic organizer about the big bang theory as you answer Question 1 below.

Reviewing Key Concepts

1. a. **Defining** What was the big bang?
   b. **Summarizing** When did the big bang occur?
   c. **Describing** Describe two pieces of evidence that support the big bang theory.
2. a. **Summarizing** How old is the solar system?
   b. **Relating Cause and Effect** What force caused the solar system to form?
   c. **Sequencing** Place the following events in the proper order: planets form; planetesimals form; solar nebula shrinks; nuclear fusion begins in the sun.

3. a. **Defining** What is dark matter?
   b. **Explaining** How do scientists know that dark matter exists?
   c. **Predicting** What evidence has led scientists to predict that the universe will continue to expand forever?

Lab zone **At-Home Activity**

Stargazing Plan an evening of stargazing with adult family members. Choose a dark, clear night. Use binoculars if available and the star charts in Appendix B to locate the Milky Way and some interesting stars that you have learned about. Explain to your family what you know about the Milky Way and each constellation that you observe.

Lab zone **At-Home Activity**

Stargazing L2 Encourage students to identify a star on the chart and then try to find it in the sky. Then they can reverse the exercise, finding an interesting star in the sky and trying to locate it on the charts. Allow class time for volunteers to describe their experiences with their families.

Answer

✓ **Reading Checkpoint** It is causing the expansion of the universe to accelerate.

Assess

Reviewing Key Concepts

1. a. The big bang was a giant explosion after which all of the matter in the universe began moving apart. **b.** About 13.7 billion years ago **c.** Hubble's law, the observation that the farther away a galaxy is, the faster it is moving away from Earth, and cosmic background radiation, which is radiation left over from the big bang
2. a. About five billion years old **b.** Gravity pulled the solar nebula together and then pulled most of the gas into the center of the disk, where the gas eventually became hot and dense enough for nuclear fusion to begin and form the sun. **c.** Solar nebula shrinks; nuclear fusion begins in the sun; planetesimals form; planets form
3. a. Matter that does not give off electromagnetic radiation **b.** Its presence can be inferred by observing the effect of its gravity on visible objects, such as stars, or on light. **c.** The expansion rate of the universe appears to be increasing.

Reteach L1

Have students summarize the evidence for the big bang theory.

Performance Assessment L2
Writing Tell students to assume the identity of a planet in our solar system. Then have each of them write a narrative that describes how the chosen planet formed.

All in One Teaching Resources

• Section Summary: *The Expanding Universe*
• Review and Reinforce: *The Expanding Universe*
• Enrich: *The Expanding Universe*

Study Guide
Chapter 4

Study Guide

① Telescopes
Key Concepts
- The electromagnetic spectrum includes radio waves, infrared radiation, visible light, ultraviolet radiation, X-rays, and gamma rays.
- Telescopes are instruments that collect and focus light and other forms of electromagnetic radiation.
- Many large observatories are located on mountaintops or in space.

Key Terms
- telescope
- visible light
- wavelength
- spectrum
- optical telescope
- electromagnetic radiation
- refracting telescope
- convex lens
- reflecting telescope
- radio telescope
- observatory

② Characteristics of Stars
Key Concepts
- Characteristics used to classify stars include color, temperature, size, composition, and brightness.
- The brightness of a star depends upon both its size and temperature.
- Astronomers use a unit called the light-year to measure distances between the stars.
- Astronomers often use parallax to measure distances to nearby stars.
- Astronomers use H-R diagrams to classify stars and to understand how stars change over time.

Key Terms
- constellation
- spectrograph
- apparent brightness
- absolute brightness
- light-year
- parallax
- Hertzsprung-Russell diagram
- main sequence

③ Lives of Stars
Key Concepts
- A star is born when the contracting gas and dust from a nebula become so dense and hot that nuclear fusion starts.
- How long a star lives depends on its mass.
- After a star runs out of fuel, it becomes a white dwarf, a neutron star, or a black hole.

Key Terms
- nebula
- protostar
- white dwarf
- supernova
- neutron star
- pulsar
- black hole

④ Star Systems and Galaxies
Key Concepts
- Most stars are members of groups of two or more stars called star systems.
- Astronomers classify most galaxies into the following types: spiral, elliptical, and irregular.
- Our solar system is located in a spiral galaxy called the Milky Way.
- Astronomers often use scientific notation to describe sizes and distances in the universe.

Key Terms
- binary star
- eclipsing binary
- open cluster
- globular cluster
- galaxy
- spiral galaxy
- elliptical galaxy
- irregular galaxy
- quasar
- universe
- scientific notation

⑤ The Expanding Universe
Key Concepts
- According to the big bang theory, the universe formed in an instant, billions of years ago, in an enormous explosion.
- About five billion years ago, a giant cloud of gas and dust collapsed to form our solar system.
- New observations lead astronomers to conclude that the universe will likely expand forever.

Key Terms
- big bang
- Hubble's law
- cosmic background radiation
- solar nebula
- planetesimal
- dark matter
- dark energy

Help Students Read
Building Vocabulary

Paraphrase Ask students to write the vocabulary words on a separate sheet of paper. Instruct students to write a definition in their own words for each term. Have each student write a complete sentence using the term after writing the definition.

Plural Forms Have students use dictionaries to look up the plural forms of the words *nebula (nebulae* or *nebulas)* and *supernova (supernovae* or *supernovas)*. Students also can study the Latin meanings of the words. (Nebula *means "cloud" and* nova *means "new star.")*

Connecting Concepts
Concept Maps Help students develop a concept map to show how the information in this chapter is related. Stars are classified by their physical characteristics; depending on their mass, stars progress through a consistent series of stages in their life cycles, and are part of galaxies, which are likely to continue to move farther apart as the universe expands. Have students brainstorm to identify the key concepts, key terms, details, and examples. Then have students write these items on self-stick notes and attach them at random on chart paper or on the board.

Tell students that this concept map will be organized in hierarchical order, so they will begin by placing the key concepts at the top. Ask students these questions to guide them to categorize the information on the stickies: **How are stars classified? What are the stages of a star? How are stars grouped?**

Prompt students by using such connecting words or phrases as "consists of," "to form," and "belong to" to indicate the basis for the organization of the map. The phrases should form a sentence between or among a set of concepts.

Answer Accept all logical presentations.

Interactive Textbook
- Complete student edition
- Section and chapter self-assessments
- Assessment reports for teachers

All in One Teaching Resources
- Key Terms Review: *Stars, Galaxies, and the Universe*
- Connecting Concepts: *Stars, Galaxies, and the Universe*

Review and Assessment

Go Online
PHSchool.com
For: Self-Assessment
Visit: PHSchool.com
Web Code: cfa-5040

Organizing Information

Concept Mapping Copy the concept map about telescopes onto a separate sheet of paper. Then complete it and add a title. (For more on Concept Mapping, see the Skills Handbook.)

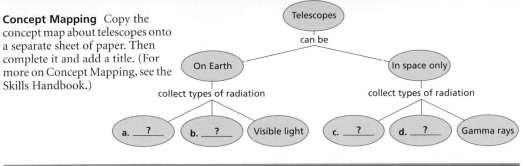

Reviewing Key Terms

Choose the letter of the best answer.

1. Visible light is a form of
   a. spectrum.
   b. electromagnetic radiation.
   c. wavelength.
   d. cosmic background radiation.

2. An H-R diagram is a graph of stars' temperature and
   a. apparent brightness.
   b. main sequence.
   c. absolute brightness.
   d. parallax.

3. A low-mass main sequence star will eventually evolve into a
   a. white dwarf.   b. protostar.
   c. black hole.   d. nebula.

4. A star system in which one star blocks the light from another is called a(n)
   a. open cluster.
   b. quasar.
   c. binary star.
   d. eclipsing binary.

5. Astronomers theorize that the universe began in an enormous explosion called the
   a. solar nebula.
   b. supernova.
   c. big bang.
   d. big crunch.

If the statement is true, write _true_. If it is false, change the underlined word or words to make the statement true.

6. A reflecting telescope uses convex lenses to gather and focus light.

7. Astronomers use spectrographs to determine the chemical composition of stars.

8. Pulsars are a kind of neutron star.

9. A galaxy shaped like a ball and containing only older stars is most likely a spiral galaxy.

10. Globular clusters are small asteroid-like bodies that formed the building blocks of the planets.

Writing in Science

News Article Imagine that you are a journalist covering current research in astronomy, including stars and black holes. Write an article explaining what black holes are, how they form, and how they can be detected.

Stars, Galaxies, and the Universe
Video Preview
Video Field Trip
▶ Video Assessment

Go Online
PHSchool.com
For: Self-Assessment
Visit: PHSchool.com
Web Code: cfa-5040

Students can take an online practice test that is automatically scored.

All in One Teaching Resources

- Transparency J48
- Chapter Test
- Performance Assessment Teacher Notes
- Performance Assessment Teacher Worksheet
- Performance Assessment Scoring Rubric

ExamView® Computer Test Bank CD-ROM

Review and Assessment

Organizing Information
a. radio waves
b. infrared
c. ultraviolet
d. X-rays

Reviewing Key Terms
1. b   2. c   3. a   4. d   5. c
6. refracting telescope
7. true
8. true
9. elliptical galaxy
10. Planetesimals

Writing in Science

Writing Skill Research

Scoring Rubric
4 Exceeds criteria by including accurate information presented in an interesting manner
3 Meets criteria by including accurate information, but presentation is not interesting
2 Includes only basic information about what a black hole is, how it forms, or how it is detected
1 Is inaccurate and incomplete

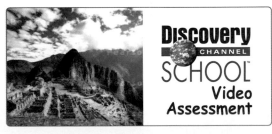

Video Assessment

Stars, Galaxies, and the Universe

Show the Video Assessment to review chapter content and as a prompt for the writing assignment. Discussion questions: **How are a star's mass and its lifespan related?** *(More massive stars have shorter lifespans.)* **Explain what can happen when a star dies.** *(How a star dies depends on its mass. If a star is massive enough, it can form a neutron star or a black hole. Gravity causes what remains after the star explodes to collapse. If the mass of the star is similar to or smaller than that of the sun, it will eventually become a white dwarf.)*

Checking Concepts

11. A light-year is a unit of distance. It measures how far light travels in one year.

12. The distance that a star so far away would appear to move when seen from opposite sides of Earth's orbit would be too small to measure accurately.

13. A star is born when nuclear fusion begins.

14. Most star formation takes place in the spiral arms of our galaxy.

15. Hubble's law states that the farther away a galaxy is, the faster it is moving away from us.

16. Its presence can be inferred by observing the effect of its gravity on visible objects, such as stars, or on light.

Math Practice

17. Spica is about 2.5×10^{15} kilometers from our solar system.

18. The star Antares is 6.04×10^2 light-years from Earth.

Review and Assessment

Checking Concepts

11. Is a light-year a unit of distance or a unit of time? Explain.

12. Why can't astronomers measure the parallax of a star that is a million light-years away?

13. At what point in the evolution of a star is the star actually born?

14. Where in our galaxy does most star formation take place?

15. What is Hubble's law?

16. How can astronomers detect dark matter if they cannot observe it directly?

Math Practice

17. Calculating The bright star Spica is 262 light-years from our solar system. How many kilometers is this?

18. Scientific Notation The star Antares is approximately 604 light-years from Earth. Write this distance in scientific notation.

Thinking Critically

19. Inferring What advantage might there be to locating a telescope, such as the one shown below, on the moon?

20. Applying Concepts Describe a real-world situation involving absolute and apparent brightness. (*Hint:* Think about riding in a car at night.)

21. Relating Cause and Effect How does a star's mass affect its lifetime?

22. Comparing and Contrasting Compare the conditions that led to the formation of the terrestrial planets with those that led to the formation of the gas giants.

Applying Skills

Use the data in the H-R diagram below to answer Questions 23–26.

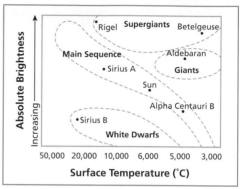

Hertzsprung-Russell Diagram

23. Interpreting Diagrams Which star has a greater absolute brightness, Aldebaran or Sirius B?

24. Interpreting Diagrams Which stars have higher surface temperatures than Sirius A?

25. Applying Concepts Which star is most likely to be red: Rigel, Sirius B, or Betelgeuse?

26. Comparing and Contrasting Compare Aldebaran and the sun in terms of size, temperature, and absolute brightness.

Performance Assessment Check the final draft of your constellation story for correct spelling, grammar, punctuation, and usage. Then decide how you will present your story. For example, you could make a poster, read your story aloud, or perform it as a skit or a play.

 **L3**

Performance Assessment Advise students to be ready to answer questions from you and from other students about the classical myths associated with their constellations. Encourage students who have studied the same constellation to compare their different approaches to writing new stories for it.

Encourage students to reflect on the research and writing process. Ask students to identify points on which they spent too much time, as well as points on which they spent too little time. Have students make suggestions on how they would improve their projects.

Standardized Test Prep

Test-Taking Tip

Sequencing Events

Some questions ask you to arrange a series of events in order. For example, you might be asked which event comes first or last, or which event comes before another event. Before looking at the answer choices, first try to recall the sequence of events in the entire process. If you have an idea of the sequence beforehand, you should find it easier to identify the correct answer.

Sample Question

Which of the following correctly describes the evolution of a sun-like star from young to old?

A white dwarf, red giant, main-sequence star, protostar

B red giant, main-sequence star, white dwarf, protostar

C protostar, main-sequence star, white dwarf, red giant

D protostar, main-sequence star, red giant, white dwarf

Answer

The correct answer is **D**. Choice **A** gives the correct order from old to young, rather than young to old. Choices **B** and **C** do not correctly sequence the life cycle of any star.

Choose the letter of the best answer.

1. The most common chemical element in most stars is
   A oxygen.
   B hydrogen
   C helium.
   D nitrogen.

2. The main factor that affects the evolution of a star is its
   F color.
   G apparent brightness.
   H mass.
   J parallax.

3. The color of a star is related to its temperature. Which of the following color sequences correctly identifies the temperatures of stars in order from hottest to coldest?
   A red, red-orange, yellow, white, blue
   B yellow, white, blue, red, red-orange
   C blue, yellow, red-orange, red, white
   D blue, white, yellow, red-orange, red

The table below gives an estimate of the distribution of stars in the Milky Way galaxy. Use the table and your knowledge of science to answer Questions 4 and 5.

Type of Star	Percentage of Total
Main sequence	90.75%
Red Giant	0.50%
Supergiant	< 0.0001%
White Dwarf	8.75%

4. According to the table, the most common type of stars in the Milky Way is
   F main-sequence stars.
   G red giants.
   H supergiants.
   J white dwarfs.

5. If there are a total of 400 billion stars in the Milky Way, about how many white dwarfs are there in the galaxy?
   A 8.75 billion
   B 35 billion
   C 87.5 billion
   D 3,500 billion

Constructed Response

6. Describe the appearance of the Milky Way as you would see it both from Earth and from a point directly above or below the galaxy. Why does the galaxy look different from different vantage points?

Thinking Critically

19. The moon has no atmosphere that could distort telescope images.

20. High beams on car headlights have a greater absolute magnitude than low beams do. Also, the closer an oncoming car is to you, the greater the apparent brightness of its headlights (on low or high).

21. Low-mass stars have longer lifetimes than do high-mass stars because low-mass stars burn their fuel much more slowly.

22. Because of high temperatures in the inner solar system, most gases escaped the gravity of planets forming in this region, causing the inner planets to be rocky. The outer solar system, being farther from the sun, was cooler. As a result, planets forming in this region were able to capture gases and so became gas giants.

Applying Skills

23. Aldebaran has a greater absolute brightness.

24. Rigel and Sirius B have higher surface temperatures than Sirius A.

25. Betelgeuse is most likely to be red.

26. The sun is a medium-sized star with average absolute brightness and a surface temperature of about 5,800°C. Aldebaran is a giant with a high absolute brightness and a surface temperature of about 4,000°C.

Standardized Test Prep

1. B **2.** H **3.** D **4.** F **5.** B

6. From Earth, the Milky Way looks like a thick ribbon of stars across the night sky. This is because we are looking at it from one of its arms, so it is like looking at the edge of a dinner plate. From above and below, the Milky Way would look like a disc or a spiral because you would be outside of it and able to see the entire galaxy.

Interdisciplinary Exploration

Journey to Mars

This interdisciplinary feature presents the central theme of exploring Mars by connecting four different disciplines: language arts, mathematics, social studies, and science. The four explorations are designed to capture students' interest and help them see how the content they are studying in science relates to other school subjects and to real-world events. Share with others for a team-teaching experience.

All in One Teaching Resources

- Interdisciplinary Exploration: *Language Arts*
- Interdisciplinary Exploration: *Mathematics*
- Interdisciplinary Exploration: *Social Studies*
- Interdisciplinary Exploration: *Science*

Build Background Knowledge

Mars is one of the inner planets

Help students recall what they learned in the chapter *The Solar System*. Ask: **How many moons does Mars have?** *(Two)* **How does Mars compare in size with Earth?** *(Mars has a diameter that is a little more than half that of Earth.)* **Is Mars closer to or farther away from the sun than Earth is?** *(Farther away)* **What type of atmosphere does Mars have?** *(A thin atmosphere made mostly of carbon dioxide.)*

Introduce the Exploration

Remind students that space exploration is a popular theme in movies and on television. However, in reality humans have explored very little of space so far. Ask: **Why is it so difficult for humans to explore space?** *(It is expensive, and new technologies have to be developed. Accept all reasonable responses.)* Ask: **Where have humans been in the solar system outside of Earth?** *(In space stations orbiting Earth and on the moon)*

Interdisciplinary Exploration

Journey to Mars

The six-wheeled rover inched onto the surface of Mars.
Scientists on Earth held their breaths.
Then, *Spirit* hummed into action.

Spirit was the first star of the 2004 Mars mission. Engineers at the Jet Propulsion Laboratory in Pasadena, California, guided the rover from Earth by remote control. *Spirit* carried a high-tech microscope, cameras, and geologic instruments. Within hours of landing in Gusev Crater, *Spirit* was beaming images of the rocks and red soil back to Earth. Engineers on Earth "drove" *Spirit* to its first target, a large rock that they named "Adirondack."

A major goal of the Mars Exploration Mission was to look for evidence of past liquid water on Mars. Earlier photos of the red planet lead scientists to believe that Gusev Crater was once a dried-up lake bed. The presence of water increases the likelihood that life may have once existed on Mars.

Just three weeks later, another rover called *Opportunity* landed on the opposite side of Mars in a strange, flat landscape. It sent back images of a shallow red crater with bedrock in the distance.

***Spirit* Rover**
The artwork below shows *Spirit* exploring Mars. The image of the Martian landscape at right was taken by *Spirit*.

When People Go to Mars

In 1983, Sally Ride became the first American woman in space as a crew member on the space shuttle *Challenger*. Since retiring from NASA in 1987, she has encouraged young people to explore their interests in science, math, and technology. Sally continues to dream of future achievements in space. The following passage is from *The Mystery of Mars*, a book Sally Ride co-wrote with Tam O'Shaughnessy.

Dr. Sally Ride at NASA

When the first astronauts visit Mars, what will they find? Though an astronaut could not survive without a spacesuit, she would feel more at home on Mars than anywhere else in the solar system. She could stand on a rocky surface, scoop up a gloveful of dirt, and explore extinct volcanoes and ancient canyons.

She would need the spacesuit to protect her from the thin Martian air and the extreme cold. The spacesuit would be bulky, but not heavy. Because Mars is smaller than Earth, the pull of gravity on its surface is lower. She and her spacesuit would weigh about one-third what they weighed on Earth.

As the astronaut hiked across the rugged, rocky terrain, her boots would leave deep footprints in the dusty red soil. Fine red dust would cling to her spacesuit. Even on days when the wind was calm, she would look up at a pink sky loaded with red dust. As she headed back to the warmth of her spacecraft at the end of the day, she would look past the silhouettes of crater rims at a dimmer setting sun.

The planet she was exploring would seem strangely familiar. But it would be missing the air and water that make Earth habitable, and the plants and animals that share her home world.

Language Arts Activity

Suppose you are a member of the team that has sent Sally Ride's imaginary astronaut to Mars. What is your job? Did you design the spacesuit or outfit the spacecraft? Were you a scientist or an engineer or a different team member? Write a description of your job. Include as many details as you can.

J ◆ 159

Background

Facts and Figures
It isn't easy to get a spacecraft to another planet. About two-thirds of all missions to Mars have failed.

- The first mission to Mars by the Soviet Union in 1960 failed during launch.
- The first lander to touch down on Mars was the Soviet Union's *Mars 3* in 1971, which failed shortly after landing.

- The first successful landers were *Vikings 1* and *2,* launched by the United States in 1975. Then, in the 1997 *Pathfinder* mission to Mars, the six-wheeled rover *Sojourner* successfuly took photographs and collected data for scientists on Earth to analyze.

Explore Language Arts Concepts

Descriptive Writing Have four volunteers each read one paragraph of the excerpt aloud. As they read, write descriptive phrases from the passage on the board. *(Rocky surface, extinct volcanoes, ancient canyons, thin air, lower gravity, rugged terrain, dusty soil, red dust, pink sky, dimmer sun)* Ask: **Where on Earth might you find examples of this description?** *(Examples might be found for all but lower gravity. Accept all reasonable responses.)* **Why is the sun dimmer on Mars?** *(Mars is farther away from the sun than Earth is.)* **Why is gravity lower on Mars?** *(Mars has less mass than Earth.)* **Why is Mars generally colder than Earth?** *(It is farther from the sun, and it has a thinner atmosphere than Earth's.)* Ask: **Do you think people could live on Mars?** *(With technology that could provide spacesuits and enclosed living quarters, people might be able to live on Mars. Accept all reasonable responses.)*

Show Examples Show students examples of Martian terrain. Photos can be clipped from magazines or downloaded from the Internet. Ask students to use descriptive language to tell about the surface features they see in the photos. Write some of their responses on the board as examples of descriptive writing about Mars.

Language Arts Activity

Focus Ask: **What are some of the jobs of the team that sent the astronaut to Mars?** *(Designing the spacesuit, outfitting spacecraft; other related jobs may be mentioned, such as preserving food, providing a communication link, and designing a vehicle.)*

Teach Help students brainstorm jobs that could be done by the team that sent the astronaut to Mars. Write suggestions on the board as they are offered by students.

Scoring Rubric
4 Exceeds criteria by including lively verbs and colorful adjectives to provide a detailed job description
3 Meets criteria by providing a detailed job description
2 Provides a job description but does not include details
1 Is inaccurate and incomplete

Explore Mathematics Concepts

Use Math Skills Point out to students that the values of the percents in the circle graph shown should correspond to the relative sizes of the segments of the circle. Inform students that the northern and southern hemispheres on Mars have seasons of different lengths.

Discuss Review what causes days, years, and seasons. Ask: **Could a planet have a day shorter than an Earth day but have a year longer than an Earth year?** (*Yes, if the planet were spinning on its axis faster than Earth but revolving around the sun slower than Earth*)

Review Help students recall the use of circle graphs. Ask: **What kind of data are best represented by circle graphs?** (*Percentages, or parts of the whole*)

Math Activity

Focus Refer students to the incomplete circle graphs on the student pages.

Teach Ask: **How many sols are in a Martian year?** (*669*) Remind students that winter and summer are already shown on the graphs. Ask: **What is the longest season in the northern hemisphere?** (*Spring*) **Which segment of the circle graph represents the longest season?** (*The biggest segment*)

Answers

Northern hemisphere—Fall: 21 percent, Spring: 29 percent; Southern Hemisphere—Fall: 29 percent, Spring: 21 percent; make sure that the size of each segment is the right size for the percentage.

Mathematics

Mars Polar Cap
An ice cap covers the northern polar region of Mars.

Math Activity

There are 669 sols (Martian days) in a Martian year. Knowing the number of sols in a season, you can figure the percent of the year that is winter. For example, winter in the northern hemisphere is 156 sols ÷ 669 sols ≈ 0.233 ≈ 23%.

Martian Seasons in Sols (Martian Days)		
	Northern Hemisphere	Southern Hemisphere
Winter	156	177
Spring	194	142
Summer	177	156
Fall	142	194

Northern Hemisphere — 23%, ?, ?, 27%

Southern Hemisphere — 27%, ?, ?, 23%

Legend: ■ Winter ■ Spring ■ Summer ■ Fall

- Use the table and circle graphs above to figure out what percent of the Martian year in each hemisphere is spring and fall. Round to the nearest hundredth.
- Make two circle graphs like those shown here. Label, color, and write the percent for each season in the northern and southern hemispheres.
- Choose a different color for each.

If you had a choice, which hemisphere would you choose to live in?

Sols of Mars

Mars is the planet most like Earth. But its smaller size, greater distance from the sun, and different orbit cause some immense differences. A Martian day, called a sol, is only about 40 minutes longer than an Earth day. The Martian year, however, is much longer—669 sols.

Mars, like Earth, tilts on its axis, so it has seasons. Each Martian season lasts longer than an Earth season because the Martian year is longer. The shape of Mars's orbit makes the seasons unequal in length (see the table at right).

The climate in the southern hemisphere is more extreme than in the northern hemisphere. Winters in the south are longer and colder, while summers are shorter and warmer. Winter in the south, for instance, lasts 177 sols. In the northern hemisphere, winter lasts only 156 sols.

Seasonal changes affect Mars's north and south poles, which are covered with polar ice caps made of water and carbon dioxide. During winter in the southern hemisphere, the polar cap covers almost half the hemisphere. Here the ice cap is mainly frozen carbon dioxide—like dry ice. In spring, the ice cap partially melts, releasing carbon dioxide into the air. In a similar way, when spring comes in the northern hemisphere, the north polar cap melts. But in the north, the frozen core is made mainly of water ice.

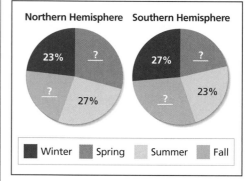

Background

Integrating Science and Technology Space scientists and engineers who have considered missions to Mars have taken two different approaches. One approach, in general, depends on transporting buildings, supplies, rocket fuel, and billions of dollars worth of other equipment to the planet—in short, taking everything necessary to get along for two or three years. By contrast, the other approach depends on the pioneer settler quickly making use of what is available on Mars. For example, an initial flight would not include humans. It would take just the equipment needed to use chemicals in the Martian atmosphere to make enough rocket fuel to get home.

Partners in Space

Many engineers and scientists are sure that humans will travel to Mars sometime in the next 20 years. Meanwhile, people have gotten a preview of a space voyage from astronauts and cosmonauts traveling on space shuttles, on *Mir* (Russia's space station), and most recently, aboard the International Space Station.

For years, the United States and the Soviet Union competed in the race to send missions into space. Now the race has become a cooperative effort. On *Mir*, astronauts worked with cosmonauts to solve problems, make repairs, take space walks, and run the ship's computers. Since 2000, cosmonauts and astronauts have lived and worked together on the International Space Station, which is in orbit about 354 kilometers above the surface of Earth.

What's it like for crew members from different backgrounds to live and work together in a cramped spacecraft? Besides having cultural and language differences, Russian and American crews have different training and different equipment. Still, it seems they have learned how to get along. They even celebrated the first-ever space wedding together in August of 2003!

This experience of living and working together and solving problems will be invaluable should we ever send a manned expedition to Mars.

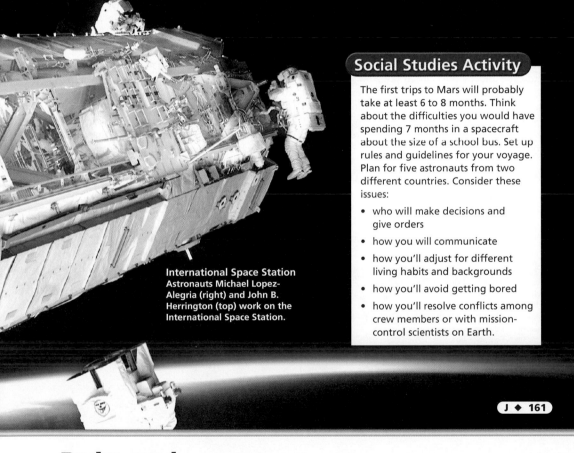

International Space Station Astronauts Michael Lopez-Alegria (right) and John B. Herrington (top) work on the International Space Station.

Social Studies Activity

The first trips to Mars will probably take at least 6 to 8 months. Think about the difficulties you would have spending 7 months in a spacecraft about the size of a school bus. Set up rules and guidelines for your voyage. Plan for five astronauts from two different countries. Consider these issues:

- who will make decisions and give orders
- how you will communicate
- how you'll adjust for different living habits and backgrounds
- how you'll avoid getting bored
- how you'll resolve conflicts among crew members or with mission-control scientists on Earth.

J ◆ 161

Background

Facts and Figures The first section of the International Space Station (ISS) was a Russian-built module that was put into Earth orbit in November 1998. In December of that year a section that was made in the United States was launched. Shuttle astronauts connected the two sections during the 12-day construction mission that followed. In June 1999 a third piece was assembled in orbit. A year later another module that was made in Russia arrived. This was the crew living quarters. By November 2000, enough of the station had been assembled that a crew could live on board. Modules installed since then include the laboratory, a robot arm, an airlock, two logistics modules, and a docking compartment.

Explore Social Studies Concepts

History of Cooperation Tell students that *Mir,* pronounced "mere," means "peace." Explain that things were not always peaceful between Russia and the United States, however. Both nations saw the military value of space research and competed with each other until the end of the Cold War in 1990. *Mir* bridged the time from competition to cooperation in space exploration. *Mir* was put into orbit in 1986. It was brought down in a controlled reentry to crash into the Pacific Ocean in 2001. But during its lifetime *Mir* had been supplied by 11 United States space shuttle flights. The International Space Station, begun in 1999, has taken over as platform for international research in Earth orbit.

Research Ask students to research the international nature of the International Space Station. Have them find out where the astronauts have come from. How did they learn to cooperate with one another?

Extend Have students think about experiences they have had where people had to cooperate in cramped conditions. Ask students to brainstorm things they learned about how to get along with one another under stressful conditions.

Social Studies Activity

Focus Help students understand that the crew on the space mission will be a small community. Remind them that the crew will not be able to leave or bring in new people and that they will be with one another for about seven months.

Teach Have students work alone at first and then in groups. Use the conflicts that might arise within student groups as opportunities to discuss how the astronauts might resolve their conflicts. Ask students to suggest strategies that people can use to make group decision-making easier. Ask: **What kinds of behavior help members of the group get along?** (*Accept all reasonable responses.*)

Scoring Rubric

4 Exceeds criteria by addressing all five issues itemized in activity and considering issues not on list

3 Meets criteria by addressing all issues

2 Addresses at least three of the five issues

1 Largely incomplete or inaccurate

Explore Science Concepts

Review As a class, review the conditions that humans need to survive. Remind students that Earth is a unique planet in the solar system.

Organize Information Have students make concept maps about the environment on Mars. Ask them to address Mars's atmosphere, surface conditions, and surface gravity in their concept maps. After students have completed their concept maps, have them contrast Mars's environment with Earth's environment.

Future Space Colony
In this painting, an artist imagines a human colony on another planet.

Essentials for Survival

You step out of your spacecraft onto a dusty red landscape under a pinkish-red sky. Now you know why Mars is called the "red planet." Water vapor in the air forms thin clouds, even fog. Because the air is so thin, the sun glares down. It's windy, too. Thick clouds of reddish dust, rich in iron, blow around you.

Without a pressurized spacesuit, you would not survive for long in the thin Martian air. Unlike the thick layers of atmosphere around Earth, this atmosphere gives almost no protection against harmful ultraviolet radiation. You also must carry oxygen. Martian air is about 95 percent carbon dioxide, which humans can't breathe.

Your spacesuit must keep you warm. Even at the Martian equator, daytime temperatures are generally below freezing. At night they plunge as low as −140°C. Walk carefully, too, because Martian gravity is weak. You'll feel only 38 percent of your Earth weight!

Mars Landscape
This is the first 360-degree image taken on Mars by *Spirit* in 2004.

162 ◆ J

Background

Facts and Figures If you've ever been in the rocky western deserts of the United States, the rugged Martian landscape of reddish rocks may look familiar. Mars has a "Grand Canyon," too, a series of huge canyons called Valles Marineris. These canyons are five times as deep as the Grand Canyon and more than 4,500 kilometers long, about the width of the continental Unites States.

Since there are no oceans, the total land area of Mars is about equal to the continents and islands on Earth. In the south, the rugged surface is pitted with craters. The northern hemisphere is sandy dunes or rolling plains covered with thin lava. Volcanoes have helped form Mars's landscape. One huge volcano, Olympus Mons, towers above the surface, three times as high as Mt. Everest.

Any human settlement on Mars would have to grow some of its own food. Experiment with a method called hydroponics—growing plants mainly in water, without soil. Set up two plant containers to grow tomatoes or peppers.

- Decide what variables to control.

- In one container, use just water and plant food, with a wire mesh support.

- In the other, add sand or gravel to root plants; add water and plant food.

- Record the rate of growth and strength of each plant over a two-to three-week period.

Which technique worked best? How do you think hydroponics would work on Mars?

Plant Grown in Water

Wire mesh

Water

Plastic container

Plant Grown in Gravel

Wire mesh

Water

Sand or gravel

Plastic container

Tie It Together

Plan a Martian Station

At last, you will be going to Mars to set up the first human research station. For an expedition this long, good planning is essential. Review the major problems that Mars presents to humans, such as a thin atmosphere, a lack of oxygen, and extreme temperatures.

Remember that it's too expensive to send most supplies to Mars. Work in groups to make a plan for setting up Earth's research station. Include maps and drawings. As you make your plan, consider questions such as these:

Rocky Plains of Mars
This painting shows a future scene in which humans walk on Mars.

- How will you supply oxygen? Water? Fuel?

- What site will you choose for your settlement? Consider the landscape and climate on Mars.

- What supplies will you bring with you?

- What will you use for building materials?

- What kinds of food will you get? How will you get food?

Materials 2 pots, water, plant food, fine wire mesh, sand or gravel

Focus Ask: **What requirements do plants have for growth?** *(Water, nutrients, light)* Some students might mention soil. Tell them that they will learn how plants can be grown without soil.

Teach Ask: **What do plants get from soil?** *(Water, nutrients, support)* **How do hydroponic growth techniques provide these things?** *(Wire mesh provides support, nutrients are added to water)*

Expected Outcome If the plant food contains all of the important major nutrients and micronutrients, both plants should
do well.

Tie It Together

Plan a Martian Station

Time 1 week (1 day for planning, 2 days for research, 2 days for preparing maps, plans, and drawings.)

Tips
- Make a list of needs that must be provided, such as food, water, oxygen, electricity, heat, and protection from sun. Encourage students to address each need in their designs.

- Because transporting materials from Earth is difficult and expensive, challenge students to make use of Martian resources whenever possible.

Extend Challenge students to find out what scientists have learned about building self-contained biospheres for humans.

Think Like a Scientist

The Skills Handbook is designed as a reference for students to use whenever they need to review inquiry, reading, or math skills. You can use the activities in this part of the Skills Handbook to teach or reinforce inquiry skills.

Observing

Focus Remind students that an observation is what they can see, hear, smell, taste, or feel.

Teach Invite students to make observations of the classroom. List these observations on the board. Challenge students to identify the senses they used to make each observation. Then, ask: **Which senses will you use to make observations from the photograph on this page?** (*Sight is the only sense that can be used to make observations from the photograph.*)

Activity

Some observations that students might make include that the boy is skateboarding, wearing a white helmet, and flying in the air. Make sure that students' observations are confined to only things that they can actually see in the photograph.

Inferring

Focus Choose one or two of the classroom observations listed on the board, and challenge students to interpret them. Guide students by asking why something appears as it does.

Teach Encourage students to describe their thought processes in making their inferences. Point out where they used their knowledge and experience to interpret the observations. Then invite students to suggest other possible interpretations for the observations. Ask: **How can you find out whether an inference is correct?** (*By further investigation*)

Activity

One possible inference is that the boy just skated off a ramp at a skate park. Invite students to share their experiences that helped them make the inference.

Predicting

Focus Discuss the weather forecast for the next day. Point out that this prediction is an inference about what will happen in the

---

Think Like a Scientist

Scientists have a particular way of looking at the world, or scientific habits of mind. Whenever you ask a question and explore possible answers, you use many of the same skills that scientists do. Some of these skills are described on this page.

Observing

When you use one or more of your five senses to gather information about the world, you are **observing.** Hearing a dog bark, counting twelve green seeds, and smelling smoke are all observations. To increase the power of their senses, scientists sometimes use microscopes, telescopes, or other instruments that help them make more detailed observations.

An observation must be an accurate report of what your senses detect. It is important to keep careful records of your observations in science class by writing or drawing in a notebook. The information collected through observations is called evidence, or data.

Inferring

When you interpret an observation, you are **inferring,** or making an inference. For example, if you hear your dog barking, you may infer that someone is at your front door. To make this inference, you combine the evidence—the barking dog—and your experience or knowledge—you know that your dog barks when strangers approach—to reach a logical conclusion.

Notice that an inference is not a fact; it is only one of many possible interpretations for an observation. For example, your dog may be barking because it wants to go for a walk. An inference may turn out to be incorrect even if it is based on accurate observations and logical reasoning. The only way to find out if an inference is correct is to investigate further.

Predicting

When you listen to the weather forecast, you hear many predictions about the next day's weather—what the temperature will be, whether it will rain, and how windy it will be. Weather forecasters use observations and knowledge of weather patterns to predict the weather. The skill of **predicting** involves making an inference about a future event based on current evidence or past experience.

Because a prediction is an inference, it may prove to be false. In science class, you can test some of your predictions by doing experiments. For example, suppose you predict that larger paper airplanes can fly farther than smaller airplanes. How could you test your prediction?

Activity

Use the photograph to answer the questions below.

Observing Look closely at the photograph. List at least three observations.

Inferring Use your observations to make an inference about what has happened. What experience or knowledge did you use to make the inference?

Predicting Predict what will happen next. On what evidence or experience do you base your prediction?

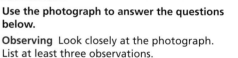

---

future based on observations and experience.

Teach Help students differentiate between a prediction and an inference. You might organize the similarities and differences in a Venn diagram on the board. Both are interpretations of observations using experience and knowledge, and both can be incorrect. Inferences describe current or past events. Predictions describe future events.

Activity

Students might predict that the boy will land and skate to the other side. Others might predict that the boy will fall. Students should also describe the evidence or experience on which they based their predictions.

Classifying

Could you imagine searching for a book in the library if the books were shelved in no particular order? Your trip to the library would be an all-day event! Luckily, librarians group together books on similar topics or by the same author. Grouping together items that are alike in some way is called **classifying.** You can classify items in many ways: by size, by shape, by use, and by other important characteristics.

Like librarians, scientists use the skill of classifying to organize information and objects. When things are sorted into groups, the relationships among them become easier to understand.

Activity

Classify the objects in the photograph into two groups based on any characteristic you choose. Then use another characteristic to classify the objects into three groups.

Activity

This student is using a model to demonstrate what causes day and night on Earth. What do the flashlight and the tennis ball in the model represent?

Making Models

Have you ever drawn a picture to help someone understand what you were saying? Such a drawing is one type of model. A model is a picture, diagram, computer image, or other representation of a complex object or process. **Making models** helps people understand things that they cannot observe directly.

Scientists often use models to represent things that are either very large or very small, such as the planets in the solar system, or the parts of a cell. Such models are physical models—drawings or three-dimensional structures that look like the real thing. Other models are mental models—mathematical equations or words that describe how something works.

Communicating

Whenever you talk on the phone, write a report, or listen to your teacher at school, you are communicating. **Communicating** is the process of sharing ideas and information with other people. Communicating effectively requires many skills, including writing, reading, speaking, listening, and making models.

Scientists communicate to share results, information, and opinions. Scientists often communicate about their work in journals, over the telephone, in letters, and on the Internet.

They also attend scientific meetings where they share their ideas with one another in person.

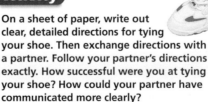

Activity

On a sheet of paper, write out clear, detailed directions for tying your shoe. Then exchange directions with a partner. Follow your partner's directions exactly. How successful were you at tying your shoe? How could your partner have communicated more clearly?

Classifying

Focus Encourage students to think of common things that are classified.

Teach Ask: **What things at home are classified?** (*Clothing might be classified in order to place it in the appropriate dresser drawer; glasses, plates, and silverware are grouped in different parts of the kitchen; screws, nuts, bolts, washers, and nails might be separated into small containers.*) **What are some things that scientists classify?** (*Scientists classify many things they study, including organisms, geological features and processes, and kinds of machines.*)

Activity

Some characteristics students might use include color, pattern of color, use of balls, and size. Students' criteria for classification should clearly divide the balls into two, and then three, distinct groups.

Making Models

Focus Ask: **What are some models you have used to study science?** (*Students might have used human anatomical models, solar system models, maps, or stream tables.*) **How have these models helped you?** (*Models can help you learn about things that are difficult to study because they are very large, very small, or highly complex.*)

Teach Be sure students understand that a model does not have to be three-dimensional. For example, a map is a model, as is a mathematical equation. Have students look at the photograph of the student modeling the causes of day and night on Earth. Ask: **What quality of each item makes this a good model?** (*The flashlight gives off light, and the ball is round and can be rotated by the student.*)

Activity

The flashlight represents the sun and the ball represents Earth.

Communicating

Focus Have students identify the methods of communication they have used today.

Teach Ask: **How is the way you communicate with a friend similar to and different from the way scientists communicate about their work to other scientists?** (*Both may communicate using various methods, but scientists must be very detailed and precise, whereas communication between friends may be less detailed and precise.*) Encourage students to communicate like a scientist as they carry out the activity.

Activity

Students' answers will vary but should identify a step-by-step process for tying a shoe. Help students identify communication errors such as leaving out a step, putting steps in the wrong order, or disregarding the person's handedness.

Making Measurements

Students can refer to this part of the Skills Handbook whenever they need to review how to make measurements with SI units. You can use the activities here to teach or reinforce SI units.

Measuring in SI

Focus Review SI units with students. Begin by providing metric rulers, graduated cylinders, balances, and Celsius thermometers. Use these tools to reinforce that the meter is the unit of length, the liter is the unit of volume, the gram is the unit of mass, and the degree Celsius is the unit of temperature.

Teach Ask: **If you want to measure the length and the width of the classroom, which SI unit would you use?** *(Meter)* **Which unit would you use to measure the amount of mass in your textbook?** *(Gram)* **Which would you use to measure how much water a drinking glass holds?** *(Liter)* **When would you use the Celsius scale?** *(To measure the temperature of something)* Then use the measuring equipment to review SI prefixes. For example, ask: **What are the smallest units on the metric ruler?** *(Millimeters)* **How many millimeters are there in one centimeter?** *(10 millimeters)* **How many in 10 centimeters?** *(100 millimeters)* **How many centimeters are there in one meter?** *(100 centimeters)* **What does 1,000 meters equal?** *(One kilometer)*

Activity

Length The length of the shell is 7.8 centimeters, or 78 millimeters. If students need more practice measuring length, have them use meter sticks and metric rulers to measure various objects in the classroom.

Activity

Liquid Volume The volume of water in the graduated cylinder is 62 milliliters. If students need more practice, have them use a graduated cylinder to measure different volumes of water.

Making Measurements

By measuring, scientists can express their observations more precisely and communicate more information about what they observe.

Measuring in SI

The standard system of measurement used by scientists around the world is known as the International System of Units, which is abbreviated as SI (**Système International d'Unités,** in French). SI units are easy to use because they are based on multiples of 10. Each unit is ten times larger than the next smallest unit and one tenth the size of the next largest unit. The table lists the prefixes used to name the most common SI units.

Common SI Prefixes		
Prefix	**Symbol**	**Meaning**
kilo-	k	1,000
hecto-	h	100
deka-	da	10
deci-	d	0.1 (one tenth)
centi-	c	0.01 (one hundredth)
milli-	m	0.001 (one thousandth)

Length To measure length, or the distance between two points, the unit of measure is the **meter (m).** The distance from the floor to a doorknob is approximately one meter. Long distances, such as the distance between two cities, are measured in kilometers (km). Small lengths are measured in centimeters (cm) or millimeters (mm). Scientists use metric rulers and meter sticks to measure length.

Common Conversions		
1 km	=	1,000 m
1 m	=	100 cm
1 m	=	1,000 mm
1 cm	=	10 mm

Activity

The larger lines on the metric ruler in the picture show centimeter divisions, while the smaller, unnumbered lines show millimeter divisions. How many centimeters long is the shell? How many millimeters long is it?

Liquid Volume To measure the volume of a liquid, or the amount of space it takes up, you will use a unit of measure known as the **liter (L).** One liter is the approximate volume of a medium-size carton of milk. Smaller volumes are measured in milliliters (mL). Scientists use graduated cylinders to measure liquid volume.

Activity

The graduated cylinder in the picture is marked in milliliter divisions. Notice that the water in the cylinder has a curved surface. This curved surface is called the *meniscus.* To measure the volume, you must read the level at the lowest point of the meniscus. What is the volume of water in this graduated cylinder?

Common Conversion
1 L = 1,000 mL

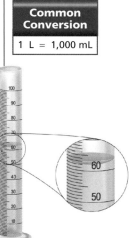

Mass To measure mass, or the amount of matter in an object, you will use a unit of measure known as the **gram (g).** One gram is approximately the mass of a paper clip. Larger masses are measured in kilograms (kg). Scientists use a balance to find the mass of an object.

Common Conversion
1 kg = 1,000 g

Activity

The mass of the potato in the picture is measured in kilograms. What is the mass of the potato? Suppose a recipe for potato salad called for one kilogram of potatoes. About how many potatoes would you need?

0.25 KG

Temperature To measure the temperature of a substance, you will use the **Celsius scale.** Temperature is measured in degrees Celsius (°C) using a Celsius thermometer. Water freezes at 0°C and boils at 100°C.

Time The unit scientists use to measure time is the **second (s).**

Activity

What is the temperature of the liquid in degrees Celsius?

Converting SI Units

To use the SI system, you must know how to convert between units. Converting from one unit to another involves the skill of **calculating,** or using mathematical operations. Converting between SI units is similar to converting between dollars and dimes because both systems are based on multiples of ten.

Suppose you want to convert a length of 80 centimeters to meters. Follow these steps to convert between units.

1. Begin by writing down the measurement you want to convert—in this example, 80 centimeters.

2. Write a conversion factor that represents the relationship between the two units you are converting. In this example, the relationship is 1 meter = 100 centimeters. Write this conversion factor as a fraction, making sure to place the units you are converting from (centimeters, in this example) in the denominator.

3. Multiply the measurement you want to convert by the fraction. When you do this, the units in the first measurement will cancel out with the units in the denominator. Your answer will be in the units you are converting to (meters, in this example).

Example

80 centimeters = ■ meters

$$80 \text{ centimeters} \times \frac{1 \text{ meter}}{100 \text{ centimeters}} = \frac{80 \text{ meters}}{100}$$

$$= 0.8 \text{ meters}$$

Activity

Convert between the following units.
1. 600 millimeters = ■ meters
2. 0.35 liters = ■ milliliters
3. 1,050 grams = ■ kilograms

Skills Handbook ◆ 167

Activity

Mass The mass of the potato is 0.25 kilograms. You would need 4 potatoes to make one kilogram. If students need more practice, give them various objects, such as coins, paper clips, and books, to measure mass.

Activity

Temperature The temperature of the liquid is 35°C. Students who need more practice can measure the temperatures of various water samples.

Converting SI Units

Focus Review the steps for converting SI units, and work through the example with students.

Teach Ask: **How many millimeters are in 80 centimeters?** *(With the relationship 10 millimeters = 1 centimeter, students should follow the steps to calculate that 80 centimeters is equal to 800 millimeters.)* Have students do the conversion problems in the activity.

Activity

1. *600 millimeters = 0.6 meters*
2. *0.35 liters = 350 milliliters*
3. *1,050 grams = 1.05 kilograms*
If students need more practice converting SI units, have them make up conversion problems to trade with partners.

Conducting a Scientific Investigation

Students can refer to this part of the Skills Handbook whenever they need to review the steps of a scientific investigation. You can use the activities here to teach or reinforce these steps.

Posing Questions

Focus Ask: **What do you do when you want to learn about something?** (*Answers might include asking questions about it or looking for information in books or on the Internet.*) Explain that scientists go through the same process to learn about something.

Teach Tell students that the questions scientists ask may have no answers or many different answers. To answer their questions, scientists often conduct experiments. Ask: **Why is a scientific question important to a scientific investigation?** (*It helps the scientist decide if an experiment is necessary; the answer might already be known. It also helps focus the idea so that the scientist can form a hypothesis.*) **What is the scientific question in the activity on the next page?** (*Is a ball's bounce affected by the height from which it is dropped?*)

Developing a Hypothesis

Focus Emphasize that a hypothesis is one possible explanation for a set of observations. It is *not* a guess. It is often based on an inference.

Teach Ask: **On what information do scientists base their hypotheses?** (*Their observations and previous knowledge or experience*) Point out that a hypothesis does not always turn out to be correct. Ask: **When a hypothesis turns out to be incorrect, do you think the scientist wasted his or her time? Explain.** (*No. The scientist learned from the investigation and will develop another hypothesis that could prove to be correct.*)

Designing an Experiment

Focus Have a volunteer read the Experimental Procedure in the box. Invite students to identify the manipulated variable (*amount of salt*), the variables kept constant (*amount and temperature of water, location of containers*), the control (*Container 3*), and the responding variable (*time required for the water to freeze*).

Conducting a Scientific Investigation

In some ways, scientists are like detectives, piecing together clues to learn about a process or event. One way that scientists gather clues is by carrying out experiments. An experiment tests an idea in a careful, orderly manner. Although experiments do not all follow the same steps in the same order, many follow a pattern similar to the one described here.

Posing Questions

Experiments begin by asking a scientific question. A scientific question is one that can be answered by gathering evidence. For example, the question "Which freezes faster—fresh water or salt water?" is a scientific question because you can carry out an investigation and gather information to answer the question.

Developing a Hypothesis

The next step is to form a hypothesis. A **hypothesis** is a possible explanation for a set of observations or answer to a scientific question. In science, a hypothesis must be something that can be tested. A hypothesis can be worded as an *If . . . then . . .* statement. For example, a hypothesis might be *"If I add salt to fresh water, then the water will take longer to freeze."* A hypothesis worded this way serves as a rough outline of the experiment you should perform.

Teach Ask: **How might the experiment be affected if Container 1 had only 100 milliliters of water?** (*It wouldn't be an accurate comparison with the containers that have more water.*) Also make sure that students understand the importance of the control. Then, ask: **What operational definition is used in this experiment?** (*"Frozen" means the time at which a wooden stick can no longer move in a container.*)

Designing an Experiment

Next you need to plan a way to test your hypothesis. Your plan should be written out as a step-by-step procedure and should describe the observations or measurements you will make.

Two important steps involved in designing an experiment are controlling variables and forming operational definitions.

Controlling Variables In a well-designed experiment, you need to keep all variables the same except for one. A **variable** is any factor that can change in an experiment. The factor that you change is called the **manipulated variable**. In this experiment, the manipulated variable is the amount of salt added to the water. Other factors, such as the amount of water or the starting temperature, are kept constant.

The factor that changes as a result of the manipulated variable is called the **responding variable.** The responding variable is what you measure or observe to obtain your results. In this experiment, the responding variable is how long the water takes to freeze.

An experiment in which all factors except one are kept constant is called a **controlled experiment.** Most controlled experiments include a test called the control. In this experiment, Container 3 is the control. Because no salt is added to Container 3, you can compare the results from the other containers to it. Any difference in results must be due to the addition of salt alone.

Forming Operational Definitions Another important aspect of a well-designed experiment is having clear operational definitions. An **operational definition** is a statement that describes how a particular variable is to be measured or how a term is to be defined. For example, in this experiment, how will you determine if the water has frozen? You might decide to insert a stick in each container at the start of the experiment. Your operational definition of "frozen" would be the time at which the stick can no longer move.

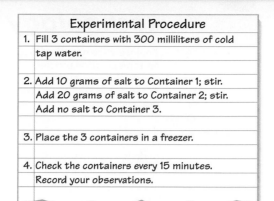

Experimental Procedure
1. Fill 3 containers with 300 milliliters of cold tap water.
2. Add 10 grams of salt to Container 1; stir. Add 20 grams of salt to Container 2; stir. Add no salt to Container 3.
3. Place the 3 containers in a freezer.
4. Check the containers every 15 minutes. Record your observations.

Interpreting Data

The observations and measurements you make in an experiment are called **data.** At the end of an experiment, you need to analyze the data to look for any patterns or trends. Patterns often become clear if you organize your data in a data table or graph. Then think through what the data reveal. Do they support your hypothesis? Do they point out a flaw in your experiment? Do you need to collect more data?

Drawing Conclusions

A **conclusion** is a statement that sums up what you have learned from an experiment. When you draw a conclusion, you need to decide whether the data you collected support your hypothesis or not. You may need to repeat an experiment several times before you can draw any conclusions from it. Conclusions often lead you to pose new questions and plan new experiments to answer them.

Activity

Is a ball's bounce affected by the height from which it is dropped? Using the steps just described, plan a controlled experiment to investigate this problem.

Interpreting Data

Focus Ask: **What kind of data would you collect from the experiment with freezing salt water?** (*Time and state of the water*)

Teach Ask: **What if you forgot to record some data during an investigation?** (*You wouldn't be able to draw valid conclusions because some data are missing.*) Then, ask: **Why are data tables and graphs a good way to organize data?** (*They make it easier to record data accurately, as well as compare and analyze data.*) **What kind of data table and graph might you use for this experiment?** (*A table would have columns for each container with a row for each time interval in which the state of water is recorded. A bar graph would show the time elapsed until water froze for each container.*)

Drawing Conclusions

Focus Help students understand that a conclusion is not necessarily the end of a scientific investigation. A conclusion about one experiment may lead right into another experiment.

Teach Point out that in scientific investigations, a conclusion is a summary and explanation of the results of an experiment. For the Experimental Procedure described on this page, tell students to suppose that they obtained the following results: Container 1 froze in 45 minutes, Container 2 in 80 minutes, and Container 3 in 25 minutes. Ask: **What conclusions can you draw from this experiment?** (*Students might conclude that water takes longer to freeze as more salt is added to it. The hypothesis is supported, and the question of which freezes faster is answered—fresh water.*)

Activity

You might wish to have students work in pairs to plan the controlled experiment. Students should develop a hypothesis, such as, "If I increase the height from which a ball is dropped, then the height of its bounce will increase." They can test the hypothesis by dropping a ball from varying heights (the manipulated variable). All trials should be done with the same kind of ball and on the same surface (constants). For each trial, they should measure the height of the bounce (responding variable). After students have designed the experiment, provide rubber balls, and invite them to carry out the experiment so they can collect and interpret data and draw conclusions.

Technology Design Skills

Students can refer to this part of the Skills Handbook whenever they need to review the process of designing new technologies. You can use the activities here to teach or reinforce the steps in this process.

Identify a Need

Focus Solicit from students any situations in which they have thought that a tool, machine, or other object would be really helpful to them or others. Explain that this is the first step in the design of new products.

Teach Point out that identifying specific needs is very important to the design process. Ask: **If it was specified that the toy boat be wind-powered, how might that affect the design?** (*The boat would likely be designed with sails.*)

Research the Problem

Focus Explain that research focuses the problem so that the design is more specific.

Teach Ask: **What might happen if you didn't research the problem before designing the solution?** (*Answers include developing a design that has already been found to fail, using materials that aren't the best, or designing a solution that already exists.*) **What would you research before designing your toy boat?** (*Students might research designs and materials.*)

Design a Solution

Focus Emphasize the importance of a design team. Ask: **Why are brainstorming sessions important in product design?** (*A group will propose more new ideas than one person.*)

Teach Divide the class into teams to design the toy boat. Instruct them to brainstorm design ideas. Then, ask: **Why do you think engineers evaluate constraints after brainstorming?** (*Evaluating constraints while brainstorming often stops the flow of new ideas.*) **What design constraints do you have for your toy boat?** (*Materials must be readily available and teacher-approved. The boat must be 15 centimeters or less in length and must travel 2 meters in a straight line carrying a load of 20 pennies.*)

Technology Design Skills

Engineers are people who use scientific and technological knowledge to solve practical problems. To design new products, engineers usually follow the process described here, even though they may not follow these steps in the exact order. As you read the steps, think about how you might apply them in technology labs.

Identify a Need

Before engineers begin designing a new product, they must first identify the need they are trying to meet. For example, suppose you are a member of a design team in a company that makes toys. Your team has identified a need: a toy boat that is inexpensive and easy to assemble.

Research the Problem

Engineers often begin by gathering information that will help them with their new design. This research may include finding articles in books, magazines, or on the Internet. It may also include talking to other engineers who have solved similar problems. Engineers often perform experiments related to the product they want to design.

For your toy boat, you could look at toys that are similar to the one you want to design. You might do research on the Internet. You could also test some materials to see whether they will work well in a toy boat.

Drawing for a boat design ▼

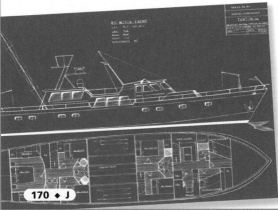

Design a Solution

Research gives engineers information that helps them design a product. When engineers design new products, they usually work in teams.

Generating Ideas Often design teams hold brainstorming meetings in which any team member can contribute ideas. **Brainstorming** is a creative process in which one team member's suggestions often spark ideas in other group members. Brainstorming can lead to new approaches to solving a design problem.

Evaluating Constraints During brainstorming, a design team will often come up with several possible designs. The team must then evaluate each one.

As part of their evaluation, engineers consider constraints. **Constraints** are factors that limit or restrict a product design. Physical characteristics, such as the properties of materials used to make your toy boat, are constraints. Money and time are also constraints. If the materials in a product cost a lot, or if the product takes a long time to make, the design may be impractical.

Making Trade-offs Design teams usually need to make trade-offs. In a **trade-off,** engineers give up one benefit of a proposed design in order to obtain another. In designing your toy boat, you will have to make trade-offs. For example, suppose one material is sturdy but not fully waterproof. Another material is more waterproof, but breakable. You may decide to give up the benefit of sturdiness in order to obtain the benefit of waterproofing.

Build and Evaluate a Prototype

Once the team has chosen a design plan, the engineers build a prototype of the product. A **prototype** is a working model used to test a design. Engineers evaluate the prototype to see whether it works well, is easy to operate, is safe to use, and holds up to repeated use.

Think of your toy boat. What would the prototype be like? Of what materials would it be made? How would you test it?

Troubleshoot and Redesign

Few prototypes work perfectly, which is why they need to be tested. Once a design team has tested a prototype, the members analyze the results and identify any problems. The team then tries to **troubleshoot,** or fix the design problems. For example, if your toy boat leaks or wobbles, the boat should be redesigned to eliminate those problems.

Communicate the Solution

A team needs to communicate the final design to the people who will manufacture and use the product. To do this, teams may use sketches, detailed drawings, computer simulations, and word descriptions.

Activity

You can use the technology design process to design and build a toy boat.

Research and Investigate

1. Visit the library or go online to research toy boats.

2. Investigate how a toy boat can be powered, including wind, rubber bands, or baking soda and vinegar.

3. Brainstorm materials, shapes, and steering for your boat.

Design and Build

4. Based on your research, design a toy boat that
   • is made of readily available materials
   • is no larger than 15 cm long and 10 cm wide

   • includes a power system, a rudder, and an area for cargo
   • travels 2 meters in a straight line carrying a load of 20 pennies

5. Sketch your design and write a step-by-step plan for building your boat. After your teacher approves your plan, build your boat.

Evaluate and Redesign

6. Test your boat, evaluate the results, and troubleshoot any problems.

7. Based on your evaluation, redesign your toy boat so it performs better.

Skills Handbook ◆ 171

Build and Evaluate a Prototype

Focus Explain that building a prototype enables engineers to test design ideas.

Teach Relate building and testing a prototype to conducting an experiment. Explain that engineers set up controlled experiments to test the prototype. Ask: **Why do you think engineers set up controlled experiments?** (*From the data, they can determine which component of the design is working and which is failing.*) **How would you test your prototype of the toy boat?** (*Answers will vary depending on the toy boat's propulsion system.*)

Troubleshoot and Redesign

Focus Make sure students know what it means to troubleshoot. If necessary, give an example. One example is a stapler that isn't working. In that case, you would check to see if it is out of staples or if the staples are jammed. Then you would fix the problem and try stapling again. If it still didn't work, you might check the position of staples and try again.

Teach Explain that engineers often are not surprised if the prototype doesn't work. Ask: **Why isn't it a failure if the prototype doesn't work?** (*Engineers learn from the problems and make changes to address the problems. This process makes the design better.*) Emphasize that prototypes are completely tested before the product is made in the factory.

Communicate the Solution

Focus Inquire whether students have ever read the instruction manual that comes with a new toy or electronic device.

Teach Emphasize the importance of good communication in the design process. Ask: **What might happen if engineers did not communicate their design ideas clearly?** (*The product might not be manufactured correctly or used properly.*)

Activity

The design possibilities are endless. Students might use small plastic containers, wood, foil, or plastic drinking cups for the boat. Materials may also include toothpicks, straws, or small wooden dowels. Brainstorm with students the different ways in which a toy boat can be propelled. The boats may be any shape, but must be no longer than 15 centimeters.

As student groups follow the steps in the design process, have them record their sources, brainstorming ideas, and prototype design in a logbook. Also give them time to troubleshoot and redesign their boats. When students turn in their boats, they should include assembly directions with a diagram, as well as instructions for use.

Creating Data Tables and Graphs

Students can refer to this part of the Skills Handbook whenever they need to review the skills required to create data tables and graphs. You can use the activities provided here to teach or reinforce these skills.

Data Tables

Focus Emphasize the importance of organizing data. Ask: **What might happen if you didn't use a data table for an experiment?** (*Possible answers include that data might not be collected or they might be forgotten.*)

Teach Have students create a data table to show how much time they spend on different activities during one week. Suggest that students first list the main activities they do every week. Then they should determine the amount of time they spend on each activity each day. Remind students to give the data table a title. A sample data table is shown below.

Bar Graphs

Focus Have students compare and contrast the data table and the bar graph on this page. Ask: **Why would you make a bar graph if the data are already organized in a table?** (*The bar graph organizes the data in a visual way that makes them easier to interpret.*)

Teach Students can use the data from the data table they created to make a bar graph that shows the amount of time they spend on different activities during a week. The vertical axis should be divided into units of time, such as hours. Remind students to label both axes and give their graph a title. A sample bar graph is shown below.

Creating Data Tables and Graphs

**How can you make sense of the data in a science experiment?
The first step is to organize the data to help you understand them.
Data tables and graphs are helpful tools for organizing data.**

Data Tables

You have gathered your materials and set up your experiment. But before you start, you need to plan a way to record what happens during the experiment. By creating a data table, you can record your observations and measurements in an orderly way.

Suppose, for example, that a scientist conducted an experiment to find out how many Calories people of different body masses burn while doing various activities. The data table shows the results.

Notice in this data table that the manipulated variable (body mass) is the heading of one column. The responding variable (for

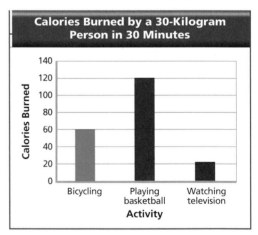

Calories Burned in 30 Minutes			
Body Mass	Experiment 1: Bicycling	Experiment 2: Playing Basketball	Experiment 3: Watching Television
30 kg	60 Calories	120 Calories	21 Calories
40 kg	77 Calories	164 Calories	27 Calories
50 kg	95 Calories	206 Calories	33 Calories
60 kg	114 Calories	248 Calories	38 Calories

Experiment 1, the number of Calories burned while bicycling) is the heading of the next column. Additional columns were added for related experiments.

Bar Graphs

To compare how many Calories a person burns doing various activities, you could create a bar graph. A bar graph is used to display data in a number of separate, or distinct, categories. In this example, bicycling, playing basketball, and watching television are the three categories.

To create a bar graph, follow these steps.

1. On graph paper, draw a horizontal, or *x*-, axis and a vertical, or *y*-, axis.

2. Write the names of the categories to be graphed along the horizontal axis. Include an overall label for the axis as well.

3. Label the vertical axis with the name of the responding variable. Include units of measurement. Then create a scale along the axis by marking off equally spaced numbers that cover the range of the data collected.

4. For each category, draw a solid bar using the scale on the vertical axis to determine the height. Make all the bars the same width.

5. Add a title that describes the graph.

Calories Burned by a 30-Kilogram Person in 30 Minutes

(Bar graph: Calories Burned vs. Activity — Bicycling ≈ 60, Playing basketball ≈ 120, Watching television ≈ 22)

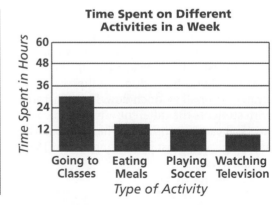

Time Spent on Different Activities in a Week				
	Going to Classes	Eating Meals	Playing Soccer	Watching Television
Monday	6	2	2	0.5
Tuesday	6	1.5	1.5	1.5
Wednesday	6	2	1	2
Thursday	6	2	2	1.5
Friday	6	2	2	0.5
Saturday	0	2.5	2.5	1
Sunday	0	3	1	2

Time Spent on Different Activities in a Week

(Bar graph: Time Spent in Hours vs. Type of Activity — Going to Classes, Eating Meals, Playing Soccer, Watching Television)

Line Graphs

To see whether a relationship exists between body mass and the number of Calories burned while bicycling, you could create a line graph. A line graph is used to display data that show how one variable (the responding variable) changes in response to another variable (the manipulated variable). You can use a line graph when your manipulated variable is **continuous,** that is, when there are other points between the ones that you tested. In this example, body mass is a continuous variable because there are other body masses between 30 and 40 kilograms (for example, 31 kilograms). Time is another example of a continuous variable.

Line graphs are powerful tools because they allow you to estimate values for conditions that you did not test in the experiment. For example, you can use the line graph to estimate that a 35-kilogram person would burn 68 Calories while bicycling.

To create a line graph, follow these steps.

1. On graph paper, draw a horizontal, or *x*-, axis and a vertical, or *y*-, axis.

2. Label the horizontal axis with the name of the manipulated variable. Label the vertical axis with the name of the responding variable. Include units of measurement.

3. Create a scale on each axis by marking off equally spaced numbers that cover the range of the data collected.

4. Plot a point on the graph for each piece of data. In the line graph above, the dotted lines show how to plot the first data point (30 kilograms and 60 Calories). Follow an imaginary vertical line extending up from the horizontal axis at the 30-kilogram mark. Then follow an imaginary horizontal line extending across from the vertical axis at the 60-Calorie mark. Plot the point where the two lines intersect.

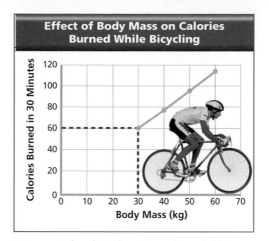

Effect of Body Mass on Calories Burned While Bicycling

5. Connect the plotted points with a solid line. (In some cases, it may be more appropriate to draw a line that shows the general trend of the plotted points. In those cases, some of the points may fall above or below the line. Also, not all graphs are linear. It may be more appropriate to draw a curve to connect the points.)

6. Add a title that identifies the variables or relationship in the graph.

Activity

Create line graphs to display the data from Experiment 2 and Experiment 3 in the data table.

Activity

You read in the newspaper that a total of 4 centimeters of rain fell in your area in June, 2.5 centimeters fell in July, and 1.5 centimeters fell in August. What type of graph would you use to display these data? Use graph paper to create the graph.

Line Graphs

Focus Ask: **Would a bar graph show the relationship between body mass and the number of Calories burned in 30 minutes?** (*No. Bar graphs can only show data in distinct categories.*) Explain that line graphs are used to show how one variable changes in response to another variable.

Teach Walk students through the steps involved in creating a line graph using the example illustrated on the page. For example, ask: **What is the label on the horizontal axis? On the vertical axis?** (*Body Mass (kg); Calories Burned in 30 Minutes*) **What scale is used on each axis?** (*10 kg on the x-axis and 20 Calories on the y-axis*) **What does the second data point represent?** (*77 Calories burned for a body mass of 40 kg*) **What trend or pattern does the graph show?** (*The number of Calories burned in 30 minutes of cycling increases with body mass.*)

Activity

Students should make a different graph for each experiment. Each graph should have a different *x*-axis scale that is appropriate for the data. See sample graphs below.

Activity

Students should conclude that a bar graph would be best for displaying the data.

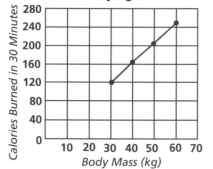

Effect of Body Mass on Calories Burned While Playing Basketball

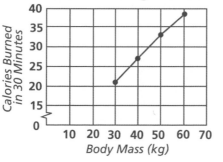

Effect of Body Mass on Calories Burned While Watching Television

J ● 173

Circle Graphs

Focus Emphasize that a circle graph must include 100 percent of the categories for the topic being graphed. For example, ask: **Could the data in the bar graph titled "Calories Burned by a 30-kilogram Person in Various Activities" (on the previous page) be shown in a circle graph? Why or why not?** (*No. It does not include all the possible ways a 30-kilogram person can burn Calories.*)

Teach Walk students through the steps for making a circle graph. If necessary, help them with the compass and the protractor. Use the protractor to illustrate that a circle has 360 degrees. Make sure students understand the mathematical calculations involved in making a circle graph.

Activity

You might have students work in pairs to complete the activity. Students' circle graphs should look like the graph below.

Ways Students Get to School

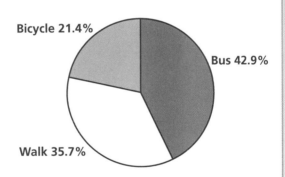

Bicycle 21.4%

Bus 42.9%

Walk 35.7%

Circle Graphs

Like bar graphs, circle graphs can be used to display data in a number of separate categories. Unlike bar graphs, however, circle graphs can only be used when you have data for *all* the categories that make up a given topic. A circle graph is sometimes called a pie chart. The pie represents the entire topic, while the slices represent the individual categories. The size of a slice indicates what percentage of the whole a particular category makes up.

The data table below shows the results of a survey in which 24 teenagers were asked to identify their favorite sport. The data were then used to create the circle graph at the right.

Favorite Sports

Sport	Students
Soccer	8
Basketball	6
Bicycling	6
Swimming	4

To create a circle graph, follow these steps.

1. Use a compass to draw a circle. Mark the center with a point. Then draw a line from the center point to the top of the circle.

2. Determine the size of each "slice" by setting up a proportion where *x* equals the number of degrees in a slice. (*Note:* A circle contains 360 degrees.) For example, to find the number of degrees in the "soccer" slice, set up the following proportion:

$$\frac{\text{Students who prefer soccer}}{\text{Total number of students}} = \frac{x}{\text{Total number of degrees in a circle}}$$

$$\frac{8}{24} = \frac{x}{360}$$

Cross-multiply and solve for x.

$$24x = 8 \times 360$$
$$x = 120$$

The "soccer" slice should contain 120 degrees.

Sports That Teens Prefer

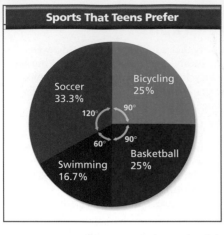

Soccer 33.3%

Bicycling 25%

120° 90°

60° 90°

Swimming 16.7%

Basketball 25%

3. Use a protractor to measure the angle of the first slice, using the line you drew to the top of the circle as the 0° line. Draw a line from the center of the circle to the edge for the angle you measured.

4. Continue around the circle by measuring the size of each slice with the protractor. Start measuring from the edge of the previous slice so the wedges do not overlap. When you are done, the entire circle should be filled in.

5. Determine the percentage of the whole circle that each slice represents. To do this, divide the number of degrees in a slice by the total number of degrees in a circle (360), and multiply by 100%. For the "soccer" slice, you can find the percentage as follows:

$$\frac{120}{360} \times 100\% = 33.3\%$$

6. Use a different color for each slice. Label each slice with the category and with the percentage of the whole it represents.

7. Add a title to the circle graph.

Activity

In a class of 28 students, 12 students take the bus to school, 10 students walk, and 6 students ride their bicycles. Create a circle graph to display these data.

Math Review

Scientists use math to organize, analyze, and present data. This appendix will help you review some basic math skills.

Mean, Median, and Mode

The **mean** is the average, or the sum of the data divided by the number of data items. The middle number in a set of ordered data is called the **median**. The **mode** is the number that appears most often in a set of data.

Example

A scientist counted the number of distinct songs sung by seven different male birds and collected the data shown below.

Male Bird Songs							
Bird	A	B	C	D	E	F	G
Number of Songs	36	29	40	35	28	36	27

To determine the mean number of songs, add the total number of songs and divide by the number of data items—in this case, the number of male birds.

Mean = $\frac{231}{7}$ = 33 songs

To find the median number of songs, arrange the data in numerical order and find the number in the middle of the series.

27 28 29 35 36 36 40

The number in the middle is 35, so the median number of songs is 35.

The mode is the value that appears most frequently. In the data, 36 appears twice, while each other item appears only once. Therefore, 36 songs is the mode.

Practice

Find out how many minutes it takes each student in your class to get to school. Then find the mean, median, and mode for the data.

Probability

Probability is the chance that an event will occur. Probability can be expressed as a ratio, a fraction, or a percentage. For example, when you flip a coin, the probability that the coin will land heads up is 1 in 2, or $\frac{1}{2}$, or 50 percent.

The probability that an event will happen can be expressed in the following formula.

$P(\text{event}) = \frac{\text{Number of times the event can occur}}{\text{Total number of possible events}}$

Example

A paper bag contains 25 blue marbles, 5 green marbles, 5 orange marbles, and 15 yellow marbles. If you close your eyes and pick a marble from the bag, what is the probability that it will be yellow?

$P(\text{yellow marbles}) = \frac{15 \text{ yellow marbles}}{50 \text{ marbles total}}$

$P = \frac{15}{50}, \text{ or } \frac{3}{10}, \text{ or } 30\%$

Practice

Each side of a cube has a letter on it. Two sides have A, three sides have B, and one side has C. If you roll the cube, what is the probability that A will land on top?

Math Review

Students can refer to this part of the Skills Handbook whenever they need to review some basic math skills. You can use the activities provided here to teach or reinforce these skills.

Mean, Median, and Mode

Focus Remind students that data from an experiment might consist of hundreds or thousands of numbers. Unless analyzed, the numbers likely will not be helpful.

Teach Work through the process of determining mean, median, and mode using the example in the book. Make sure students realize that these three numbers do not always equal each other. Point out that taken together, these three numbers give more information about the data than just one of the numbers alone.

Practice

Answers will vary based on class data. The mean should equal the total number of minutes divided by the number of students. The median should equal the number in the middle after arranging the data in numerical order. The mode should equal the number of minutes that is given most frequently.

Probability

Focus Show students a coin and ask: **What is the chance that I will get tails when I flip the coin?** (*Some students might know that there is a 1 in 2, or 50 percent, chance of getting tails.*)

Teach Set up a bag of marbles like the one in the example. Allow students to practice determining the probabilities of picking marbles of different colors. Then, encourage them to actually pick marbles and compare their actual results with those results predicted by probability.

Practice

$P(A) = 2 \text{ sides with } \frac{A}{6} \text{ sides total}$
$P = \frac{2}{6}, \text{ or } \frac{1}{3}, \text{ or } 33\%$

Area

Focus Ask: **Who knows what area is?** (*Area is equal to the number of square units needed to cover a certain shape or object.*) On the board, write the formulas for the area of a rectangle and a circle.

Teach Give students various objects of different shapes. Have them measure each object and determine its area based on the measurements. Point out that the units of the answer are squared because they are multiplied together. If students are interested, you might also explain that π is equal to the ratio of the circumference of a circle to its diameter. For circles of all sizes, π is approximately equal to the number 3.14, or $\frac{22}{7}$.

> **Practice**

The area of the circle is equal to $21 \text{ m} \times 21 \text{ m} \times \frac{22}{7}$, or $1,386 \text{ m}^2$.

Circumference

Focus Draw a circle on the board. Then trace the outline with your finger and explain that this is the circumference of the circle, or the distance around it.

Teach Show students that the radius is equal to the distance from the center of the circle to any point on it. Point out that the diameter of a circle is equal to two times the radius. Give students paper circles of various sizes, and have them calculate the circumference of each.

> **Practice**

The circumference is equal to $2 \times 28 \text{ m} \times \frac{22}{7}$, or 176 m.

Volume

Focus Fill a beaker with 100 milliliters of water. Ask: **What is the volume of water?** (*100 milliliters*) Explain that volume is the amount of space that something takes up. Then point out that one milliliter is equal to one cubic centimeter (cm^3).

Teach Write on the board the formulas for calculating the volumes of a rectangle and a cylinder. Point out that volume is equal to the area of an object multiplied by its height. Then measure the beaker to show students the relationship between liquid volume (100 milliliters) and the number of cubic units it contains (100 cubic centimeters).

Area

The **area** of a surface is the number of square units that cover it. The front cover of your textbook has an area of about 600 cm^2.

Area of a Rectangle and a Square To find the area of a rectangle, multiply its length times its width. The formula for the area of a rectangle is

$$A = \ell \times w, \text{ or } A = \ell w$$

Since all four sides of a square have the same length, the area of a square is the length of one side multiplied by itself, or squared.

$$A = s \times s, \text{ or } A = s^2$$

> **Example**
>
> A scientist is studying the plants in a field that measures 75 m × 45 m. What is the area of the field?
>
> $$A = \ell \times w$$
> $$A = 75 \text{ m} \times 45 \text{ m}$$
> $$A = 3,375 \text{ m}^2$$

Area of a Circle The formula for the area of a circle is

$$A = \pi \times r \times r, \text{ or } A = \pi r^2$$

The length of the radius is represented by r, and the value of π is approximately $\frac{22}{7}$.

> **Example**
>
> Find the area of a circle with a radius of 14 cm.
>
> $$A = \pi r^2$$
> $$A = 14 \times 14 \times \frac{22}{7}$$
> $$A = 616 \text{ cm}^2$$

> **Practice**
>
> Find the area of a circle that has a radius of 21 m.

Circumference

The distance around a circle is called the circumference. The formula for finding the circumference of a circle is

$$C = 2 \times \pi \times r, \text{ or } C = 2\pi r$$

> **Example**
>
> The radius of a circle is 35 cm. What is its circumference?
>
> $$C = 2\pi r$$
> $$C = 2 \times 35 \times \frac{22}{7}$$
> $$C = 220 \text{ cm}$$

> **Practice**
>
> What is the circumference of a circle with a radius of 28 m?

Volume

The volume of an object is the number of cubic units it contains. The volume of a wastebasket, for example, might be about $26,000 \text{ cm}^3$.

Volume of a Rectangular Object To find the volume of a rectangular object, multiply the object's length times its width times its height.

$$V = \ell \times w \times h, \text{ or } V = \ell w h$$

> **Example**
>
> Find the volume of a box with length 24 cm, width 12 cm, and height 9 cm.
>
> $$V = \ell w h$$
> $$V = 24 \text{ cm} \times 12 \text{ cm} \times 9 \text{ cm}$$
> $$V = 2,592 \text{ cm}^3$$

> **Practice**
>
> What is the volume of a rectangular object with length 17 cm, width 11 cm, and height 6 cm?

> **Practice**

The volume of the rectangular object is equal to $17 \text{ cm} \times 11 \text{ cm} \times 6 \text{ cm}$, or $1,122 \text{ cm}^3$.

Fractions

A **fraction** is a way to express a part of a whole. In the fraction $\frac{4}{7}$, 4 is the numerator and 7 is the denominator.

Adding and Subtracting Fractions To add or subtract two or more fractions that have a common denominator, first add or subtract the numerators. Then write the sum or difference over the common denominator.

To find the sum or difference of fractions with different denominators, first find the least common multiple of the denominators. This is known as the least common denominator. Then convert each fraction to equivalent fractions with the least common denominator. Add or subtract the numerators. Then write the sum or difference over the common denominator.

> **Example**
>
> $\frac{5}{6} - \frac{3}{4} = \frac{10}{12} - \frac{9}{12} = \frac{10-9}{12} = \frac{1}{12}$

Multiplying Fractions To multiply two fractions, first multiply the two numerators, then multiply the two denominators.

> **Example**
>
> $\frac{5}{6} \times \frac{2}{3} = \frac{5 \times 2}{6 \times 3} = \frac{10}{18} = \frac{5}{9}$

Dividing Fractions Dividing by a fraction is the same as multiplying by its reciprocal. Reciprocals are numbers whose numerators and denominators have been switched. To divide one fraction by another, first invert the fraction you are dividing by—in other words, turn it upside down. Then multiply the two fractions.

> **Example**
>
> $\frac{2}{5} \div \frac{7}{8} = \frac{2}{5} \times \frac{8}{7} = \frac{2 \times 8}{5 \times 7} = \frac{16}{35}$

> **Practice** ▶
>
> Solve the following: $\frac{3}{7} \div \frac{4}{5}$.

Decimals

Fractions whose denominators are 10, 100, or some other power of 10 are often expressed as decimals. For example, the fraction $\frac{9}{10}$ can be expressed as the decimal 0.9, and the fraction $\frac{7}{100}$ can be written as 0.07.

Adding and Subtracting With Decimals To add or subtract decimals, line up the decimal points before you carry out the operation.

> **Example**
>
> $\begin{array}{r} 27.4 \\ + 6.19 \\ \hline 33.59 \end{array}$ $\qquad$ $\begin{array}{r} 278.635 \\ - 191.4 \\ \hline 87.235 \end{array}$

Multiplying With Decimals When you multiply two numbers with decimals, the number of decimal places in the product is equal to the total number of decimal places in each number being multiplied.

> **Example**
>
> $\begin{array}{r} 46.2 \text{ (one decimal place)} \\ \times\ 2.37 \text{ (two decimal places)} \\ \hline 109.494 \text{ (three decimal places)} \end{array}$

Dividing With Decimals To divide a decimal by a whole number, put the decimal point in the quotient above the decimal point in the dividend.

> **Example**
>
> $15.5 \div 5$
>
> $\begin{array}{r} 3.1 \\ 5)\overline{15.5} \end{array}$

To divide a decimal by a decimal, you need to rewrite the divisor as a whole number. Do this by multiplying both the divisor and dividend by the same multiple of 10.

> **Example**
>
> $1.68 \div 4.2 = 16.8 \div 42$
>
> $\begin{array}{r} 0.4 \\ 42)\overline{16.8} \end{array}$

> **Practice** ▶
>
> Multiply 6.21 by 8.5.

Fractions

Focus Draw a circle on the board, and divide it into eight equal sections. Shade in one of the sections, and explain that one out of eight, or one eighth, of the sections is shaded. Also use the circle to show that four eighths is the same as one half.

Teach Write the fraction $\frac{3}{4}$ on the board. Ask: **What is the numerator?** *(Three)* **What is the denominator?** *(Four)* Emphasize that when adding and subtracting fractions, the denominators of the two fractions must be the same. If necessary, review how to find the least common denominator. Remind students that when multiplying and dividing, the denominators do not have to be the same.

> **Practice** ▶
>
> $\frac{3}{7} \div \frac{4}{5} = \frac{3}{7} \times \frac{5}{4} = \frac{15}{28}$

Decimals

Focus Write the number *129.835* on the board. Ask: **What number is in the ones position?** *(9)* **The tenths position?** *(8)* **The hundredths position?** *(3)* Make sure students know that 0.8 is equal to $\frac{8}{10}$ and 0.03 is equal to $\frac{3}{100}$.

Teach Use the examples in the book to review addition, subtraction, multiplication, and division with decimals. Make up a worksheet of similar problems to give students additional practice. Also show students how a fraction is converted to a decimal by dividing the numerator by the denominator. For example, $\frac{1}{2}$ is equal to 0.5.

> **Practice** ▶
>
> $6.21 \times 8.5 = 52.785$

Ratio and Proportion

Focus Differentiate a ratio from a fraction. Remind students that a fraction tells how many parts of the whole. In contrast, a ratio compares two different numbers. For example, $\frac{12}{22}$, or $\frac{6}{11}$, of a class are girls. But the ratio of boys to girls in the class is 10 to 12, or $\frac{5}{6}$.

Teach Use the example in the book to explain how to use a proportion to find an unknown quantity. Provide students with additional practice problems, if needed.

Practice

$6 \times 49 = 7x$
$294 = 7x$
$294 \div 7 = x$
$x = 42$

Percentage

Focus On the board, write $50\% = \frac{50}{100}$. Explain that a percentage is a ratio that compares a number to 100.

Teach Point out that when calculating percentages, you are usually using numbers other than 100. In this case, you set up a proportion. Go over the example in the book. Emphasize that the number representing the total goes on the bottom of the ratio, as does the 100%.

Practice

Students should set up the proportion

$$\frac{42 \text{ marbles}}{300 \text{ marbles}} = \frac{x\%}{100\%}$$

$42 \times 100 = 300x$

$4200 = 300x$

$4200 \div 300 = 14\%$

Ratio and Proportion

A **ratio** compares two numbers by division. For example, suppose a scientist counts 800 wolves and 1,200 moose on an island. The ratio of wolves to moose can be written as a fraction, $\frac{800}{1,200}$, which can be reduced to $\frac{2}{3}$. The same ratio can also be expressed as 2 to 3 or 2 : 3.

A **proportion** is a mathematical sentence saying that two ratios are equivalent. For example, a proportion could state that $\frac{800 \text{ wolves}}{1,200 \text{ moose}} = \frac{2 \text{ wolves}}{3 \text{ moose}}$. You can sometimes set up a proportion to determine or estimate an unknown quantity. For example, suppose a scientist counts 25 beetles in an area of 10 square meters. The scientist wants to estimate the number of beetles in 100 square meters.

> **Example**
>
> 1. Express the relationship between beetles and area as a ratio: $\frac{25}{10}$, simplified to $\frac{5}{2}$.
> 2. Set up a proportion, with x representing the number of beetles. The proportion can be stated as $\frac{5}{2} = \frac{x}{100}$.
> 3. Begin by cross-multiplying. In other words, multiply each fraction's numerator by the other fraction's denominator.
>
> $5 \times 100 = 2 \times x$, or $500 = 2x$
>
> 4. To find the value of x, divide both sides by 2. The result is 250, or 250 beetles in 100 square meters.

> **Practice**
>
> Find the value of x in the following proportion: $\frac{6}{7} = \frac{x}{49}$.

Percentage

A **percentage** is a ratio that compares a number to 100. For example, there are 37 granite rocks in a collection that consists of 100 rocks. The ratio $\frac{37}{100}$ can be written as 37%. Granite rocks make up 37% of the rock collection.

You can calculate percentages of numbers other than 100 by setting up a proportion.

> **Example**
>
> Rain falls on 9 days out of 30 in June. What percentage of the days in June were rainy?
>
> $$\frac{9 \text{ days}}{30 \text{ days}} = \frac{d\%}{100\%}$$
>
> To find the value of d, begin by cross-multiplying, as for any proportion:
>
> $9 \times 100 = 30 \times d$ $\quad d = \frac{900}{30}$ $\quad d = 30$

> **Practice**
>
> There are 300 marbles in a jar, and 42 of those marbles are blue. What percentage of the marbles are blue?

Significant Figures

The **precision** of a measurement depends on the instrument you use to take the measurement. For example, if the smallest unit on the ruler is millimeters, then the most precise measurement you can make will be in millimeters.

The sum or difference of measurements can only be as precise as the least precise measurement being added or subtracted. Round your answer so that it has the same number of digits after the decimal as the least precise measurement. Round up if the last digit is 5 or more, and round down if the last digit is 4 or less.

Example

Subtract a temperature of 5.2°C from the temperature 75.46°C.

75.46 − 5.2 = 70.26

5.2 has the fewest digits after the decimal, so it is the least precise measurement. Since the last digit of the answer is 6, round up to 3. The most precise difference between the measurements is 70.3°C.

Practice

Add 26.4 m to 8.37 m. Round your answer according to the precision of the measurements.

Significant figures are the number of nonzero digits in a measurement. Zeroes between nonzero digits are also significant. For example, the measurements 12,500 L, 0.125 cm, and 2.05 kg all have three significant figures. When you multiply and divide measurements, the one with the fewest significant figures determines the number of significant figures in your answer.

Example

Multiply 110 g by 5.75 g.

110 × 5.75 = 632.5

Because 110 has only two significant figures, round the answer to 630 g.

Scientific Notation

A **factor** is a number that divides into another number with no remainder. In the example, the number 3 is used as a factor four times.

An **exponent** tells how many times a number is used as a factor. For example, $3 \times 3 \times 3 \times 3$ can be written as 3^4. The exponent 4 indicates that the number 3 is used as a factor four times. Another way of expressing this is to say that 81 is equal to 3 to the fourth power.

Example

$$3^4 = 3 \times 3 \times 3 \times 3 = 81$$

Scientific notation uses exponents and powers of ten to write very large or very small numbers in shorter form. When you write a number in scientific notation, you write the number as two factors. The first factor is any number between 1 and 10. The second factor is a power of 10, such as 10^3 or 10^6.

Example

The average distance between the planet Mercury and the sun is 58,000,000 km. To write the first factor in scientific notation, insert a decimal point in the original number so that you have a number between 1 and 10. In the case of 58,000,000, the number is 5.8.

To determine the power of 10, count the number of places that the decimal point moved. In this case, it moved 7 places.

$$58,000,000 \text{ km} = 5.8 \times 10^7 \text{ km}$$

Practice

Express 6,590,000 in scientific notation.

Significant Figures

Focus Measure the length of a paper clip using two different rulers. Use one ruler that is less precise than the other. Compare the two measurements. Ask: **Which measurement is more precise?** (*The ruler with the smallest units will give the more precise measurement.*)

Teach Give students the opportunity to take measurements of an object using tools with different precision. Encourage students to add and subtract their measurements, making sure that they round the answers to reflect the precision of the instruments. Go over the example for significant digits. Check for understanding by asking: **How many significant digits are in the number 324,000?** (*Three*) **In the number 5, 901?** (*Four*) **In the number 0.706?** (*Three*) If students need additional practice, create a worksheet with problems in multiplying and dividing numbers with various significant digits.

Practice

26.4 m + 8.37 m = 34.77 m
This answer should be rounded to 34.8 m because the least precise measurement has only one digit after the decimal. This number is rounded up to 8 because the last digit is more than 5.

Scientific Notation

Focus Write a very large number on the board, such as 100 million, using all the zeros. Then, write the number using scientific notation. Ask: **Why do you think scientists prefer to write very large numbers using scientific notation?** (*Possible answers include that it is easier to do calculations, convert units, and make comparisons with other numbers.*)

Teach Go over the examples, and ask: **In the second example, which numbers are the factors?** (*5.8 and 10^7*) **Which number is the exponent?** (^{7}) Explain that very small numbers have a negative exponent because the decimal point is moved to the right to produce the first factor. For example, 0.00000628 is equal to 6.28×10^{-6}.

Practice

$6,590,000 = 6.59 \times 10^6$

Reading Comprehension Skills

Students can refer to this part of the Skills Handbook whenever they need to review a reading skill. You can use the activities provided here to teach or reinforce these skills.

Learning From Science Textbooks

Reading in a content area presents challenges different from those encountered when reading fiction. Science texts often have more new vocabulary and more unfamiliar concepts that place greater emphasis on inferential reasoning. Students who can apply reading skills and information-organizing strategies will be more successful in reading and understanding a science textbook.

Activity

Turn with students to the first page of any section. Walk through the Reading Preview with students, showing them the Key Concepts that provide a guiding set of questions that students can answer from the text. Next, point out the Key Terms list, which highlights the science vocabulary. Last, have students find the Target Reading Skill with graphic organizer. Make the connection for students to the help in this Skills Handbook.

All in One Teaching Resources

• Target Reading Skills Handbook

Building Vocabulary

Focus Explain to students that knowing the definitions of key concept words can help them understand what they read.

Teach List on the board strategies to learn the definitions of new terms. Also solicit from students strategies that work for them—drawing a picture for the term, acting it out, or using it in conversation. Challenge students to choose a new strategy to learn the Key Terms in your next section.

Using Prior Knowledge

Focus Explain to students that using prior knowledge helps connect what they already know to what they are about to read.

Teach Point out that prior knowledge might not be accurate because memories have faded or perspectives have changed. Encourage students to ask questions to

---

Reading Comprehension Skills

Your textbook is an important source of science information. As you read your science textbook, you will find that the book has been written to assist you in understanding the science concepts.

Learning From Science Textbooks

As you study science in school, you will learn science concepts in a variety of ways. Sometimes you will do interesting activities and experiments to explore science ideas. To fully understand what you observe in experiments and activities, you will need to read your science textbook. To help you read, some of the important ideas are highlighted so that you can easily recognize what they are. In addition, a target reading skill in each section will help you understand what you read.

By using the target reading skills, you will improve your reading comprehension—that is, you will improve your ability to understand what you read. As you learn science, you will build knowledge that will help you understand even more of what you read. This knowledge will help you learn about all the topics presented in this textbook.

And—guess what?—these reading skills can be useful whenever you are reading. Reading to learn is important for your entire life. You have an opportunity to begin that process now.

The target reading skills that will improve your reading comprehension are described below.

Building Vocabulary

To understand the science concepts taught in this textbook, you need to remember the meanings of the Key Terms. One strategy consists of writing the definitions of these terms in your own words. You can also practice using the terms in sentences and make lists of words or phrases you associate with each term.

Using Prior Knowledge

Your prior knowledge is what you already know before you begin to read about a topic. Building on what you already know gives you a head start on learning new information. Before you begin a new assignment, think about what you know. You might page through your reading assignment, looking at the headings and the visuals to spark your memory. You can list what you know in the graphic organizer provided in the section opener. Then, as you read, consider questions like the ones below to connect what you learn to what you already know.

• How does what you learn relate to what you know?
• How did something you already know help you learn something new?
• Did your original ideas agree with what you have just learned? If not, how would you revise your original ideas?

Asking Questions

Asking yourself questions is an excellent way to focus on and remember new information in your textbook. You can learn how to ask good questions.

One way is to turn the text headings into questions. Then your questions can guide you to identify and remember the important information as you read. Look at these examples:

Heading: Using Seismographic Data
Question: How are seismographic data used?
Heading: Kinds of Faults
Question: What are the kinds of faults?

---

resolve discrepancies between their prior knowledge and what they have learned.

Asking Questions

Focus Demonstrate to students how to change a text heading into a question to help them anticipate the concepts, facts, and events they will read about.

Teach Encourage students to use this reading skill for the next section they read. Instruct them to turn the text headings into questions. Also challenge students to write at least four *what, how, why, who, when,* or *where* questions. Then, have students evaluate the skill. Ask: **Did asking questions about the text help you focus on the reading and remember what you read?** (*Answers will vary, but encourage honesty.*) If this reading skill didn't help, challenge them to assess why not.

You do not have to limit your questions to the text headings. Ask questions about anything that you need to clarify or that will help you understand the content. *What* and *how* are probably the most common question words, but you may also ask *why*, *who*, *when*, or *where* questions. Here is an example:

Properties of Waves

Question	Answer
What is amplitude?	Amplitude is . . .

Previewing Visuals

Visuals are photographs, graphs, tables, diagrams, and illustrations. Visuals, such as this diagram of a normal fault, contain important information. Look at visuals and their captions before you read. This will help you prepare for what you will be reading about.

Often you will be asked what you want to learn about a visual. For example, after you look at the normal fault diagram, you might ask: What is the movement along a normal fault? Questions about visuals give you a purpose for reading—to answer your questions. Previewing visuals also helps you see what you already know.

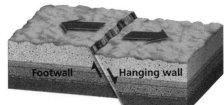

Normal Fault

Outlining

An outline shows the relationship between main ideas and supporting ideas. An outline has a formal structure. You write the main ideas, called topics, next to Roman numerals. The supporting ideas, sometimes called subtopics, are written under the main ideas and labeled A, B, C, and so on. An outline looks like this:

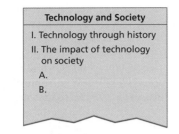

Technology and Society

I. Technology through history
II. The impact of technology on society
   A.
   B.

When you have completed an outline like this, you can see at a glance the structure of the section. You can use this outline as a study tool.

Identifying Main Ideas

When you are reading, it is important to try to understand the ideas and concepts that are in a passage. As you read science material, you will recognize that each paragraph has a lot of information and detail. Good readers try to identify the most important—or biggest—idea in every paragraph or section. That's the main idea. The other information in the paragraph supports or further explains the main idea.

Sometimes main ideas are stated directly. In this book, some main ideas are identified for you as key concepts. These are printed in bold-face type. However, you must identify other main ideas yourself. In order to do this, you must identify all the ideas within a paragraph or section. Then ask yourself which idea is big enough to include all the other ideas.

Previewing Visuals

Focus Explain to students that looking at the visuals before reading will help them activate prior knowledge and predict what they are about to read.

Teach Assign a section for students to preview the visuals. First, instruct them to write a sentence describing what the section will be about. Then, encourage them to write one or two questions for each visual to give purpose to their reading. Also have them list any prior knowledge about the subject.

Outlining

Focus Explain that using an outline format helps organize information by main topic, subtopic, and details.

Teach Choose a section in the book, and demonstrate how to make an outline for it. Make sure students understand the structure of the outline by asking: **Is this a topic or a subtopic? Where does this information go in the outline? Would I write this heading next to a Roman numeral or a capital letter?** *(Answers depend on the section being outlined.)* Also show them how to indent and add details to the outline using numerals and lowercase letters.

Identifying Main Ideas

Focus Explain that identifying main ideas and details helps sort the facts from the information into groups. Each group can have a main topic, subtopics, and details.

Teach Tell students that paragraphs are often written so that the main idea is in the first or second sentence, or in the last sentence. Assign students a page in the book. Instruct them to write the main idea for each paragraph on that page. If students have difficulty finding the main idea, suggest that they list all of the ideas given in the paragraph, and then choose the idea that is big enough to include all the others.

Comparing and Contrasting

Focus Explain that comparing and contrasting information shows how concepts, facts, and events are similar or different. The results of the comparison can have importance.

Teach Point out that Venn diagrams work best when comparing two things. To compare more than two things, students should use a compare/contrast table. Have students make a Venn diagram or compare/contrast table using two or more different sports or other activities, such as playing musical instruments. Emphasize that students should select characteristics that highlight the similarities and differences in the activities.

Sequencing

Focus Tell students that organizing information from beginning to end will help them understand a step-by-step process.

Teach Encourage students to create a flowchart to show the things they did this morning to get ready for school. Remind students that a flowchart should show the correct order in which events occur. (*A typical flowchart might include: got up ➤ took a shower ➤ got dressed ➤ ate breakfast ➤ brushed teeth ➤ gathered books and homework ➤ put on jacket.*) Then explain that a cycle diagram shows a sequence of events that is continuous. Challenge students to create a cycle diagram that shows how the weather changes with the seasons where they live. (*Most cycle diagrams will include four steps, one for each season.*)

Comparing and Contrasting

When you compare and contrast, you examine the similarities and differences between things. You can compare and contrast in a Venn diagram or in a table. Your completed diagram or table shows you how the items are alike and how they are different.

Venn Diagram A Venn diagram consists of two overlapping circles. In the space where the circles overlap, you write the characteristics that the two items have in common. In one of the circles outside the area of overlap, you write the differing features or characteristics of one of the items. In the other circle outside the area of overlap, you write the differing characteristics of the other item.

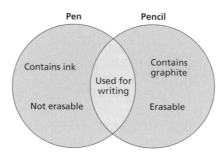

Table In a compare/contrast table, you list the items to be compared across the top of the table. Then list the characteristics or features to be compared in the left column. Complete the table by filling in information about each characteristic or feature.

Blood Vessel	Function	Structure of Wall
Artery	Carries blood away from heart	
Capillary		
Vein		

Sequencing

A sequence is the order in which a series of events occurs. Recognizing and remembering the sequence of events is important to understanding many processes in science. Sometimes the text uses words like *first, next, during,* and *after* to signal a sequence. A flowchart or a cycle diagram can help you visualize a sequence.

Flowchart To make a flowchart, write a brief description of each step or event in a box. Place the boxes in order, with the first event at the top of the page. Then draw an arrow to connect each step or event to the next.

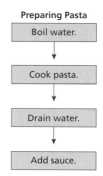

Cycle Diagram A cycle diagram shows a sequence that is continuous, or cyclical. A continuous sequence does not have an end because when the final event is over, the first event begins again. To create a cycle diagram, write the starting event in a box placed at the top of a page in the center. Then, moving in a clockwise direction around an imaginary circle, write each event in a box in its proper sequence. Draw arrows that connect each event to the one that occurs next, forming a continuous circle.

Identifying Supporting Evidence

A hypothesis is a possible explanation for observations made by scientists or an answer to a scientific question. A hypothesis is tested over and over again. The tests may produce evidence that supports the hypothesis. When enough supporting evidence is collected, a hypothesis may become a theory.

Identifying the supporting evidence for a hypothesis or theory can help you understand the hypothesis or theory. Evidence consists of facts—information whose accuracy can be confirmed by testing or observation.

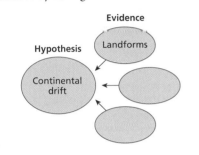

Relating Cause and Effect

Identifying causes and effects helps you understand relationships among events. A cause makes something happen. An effect is what happens. When you recognize that one event causes another, you are relating cause and effect. Words like *cause, because, effect, affect,* and *result* often signal a cause or an effect.

Sometimes an effect can have more than one cause, or a cause can produce several effects. For example, car exhaust and smoke from industrial plants are two causes of air pollution. Some effects of air pollution include breathing difficulties for some people, death of plants along some highways, and damage to some building surfaces.

Science involves many cause-and-effect relationships. Seeing and understanding these relationships helps you understand science processes.

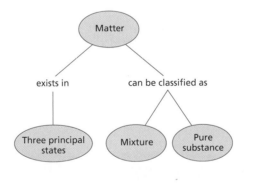

Concept Mapping

Concept maps are useful tools for organizing information on any topic. A concept map begins with a main idea or core concept and shows how the idea can be subdivided into related subconcepts or smaller ideas. In this way, relationships between concepts become clearer and easier to understand.

You construct a concept map by placing concepts (usually nouns) in ovals and connecting them with linking words. The biggest concept or idea is placed in an oval at the top of the map. Related concepts are arranged in ovals below the big idea. The linking words are often verbs and verb phrases and are written on the lines that connect the ovals.

Identifying Supporting Evidence

Focus Explain to students that identifying the supporting evidence will help them to understand the relationship between the facts and the hypothesis.

Teach Remind students that a hypothesis is neither right nor wrong, but it is either supported or not supported by the evidence from testing or observation. If evidence is found that does not support a hypothesis, the hypothesis can be changed to accommodate the new evidence, or it can be dropped.

Relating Cause and Effect

Focus Explain to students that cause is the reason for what happens. The effect is what happens in response to the cause. Relating cause and effect helps students relate the reason for what happens to what happens as a result.

Teach Emphasize that not all events that occur together have a cause-and-effect relationship. For example, tell students that you went to the grocery store and your car stalled. Ask: **Is there a cause-and-effect relationship in this situation? Explain.** (*No. Going to the grocery store could not cause a car to stall. There must be another cause to make the car stall.*)

Concept Mapping

Focus Elicit from students how a map shows the relationship of one geographic area to another. Connect this idea to how a concept map shows the relationship between terms and concepts.

Teach Challenge students to make a concept map with at least three levels of concepts to organize information about types of transportation. All students should start with the phrase *Types of transportation* at the top of the concept map. After that point, their concepts may vary. (*For example, some students might place* private transportation *and* public transportation *at the next level, while other students might choose* human-powered *and* gas-powered.) Make sure students connect the concepts with linking words.

- Complete student edition
- Video and audio
- Simulations and activities
- Section and chapter activities

Laboratory Safety

Laboratory safety is an essential element of a successful science class. Students need to understand exactly what is safe and unsafe behavior and what the rationale is behind each safety rule.

All in One Teaching Resources

- Laboratory Safety Teacher Notes
- Laboratory Safety Rules
- Laboratory Safety Symbols
- Laboratory Safety Contract

General Precautions

- Post safety rules in the classroom, and review them regularly with students before beginning every science activity.
- Familiarize yourself with the safety procedures for each activity before introducing it to your students.
- For open-ended activities like Chapter Projects, have students submit their procedures or design plans in writing and check them for safety considerations.
- Always act as an exemplary role model by displaying safe behavior.
- Know how to use safety equipment, such as fire extinguishers and fire blankets, and always have it accessible.
- Have students practice leaving the classroom quickly and orderly to prepare them for emergencies.
- Explain to students how to use the intercom or other available means of communication to get help during an emergency.
- Never leave students unattended while they are engaged in science activities.
- Provide enough space for students to safely carry out science activities.
- Instruct students to report all accidents and injuries to you immediately.

Safety Symbols

These symbols warn of possible dangers in the laboratory and remind you to work carefully.

 Safety Goggles Wear safety goggles to protect your eyes in any activity involving chemicals, flames or heating, or glassware.

 Lab Apron Wear a laboratory apron to protect your skin and clothing from damage.

Breakage Handle breakable materials, such as glassware, with care. Do not touch broken glassware.

Heat-Resistant Gloves Use an oven mitt or other hand protection when handling hot materials such as hot plates or hot glassware.

 Plastic Gloves Wear disposable plastic gloves when working with harmful chemicals and organisms. Keep your hands away from your face, and dispose of the gloves according to your teacher's instructions.

 Heating Use a clamp or tongs to pick up hot glassware. Do not touch hot objects with your bare hands.

Flames Before you work with flames, tie back loose hair and clothing. Follow instructions from your teacher about lighting and extinguishing flames.

 No Flames When using flammable materials, make sure there are no flames, sparks, or other exposed heat sources present.

Corrosive Chemical Avoid getting acid or other corrosive chemicals on your skin or clothing or in your eyes. Do not inhale the vapors. Wash your hands after the activity.

 Poison Do not let any poisonous chemical come into contact with your skin, and do not inhale its vapors. Wash your hands when you are finished with the activity.

 Fumes Work in a ventilated area when harmful vapors may be involved. Avoid inhaling vapors directly. Only test an odor when directed to do so by your teacher, and use a wafting motion to direct the vapor toward your nose.

 Sharp Object Scissors, scalpels, knives, needles, pins, and tacks can cut your skin. Always direct a sharp edge or point away from yourself and others.

 Animal Safety Treat live or preserved animals or animal parts with care to avoid harming the animals or yourself. Wash your hands when you are finished with the activity.

 Plant Safety Handle plants only as directed by your teacher. If you are allergic to certain plants, tell your teacher; do not do an activity involving those plants. Avoid touching harmful plants such as poison ivy. Wash your hands when you are finished with the activity.

 Electric Shock To avoid electric shock, never use electrical equipment around water, or when the equipment is wet or your hands are wet. Be sure cords are untangled and cannot trip anyone. Unplug equipment not in use.

 Physical Safety When an experiment involves physical activity, avoid injuring yourself or others. Alert your teacher if there is any reason you should not participate.

 Disposal Dispose of chemicals and other laboratory materials safely. Follow the instructions from your teacher.

 Hand Washing Wash your hands thoroughly when finished with the activity. Use antibacterial soap and warm water. Rinse well.

General Safety Awareness When this symbol appears, follow the instructions provided. When you are asked to develop your own procedure in a lab, have your teacher approve your plan before you go further.

End-of-Experiment Rules

- Always have students use warm water and soap for washing their hands.

Heating and Fire Safety

- No flammable substances should be in use around hot plates, light bulbs, or open flames.
- Test tubes should be heated only in water baths.

- Students should be permitted to strike matches to light candles or burners *only* with strict supervision. When possible, you should light the flames, especially when working with younger students.
- Be sure to have proper ventilation when fumes are produced during a procedure.
- All electrical equipment used in the lab should have GFI (Ground Fault Interrupter) switches.

Science Safety Rules

General Precautions

Follow all instructions. Never perform activities without the approval and supervision of your teacher. Do not engage in horseplay. Never eat or drink in the laboratory. Keep work areas clean and uncluttered.

Dress Code

Wear safety goggles whenever you work with chemicals, glassware, heat sources such as burners, or any substance that might get into your eyes. If you wear contact lenses, notify your teacher.

Wear a lab apron or coat whenever you work with corrosive chemicals or substances that can stain. Wear disposable plastic gloves when working with organisms and harmful chemicals. Tie back long hair. Remove or tie back any article of clothing or jewelry that can hang down and touch chemicals, flames, or equipment. Roll up long sleeves. Never wear open shoes or sandals.

First Aid

Report all accidents, injuries, or fires to your teacher, no matter how minor. Be aware of the location of the first-aid kit, emergency equipment such as the fire extinguisher and fire blanket, and the nearest telephone. Know whom to contact in an emergency.

Heating and Fire Safety

Keep all combustible materials away from flames. When heating a substance in a test tube, make sure that the mouth of the tube is not pointed at you or anyone else. Never heat a liquid in a closed container. Use an oven mitt to pick up a container that has been heated.

Using Chemicals Safely

Never put your face near the mouth of a container that holds chemicals. Never touch, taste, or smell a chemical unless your teacher tells you to.

Use only those chemicals needed in the activity. Keep all containers closed when chemicals are not being used. Pour all chemicals over the sink or a container, not over your work surface. Dispose of excess chemicals as instructed by your teacher.

Be extra careful when working with acids or bases. When mixing an acid and water, always pour the water into the container first and then add the acid to the water. Never pour water into an acid. Wash chemical spills and splashes immediately with plenty of water.

Using Glassware Safely

If glassware is broken or chipped, notify your teacher immediately. Never handle broken or chipped glass with your bare hands.

Never force glass tubing or thermometers into a rubber stopper or rubber tubing. Have your teacher insert the glass tubing or thermometer if required for an activity.

Using Sharp Instruments

Handle sharp instruments with extreme care. Never cut material toward you; cut away from you.

Animal and Plant Safety

Never perform experiments that cause pain, discomfort, or harm to animals. Only handle animals if absolutely necessary. If you know that you are allergic to certain plants, molds, or animals, tell your teacher before doing an activity in which these are used. Wash your hands thoroughly after any activity involving animals, animal parts, plants, plant parts, or soil.

During field work, wear long pants, long sleeves, socks, and closed shoes. Avoid poisonous plants and fungi as well as plants with thorns.

End-of-Experiment Rules

Unplug all electrical equipment. Clean up your work area. Dispose of waste materials as instructed by your teacher. Wash your hands after every experiment.

Appendix A ◆ 185

Handling Organisms Safely

- In an activity where students are directed to taste something, be sure to store the material in clean, *nonscience* containers. Distribute the material to students in *new* plastic or paper dispensables, which should be discarded after the tasting. Tasting or eating should never be done in a lab classroom.

- When growing bacterial cultures, use only disposable petri dishes. After streaking, the dishes should be sealed and not opened again by students. After the lab, students should return the unopened dishes to you.

- Two methods are recommended for the safe disposal of bacterial cultures. *First method:* Autoclave the petri dishes and discard them without opening. *Second method:* If no autoclave is available, carefully open the dishes (never have a student do this), pour full-strength bleach into the dishes, and let them stand for a day. Then pour the bleach from the petri dishes down a drain, and flush the drain with lots of water. Tape the petri dishes back together, and place them in a sealed plastic bag. Wrap the plastic bag with a brown paper bag or newspaper, and tape securely. Throw the sealed package in the trash. Thoroughly disinfect the work area with bleach.

- To grow mold, use a new, sealable plastic bag that is two to three times larger than the material to be placed inside. Seal the bag and tape it shut. After the bag is sealed, students should not open it. To dispose of the bag and mold culture, make a small cut near an edge of the bag, and cook the bag in a microwave oven on a high setting for at least one minute. Discard the bag according to local ordinance, usually in the trash.

- Students should wear disposable nitrile, latex, or food-handling gloves when handling live animals or nonliving specimens.

Using Glassware Safely

- Use plastic containers, graduated cylinders, and beakers whenever possible. If using glass, students should wear safety goggles.
- Use only nonmercury thermometers with anti-roll protectors.

Using Chemicals Safely

- When students use both chemicals and microscopes in one activity, microscopes should be in a separate part of the room from the chemicals so that when students remove their goggles to use the microscopes, their eyes are not at risk.

Use these star charts to locate bright stars and major constellations in the night sky at different times of year. Choose the appropriate star chart for the current season.

Autumn Sky

This chart works best at the following dates and times: September 1 at 10:00 P.M., October 1 at 8:00 P.M., or November 1 at 6:00 P.M. Look for the constellations Ursa Minor (the Little Dipper) and Cassiopeia in the northern sky, and for the star Deneb, which is nearly overhead in autumn.

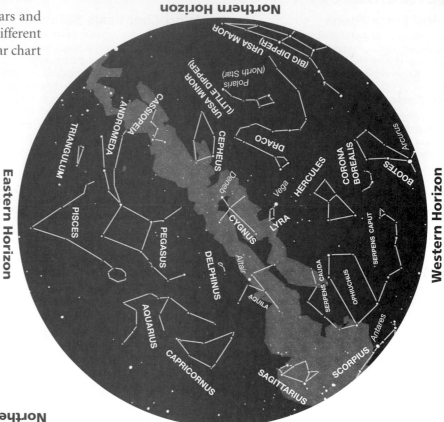

Winter Sky

This chart works best at the following dates and times: December 1 at 10:00 P.M., January 1 at 8:00 P.M., or February 1 at 6:00 P.M. Look for the constellations Orion and Gemini, the bright star Sirius, and the Pleiades, a star cluster, in the winter sky.

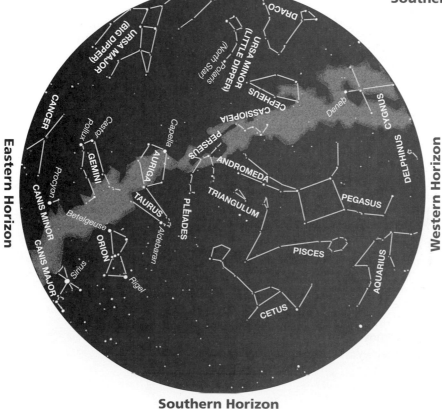

Using a flashlight and a compass, hold the appropriate chart and turn it so that the direction you are facing is at the bottom of the chart. These star charts work best at 34° north latitude, but can be used at other central latitudes.

Spring Sky

This chart works best at the following dates and times: March 1 at 10:00 P.M., March 15 at 9:00 P.M., or April 1 at 8:00 P.M. Look for the constellations Ursa Major (which contains the Big Dipper), Bootes, and Leo in the spring sky. The bright stars Arcturus and Spica can be seen in the east.

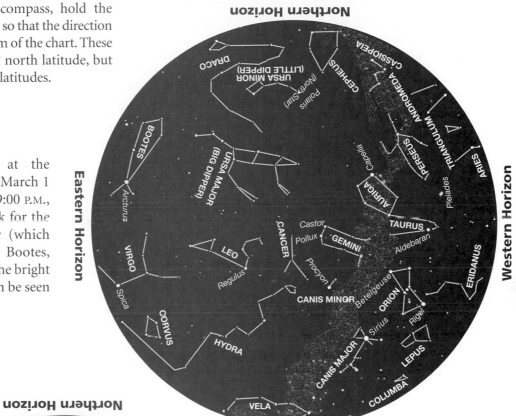

Summer Sky

This chart works best at the following dates and times: May 15 at 11:00 P.M., June 1 at 10:00 P.M., or June 15 at 9:00 P.M. Look for the bright star Arcturus in the constellations Bootes and Hercules overhead in early summer. Towards the east look for the bright stars Vega, Altair, and Deneb, which form a triangle.

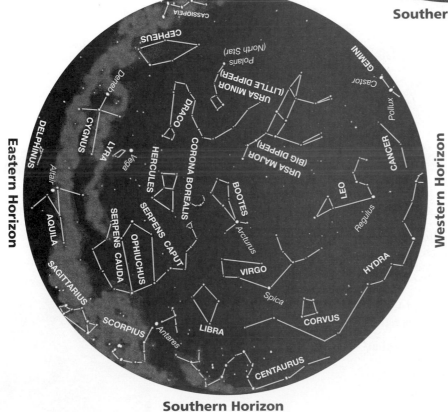

English and Spanish Glossary

A

absolute brightness The brightness a star would have if it were at a standard distance from Earth. (p. 129)
magnitud absoluta Brillo que tendría una estrella si estuviera a una distancia estándar de la Tierra.

apparent brightness The brightness of a star as seen from Earth. (p. 129)
magnitud aparente Brillo de una estrella visto desde la Tierra.

asteroid belt The region of the solar system between the orbits of Mars and Jupiter, where many asteroids are found. (p. 106)
cinturón de asteroides Región del sistema solar entre las órbitas de Marte y Júpiter, donde se encuentran muchos asteroides.

asteroids Rocky objects revolving around the sun that are too small and numerous to be considered planets. (p. 106)
asteroides Objetos rocosos que se mueven alrededor del Sol y que son demasiado pequeños y numerosos como para ser considerados planetas.

astronomy The study of the moon, stars, and other objects in space. (p. 6)
astronomía Estudio de la luna, las estrellas y otros objetos del espacio.

axis An imaginary line that passes through Earth's center and the North and South poles, about which Earth rotates. (p. 7)
eje Línca imaginaria que pasa a través del centro de la Tierra, por los polos Norte y Sur, sobre el cual gira la Tierra.

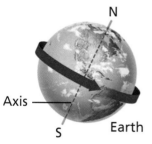

N

Axis

S   Earth

B

big bang The initial explosion that resulted in the formation and expansion of the universe. (p. 148)
big bang Explosión inicial que dio como resultado la formación y expansión del universo.

binary star A star system with two stars. (p. 142)
estrella binaria Sistema de estrellas con dos estrellas.

black hole An object whose gravity is so strong that nothing, not even light, can escape. (p. 140)
agujero negro Objeto cuya gravedad es tan fuerte que nada, ni siquiera la luz, puede escapar.

C

calendar A system of organizing time that defines the beginning, length, and divisions of a year. (p. 8)
calendario Sistema de organización del tiempo que define el principio, la duración y las divisiones de un año.

chromosphere The middle layer of the sun's atmosphere. (p. 80)
cromosfera Capa central en la atmósfera del Sol.

coma The fuzzy outer layer of a comet. (p. 105)
coma Capa exterior y difusa de un cometa.

comet A loose collection of ice, dust, and small rocky particles, typically with a long, narrow orbit. (p. 105)
cometa Conjunto no compacto de hielo, polvo y partículas rocosas pequeñas, que normalmente tiene una órbita larga y estrecha.

constellation An imaginary pattern of stars in the sky. (p. 126)
constelación Patrón imaginario de estrellas en el cielo.

convection zone The outermost layer of the sun's interior. (p. 79)
zona de convección Capa más superficial del interior del Sol.

convex lens A piece of transparent glass curved so that the middle is thicker than the edges. (p. 120)
lente convexa Trozo de cristal transparente curvado de tal manera que el centro es más grueso que los extremos.

core The central region of the sun, where nuclear fusion takes place. (p. 79)
núcleo Región central del Sol, donde ocurre la fusión nuclear.

corona The outer layer of the sun's atmosphere. (p. 80)
corona Capa externa de la atmósfera del Sol.

cosmic background radiation The electromagnetic radiation left over from the big bang. (p. 150)
radiación cósmica de fondo Radiación electromagnética que quedó del big bang.

crater A large round pit caused by the impact of a meteoroid. (p. 31)
cráter Gran cuenca redonda causada por el impacto de un meteoroide.

D

dark energy A mysterious force that appears to be causing the expansion of the universe to accelerate.
energía negra Misteriosa fuerza que parece acelerar la expansión del universo. (p. 152)

dark matter Matter that does not give off electromagnetic radiation but is quite abundant in the universe. (p. 152)
materia negra Materia que no despide radiación electromagnética, pero que es muy abundante en el universo.

E

eclipse The partial or total blocking of one object in space by another. (p. 23)
eclipse Bloqueo parcial o total de un objeto en el espacio por otro.

eclipsing binary A binary star system in which one star periodically blocks the light from the other. (p. 142)
eclipse binario Sistema de estrella binaria en el que una estrella bloquea periódicamente la luz de la otra.

electromagnetic radiation Energy that travels through space in the form of waves. (p. 119)
radiación electromagnética Energía que viaja a través del espacio en forma de ondas.

ellipse An oval shape, which may be elongated or nearly circular; the shape of the planets' orbits. (p. 75)
elipse Círculo alargado de forma ovalada; la forma de la órbita de los planetas.

elliptical galaxy A galaxy shaped like a round or flattened ball, generally containing only old stars. (p. 144)
galaxia elíptica Galaxia con forma de pelota aplastada, que generalmente está formada sólo de estrellas viejas.

equinox The two days of the year on which neither hemisphere is tilted toward or away from the sun. (p. 13)
equinoccio Los dos días del año en los que ningún hemisferio está inclinado hacia el Sol ni más lejos de él.

escape velocity The velocity an object must reach to fly beyond a planet's or moon's gravitational pull. (p. 43)
velocidad de escape Velocidad que debe alcanzar un cohete para salir del empuje gravitacional de un planeta o luna.

extraterrestrial life Life that exists other than that on Earth. (p. 108)
vida extraterrestre Vida que existe fuera de la Tierra.

F

force A push or a pull exerted on an object. (p. 16)
fuerza Empuje o atracción ejercida sobre un objeto.

G

galaxy A huge group of single stars, star systems, star clusters, dust, and gas bound together by gravity.
galaxia Enorme grupo de estrellas individuales, sistemas de estrellas, cúmulos de estrellas, polvo y gas unidos por la gravedad. (p. 144)

gas giants The name often given to the first four outer planets: Jupiter, Saturn, Uranus, and Neptune. (p. 95)
gigantes gaseosos Nombre que normalmente se da a los cuatro primeros planetas exteriores: Júpiter, Saturno, Urano y Neptuno.

geocentric A model of the universe in which Earth is at the center of the revolving planets and stars. (p. 73)
geocéntrico Modelo del universo en el que la Tierra es el centro de los planetas y estrellas que giran alrededor de ella.

geosynchronous orbit An orbit in which a satellite orbits Earth at the same rate as Earth rotates and thus stays over the same place all the time. (p. 62)
órbita geosíncrona Órbita en la que un satélite orbita la Tierra a la misma velocidad que rota la Tierra y que, por lo tanto, permanece sobre ese lugar permanentemente.

globular cluster A large, round, densely-packed grouping of older stars. (p. 143)
cúmulo globular Conjunto grande y redondo de estrellas viejas densamente apretadas.

gravity The attractive force between objects; its strength depends on their masses and the distance between them. (p. 16)
gravedad Fuerza de atracción entre los objetos; su fuerza depende de sus masas y de la distancia que les separa.

greenhouse effect The trapping of heat by a planet's atmosphere. (p. 88)
efecto invernadero Acumulación de calor en la atmósfera de un planeta.

H

heliocentric A model of the solar system in which Earth and the other planets revolve around the sun. (p. 74)
heliocéntrico Modelo del sistema solar en el que la Tierra y otros planetas giran alrededor del Sol.

Hertzsprung-Russell diagram A graph relating the surface temperatures and absolute brightnesses of stars. (p. 132)
diagrama Hertzsprung-Russel Gráfica que muestra la relación entre las temperaturas en la superficie de las estrellas y su magnitud absoluta.

Hubble's law The observation that the farther away a galaxy is, the faster it is moving away. (p. 149)
ley de Hubble Observación que enuncia que mientras más lejos de nosotros se encuentra una galaxia, más rápido se está alejando.

I

inertia The tendency of an object to resist a change in motion. (p. 18)
inercia Tendencia de un objeto a resistir un cambio en su movimiento.

irregular galaxy A galaxy that does not have a regular shape. (p. 144)
galaxia irregular Galaxia que no tiene una forma regular.

K

Kuiper belt A doughnut-shaped region that stretches from around Pluto's orbit to about 100 times Earth's distance from the sun. (p. 105)
cinturón de Kuiper Región en forma de disco que se extiende desde la órbita de Plutón hasta alrededor de 100 veces la distancia de la Tierra al Sol.

L

law of universal gravitation The scientific law that states that every object in the universe attracts every other object. (p. 16)
ley de gravitación universal Ley científica que establece que todos los objetos del universo se atraen entre ellos.

light-year The distance that light travels in one year, about 9.5 million million kilometers. (p. 130)
año luz Distancia a la que viaja la luz en un año; alrededor de 9.5 millones de millones de kilómetros.

lunar eclipse The blocking of sunlight to the moon that occurs when Earth is directly between the sun and the moon. (p. 25)
eclipse lunar Bloqueo de la luz solar sobre la Luna llena que ocurre cuando la Tierra se interpone entre el Sol y la Luna.

M

main sequence A diagonal area on an H-R diagram that includes more than 90 percent of all stars.
secuencia principal Área diagonal en un diagrama de H-R que incluye más del 90 por ciento de todas las estrellas. (p. 133)

maria Dark, flat areas on the moon's surface formed from huge ancient lava flows. (p. 31)
maria Áreas oscuras y llanas en la superficie de la Luna formadas por enormes flujos de lava antiguos.

mass The amount of matter in an object. (p. 17)
masa Cantidad de materia que hay en un objeto.

meteor A streak of light in the sky produced by the burning of a meteoroid in Earth's atmosphere. (p. 107)
meteoro Rayo de luz en el cielo producido por el incendio de un meteoroide en la atmósfera de la Tierra.

meteorite A meteoroid that passes through the atmosphere and hits Earth's surface. (p. 107)
meteorito Meteoroide que pasa por la atmósfera y golpea la superficie de la Tierra.

meteoroid A chunk of rock or dust in space. (pp. 31, 107)
meteoroide Pedazo de roca o polvo en el espacio.

microgravity The condition of experiencing weightlessness in orbit. (p. 59)
microgravedad Condición de experimentar falta de peso en órbita.

neap tide The tide with the least difference between consecutive low and high tides. (p. 27)
marea muerta Marea con la mínima diferencia entre consecutivas marea alta y marea baja.

nebula A large cloud of gas and dust in space, spread out in an immense volume. (p. 137)
nebulosa Gran nube de gas y polvo en el espacio, expandida en un volumen inmenso.

neutron star The small, dense remains of a high-mass star after a supernova. (p. 139)
estrella de neutrones Restos pequeños y densos de una estrella de gran masa después de una supernova.

Newton's first law of motion The scientific law that states that an object at rest will stay at rest and an object in motion will stay in motion with a constant speed and direction unless acted on by a force. (p. 18)
Primera ley de movimiento de Newton Ley científica que establece que un objeto en reposo se mantendrá en reposo y un objeto en movimiento se mantendrá en movimiento con una velocidad y dirección constante a menos que se ejerza una fuerza sobre él.

nuclear fusion The process by which hydrogen atoms join together in the sun's core to form helium. (p. 79)
fusión nuclear Proceso por el cual los átomos de hidrógeno se unen en el núcleo del Sol para formar helio.

nucleus The solid inner core of a comet. (p. 105)
núcleo Centro interno sólido de un cometa.

observatory A building that contains one or more telescopes. (p. 122)
observatorio Edificio que contiene uno o más telescopios.

Oort cloud A spherical region of comets that surrounds the solar system. (p. 105)
nube de Oort Región esférica de cometas que rodea el sistema solar.

open cluster A star cluster that has a loose, disorganized appearance and contains no more than a few thousand stars. (p. 143)
cúmulo abierto Cúmulo de estrellas que tiene una apariencia no compacta y desorganizada, y que no contiene más de unas pocos miles de estrellas.

optical telescope A telescope that uses lenses or mirrors to collect and focus visible light. (p. 120)
telescopio óptico Telescopio que usa lentes o espejos para captar y enfocar la luz visible.

orbit The path of an object as it revolves around another object in space. (p. 7)
órbita Trayectoria de un objeto a medida que gira alrededor de otro en el espacio.

orbital velocity The velocity a rocket must achieve to establish an orbit around a body in space. (p. 42)
velocidad orbital Velocidad que un cohete debe alcanzar para establecer una órbita alrededor de un cuerpo en el espacio.

parallax The apparent change in position of an object when seen from different places. (p. 130)
paralaje Cambio aparente en la posición de un objeto cuando es visto desde diferentes lugares.

penumbra The part of a shadow surrounding the darkest part. (p. 24)
penumbra Parte de una sombra que rodea la parte más oscura.

phase One of the different apparent shapes of the moon as seen from Earth. (p. 21)
fase Una de las diferentes formas aparentes de la Luna según se ve desde la Tierra.

photosphere The inner layer of the sun's atmosphere that gives off its visible light (p. 80)
fotosfera Capa más interna de la atmósfera del Sol que provoca la luz que vemos; superficie del Sol.

planetesimal One of the small asteroid-like bodies that formed the building blocks of the planets. (p. 151)
planetesimal Uno de los cuerpos pequeños parecidos a asteroides que dieron origen a los planetas.

prominence A huge, reddish loop of gas that protrudes from the sun's surface, linking parts of sunspot regions. (p. 82)
prominencia Enorme burbuja rojiza de gas que sobresale de la superfice del Sol, que une partes de las regiones de las manchas solares.

protostar A contracting cloud of gas and dust with enough mass to form a star. (p. 137)
protoestrella Nube de gas y polvo que se contrae, con suficiente masa como para formar una estrella.

pulsar A rapidly spinning neutron star that produces radio waves. (p. 139)
púlsar Estrella de neutrones que gira rápidamente y produce ondas de radio.

Q

quasar An enormously bright, distant galaxy with a giant black hole at its center. (p. 144)
quásar Galaxia extraordinariamente luminosa y distante con un agujero negro gigante en el centro.

R

radiation zone A region of very tightly packed gas in the sun's interior where energy is transferred mainly in the form of light. (p. 79)
zona radioactiva Región de gases estrechamente comprimidos en el interior del Sol en donde se transfiere la energía principalmente en forma de luz.

radio telescope A device used to detect radio waves from objects in space. (p. 121)
radiotelescopio Aparato usado para detectar ondas de radio de los objetos en el espacio.

reflecting telescope A telescope that uses a curved mirror to collect and focus light. (p. 121)
telescopio de reflexión Telescopio que usa un espejo curvado para captar y enfocar la luz.

refracting telescope A telescope that uses convex lenses to gather and focus light. (p. 120)
telescopio de refracción Telescopio que usa lentes convexas para captar y enfocar la luz.

remote sensing The collection of information about Earth and other objects in space using satellites or probes. (p. 62)
percepción remota Recolección de información sobre la Tierra y otros objetos en el espacio usando satélites o sondas.

revolution The movement of an object around another object. (p. 7)
revolución Movimiento de un objeto alrededor de otro.

ring A thin disk of small ice and rock particles surrounding a planet. (p. 95)
anillo Disco fino de pequeñas partículas de hielo y roca que rodea un planeta.

rocket A device that expels gas in one direction to move in the opposite direction. (p. 41)
cohete Aparato que expulsa gas en una dirección para moverse en la dirección opuesta.

rotation The spinning motion of a planet on its axis. (p. 7)
rotación Movimiento giratorio de un planeta sobre su eje.

rover A small robotic space probe that can move about the surface of a planet or moon. (p. 56)
rover Pequeña sonda espacial robótica que puede moverse sobre la superficie de un planeta o sobre la Luna.

S

satellite An object that revolves around another object in space. (p. 49)
satélite Objeto que gira alrededor de otro objeto en el espacio.

scientific notation A mathematical method of writing numbers using powers of ten. (p. 146)
notación científica Método matemático de escritura de números que usa la potencia de diez.

solar eclipse The blocking of sunlight to Earth that occurs when the moon is directly between the sun and Earth. (p. 24)
eclipse solar Bloqueo de la luz solar en su camino a la Tierra que ocurre cuando la Luna se interpone entre el Sol y la Tierra.

solar flare An eruption of gas from the sun's surface that occurs when the loops in sunspot regions suddenly connect. (p. 82)
destello solar Erupción de gas desde la superficie del Sol que ocurre cuando las burbujas en las regiones de las manchas solares se unen repentinamente.

solar nebula A large cloud of gas and dust, such as the one that formed our solar system. (p. 151)
nebulosa solar Gran nube de gas y polvo como la que forma nuestro sistema solar.

solar wind A stream of electrically charged particles that emanate from the sun's corona. (p. 80)
viento solar Flujo de partículas cargadas eléctricamente que emanan de la corona del Sol.

solstice The two days of the year on which the sun reaches its greatest distance north or south of the equator. (p. 12)
solsticio Los dos días del año en que el Sol está a mayor distancia hacia norte o hacia el sur del ecuador.

space probe A spacecraft that has various scientific instruments that can collect data, including visual images, but has no human crew. (p. 56)
sonda espacial Nave espacial que tiene varios instrumentos científicos que pueden reunir datos, incluyendo imágenes, pero que no lleva tripulación.

space shuttle A spacecraft that can carry a crew into space, return to Earth, and then be reused for the same purpose. (p. 54)
transbordador espacial Nave espacial que puede llevar a una tripulación al espacio, volver a la Tierra, y luego volver a ser usada para el mismo propósito.

space spinoff An item that has uses on Earth but was originally developed for use in space. (p. 60)
derivación espacial Objeto que se puede usar en la Tierra, pero que originalmente se construyó para ser usado en el espacio.

space station A large artificial satellite on which people can live and work for long periods. (p. 55)
estación espacial Enorme satélite artificial en el que la gente puede vivir y trabajar durante largos períodos.

spectrograph An instrument that separates light into colors and makes an image of the resulting spectrum. (p. 128)
espectrógrafo Instrumento que separa la luz en colores y crea una imagen del espectro resultante.

spectrum The range of wavelengths of electromagnetic waves. (p. 119)
espectro Abanico de longitudes de ondas electromagnéticas.

spiral galaxy A galaxy with a bulge in the middle and arms that spiral outward in a pinwheel pattern. (p. 144)
galaxia espiral Galaxia con una protuberancia en el centro y brazos que giran en espiral hacia el exterior, como un remolino.

spring tide The tide with the greatest difference between consecutive low and high tides. (p. 27)
marea viva Marea con la mayor diferencia entre mareas alta y baja consecutivas.

sunspot A dark area of gas on the sun's surface that is cooler than surrounding gases. (p. 80)
mancha solar Área oscura de gas en la superficie del Sol, que está más fría que los gases que la rodean.

supernova The brilliant explosion of a dying supergiant star. (p. 139)
supernova Explosión brillante de una estrella supergigante en extinción.

telescope A device built to observe distant objects by making them appear closer. (pp. 30, 118)
telescopio Aparato construido para observar objetos distantes que hace que aparezcan más cercanos.

terrestrial planets The name often given to the four inner planets: Mercury, Venus, Earth, and Mars. (p. 84)
planetas telúricos Nombre dado normalmente a los cuatro planetas interiores: Mercurio, Venus, Tierra y Marte.

thrust The reaction force that propels a rocket forward. (p. 42)
empuje Fuerza de reacción que propulsa un cohete hacia delante.

tide The periodic rise and fall of the level of water in the ocean. (p. 26)
marea La subida y bajada periodica del nivel de agua en el océano.

umbra The darkest part of a shadow. (p. 24)
umbra La parte más oscura de una sombra.

universe All of space and everything in it. (p. 146)
universo Todo el espacio y todo lo que hay en él.

vacuum A place that is empty of all matter. (p. 59)
vacío Lugar en donde no existe materia.

velocity Speed in a given direction. (p. 42)
velocidad Rapidez en una dirección dada.

visible light Electromagnetic radiation that can be seen with the unaided eye. (p. 119)
luz visible Radiación electromagnética que se puede ver a simple vista.

wavelength The distance between the crest of one wave and the crest of the next wave. (p. 119)
longitud de onda Distancia entre la cresta de una onda y la cresta de la siguiente onda.

weight The force of gravity on an object. (p. 17)
peso Fuerza de la gravedad que actúa sobre un objeto.

white dwarf The blue-white hot core of a star that is left behind after its outer layers have expanded and drifted out into space. (p. 138)
enana blanca Núcleo caliente azul blanquecino de una estrella, que queda después de que sus capas externas se han expandido y viajan por el espacio.

Index

Page numbers for key terms are printed in **boldface** type.
Page numbers for illustrations, maps, and charts are printed in *italics*.

Teacher's Edition entries appear in **blue type.** The page on which a term is defined is indicated in **boldface** type.

Index

Page numbers for key terms are printed in **boldface** type.
Page numbers for illustrations, maps, and charts are printed in *italics*.

Index

Page numbers for key terms are printed in **boldface** type.
Page numbers for illustrations, maps, and charts are printed in *italics*.

Acknowledgments

Activity on page 42 is from *Exploring Planets in the Classroom,* © Hawaii Space Grant Consortium. Used with permission.

Quote on page 53 by Janet Kavandi is from *Space Shuttle: The First 20 Years,* edited by Tony Reichhardt for Air & Space/Smithsonian Magazine. Published in the United States by DK Publishing, Inc.

Excerpt on page 159 is from *The Mystery of Mars* by Sally Ride and Tam O'Shaughnessy. Copyright © by Sally K. Ride and Tam E. O'Shaughnessy. Used by permission of Crown Publishers, an imprint of Random House Children's Books, a division of Random House, Inc.

Staff Credits

Scott Andrews, Jennifer Angel, Laura Baselice, Carolyn Belanger, Barbara A. Bertell, Suzanne Biron, Peggy Bliss, Stephanie Bradley, James Brady, Anne M. Bray, Kerry Cashman, Jonathan Cheney, Joshua D. Clapper, Lisa J. Clark, Bob Craton, Patricia Cully, Patricia M. Dambry, Kathy Dempsey, Emily Ellen, Thomas Ferreira, Jonathan Fisher, Patricia Fromkin, Paul Gagnon, Robert Graham, Ellen Granter, Barbara Hollingdale, Etta Jacobs, Linda Johnson, Anne Jones, John Judge, Kevin Keane, Kelly Kelliher, Toby Klang, Russ Lappa, Carolyn Lock, Rebecca Loveys, Constance J. McCarty, Carolyn B. McGuire, Ranida Touranont McKneally, Anne McLaughlin, Eve Melnechuk, Tania Mlawer, Janet Morris, Francine Neumann, Marie Opera, Jill Ort, Joan Paley, Dorothy Preston, Rashid Ross, Siri Schwartzman, Laurel Smith, Emily Soltanoff, Jennifer A. Teece, Diane Walsh, Amanda M. Watters, Merce Wilczek, Amy Winchester, Char Lyn Yeakley. **Additional Credits** Tara Allamilla, Terence Hegarty, Louise Gachet, Andrea Golden, Stephanie Rogers, Kim Schmidt, Joan Tobin.

Illustration

All art developed and produced by **Morgan Cain & Associates,** unless otherwise noted. **Kerry Cashman**: 26, 69, 86–87, 89, 98–99, 101, 104, 117, 120, 146–147. **Richard McMahon**: 8, 122.

Photography

Photo Research John Judge

Cover Image top, © 2003 Jerry Lodriguss; **bottom,** Bill Brooks/Masterfile Corporation.

Page vi, SOHO/ESA and NASA; **vii,** Richard Haynes; **viii,** Richard Haynes; **x all,** SOHO/ESA and NASA; **1,** Ken O'Donoghue; **2,** Ken O'Donoghue; **3t,** SOHO/ESA and NASA; **3b,** Ken O'Donoghue

Chapter 1
Pages 4-–5, Evad Damast; **5r,** Richard Haynes; **6t,** Richard Haynes; **6b,** Eric Lessing/Art Resource, NY; **7t,** Jeff Haynes/AFP/Corbis; **7b,** Paul Sutton/Duomo/Corbis; **8l,** Lawrence Migdale/Photo Researchers, Inc.; **8r,** Ancient Art & Architecture Collection, Ltd.; **9l,** Janet Wishnetsky/Corbis; **9m,** Hazel Hankin/Stock Boston; **9r,** The Granger Collection; **12l,** Paul A. Souders/Corbis; **12r,** Bill Ross/Corbis; **13l,** Tony Stewart/PhotoNewZealand.com; **13r,** Dennis Degnan/Corbis; **15,** Richard Haynes; **16–17,** Paul & Linda Marie Ambrose/Getty Images, Inc.; **20,** Richard Haynes; **21,** E. R. Degginger/Animals Animals/Earth Scenes; **22l,** John Bova/Photo Researchers, Inc.; **22m,** John Bova/Photo Researchers, Inc.; **22r,** John Bova/Photo Researchers, Inc.; **22–23background,** Gerry Ellis/Minden Pictures; **23tl,** John Bova/Photo Researchers, Inc.; **23tml,** John Bova/Photo Researchers, Inc.; **23tmr,** John Bova/Photo Researchers, Inc.; **23tr,** John Bova/Photo Researchers, Inc.; **23b,** Dorling Kindersley; **24,** Digital Vision/Getty Images, Inc.; **25,** G. Antonio Milani/SPL/Photo Researchers, Inc.; **26t,** Bill Bachman/Photo Researchers, Inc.; **26b,** Bill Bachman/Photo Researchers, Inc.; **29,** Richard Haynes; **30t,** Richard Haynes; **30b,** Jay M. Pasachoff; **31all,** NASA; **32t,** John Bova/Photo Researchers, Inc.; **32b,** NASA; **34tl,** Paul Sutton/Duomo/Corbis; **34tr,** Jeff Haynes/AFP/Corbis; **34b,** NASA.

Chapter 2
Pages 38–39, NASA; **39 inset,** NASA; **40t,** Richard Haynes; **40b,** Johnson Space Center/NASA; **41,** Jeff Hunter/Getty Images Inc.; **41inset,** U.S. Civil Air Patrol; **43,** Reto Stockli/GSFC/NASA; **46–47all,** Richard Haynes; **48,** TASS/Sovfoto; **49l,** NASA; **49r,** NASA; **50l,** NASA; **50r,** N. Armstrong/Corbis; **51,** World Perspectives/Getty Images, Inc.; **52,** John Frassanito & Associates; **53,** NASA; **54,** NASA; **55,** NASA; **56l,** JPL/NASA; **56r,** Roger Arno/NASA; **57l,** JPL/NASA; **57r,** David Ducros/Science Photo Library/Photo Researchers, Inc.; **58,** Richard Haynes; **59,** NASA; **60l,** Princess Margaret Rose Orthopaedic Hospital/Science Photo Library/Photo Researchers, Inc.; **60r,** Getty Images, Inc.; **61l,** FRANCK FIFE/AFP/Getty Images, Inc.; **61m,** Smith Sport Optics; **61r,** Pascal Rondeau/Getty Images, Inc.; **62,** NASA/GSFC/Boston University; **63,** Russ Lappa; **65,** Bob Daemmrich/Photo Edit; **66l,** World Perspectives/Getty Images, Inc.; **66r,** NASA.

Chapter 3
Pages 70–71, Detlev Van Ravenswaay/Photo Researchers, Inc.; **71inset,** Richard Haynes; **72,** David Malin/Anglo-Australian Observatory; **73,** The Granger Collection, NY; **74bl,** Science Photo Library/Photo Researchers, Inc.; **74bm,** Photo Researchers, Inc.; **74br,** James A. Sugar/Corbis; **74t,** Bettmann/Corbis; **75l,** Explorer-Keystone-France/Gamma Press USA; **75m,** The Art Archive/Royal Society; **75r,** Corbis Bettmann; **78,** Richard Haynes; **78–79,** SOHO/ESA and NASA; **80,** Dr. Fred Espenak/Science Photo Library/Photo Researchers, Inc.; **81bl,** National Solar Observatory; **81br,** AURA/STScI/NASA; **81t,** SOHO/ESA and NASA; **82,** Ron Sanford/Getty Images, Inc.; **86b,** NASA; **86t,** Julian Baum/Dorling Kindersley; **87b,** NASA; **87tl,** NASA; **87tr,** JPL/NASA; **88,** David Anderson/NASA/Photo Researchers, Inc.; **89b,** Hubble Heritage Team/NASA; **89t,** NASA; **90–91,** JPL/NASA; **91inset,** U.S. Geological Survey; **92b,** Pat Rawlings/NASA; **92–93t,** NASA; **93inset,** Pat Rawlings/NASA; **94,** NASA; **96l,** NASA/SPL/Photo Researchers, Inc.; **96r,** Martin Cropper/Dorling Kindersley; **97b,** David Seal/JPL/CalTech/NASA; **97ml,** JPL/NASA; **97mr,** Corbis; **97tl,** Reuters NewMedia Inc./Corbis; **97tr,** NASA; **98l,** NASA and The Hubble Heritage Team; **98r,** AFP/Corbis; **99b,** Kenneth Seidelmann, U.S. Naval Observatory/NASA; **99t,** Dorling Kindersley/Jet Propulsion Lab; **100l,** Julian Baum/Dorling Kindersley; **100r,** NASA; **101l,** Dorling Kindersley; **101r,** Lynette Cook/Photo Researchers, Inc.; **102,** Richard Haynes; **103,** Richard Haynes; **104t,** Richard Haynes; **104-105,** Jerry Lodriguss /Photo Researchers, Inc.; **105inset,** Dorling Kindersley; **106,** NEAR Project/NLR/JHUAPL/Goddard SVS/NASA; **107,** Frank Zullo /Photo Researchers, Inc.; **108,** Ghislaine Grozaz; **109,** Douglas Faulkner/Photo Researchers, Inc.; **110l,** Calvin J. Hamilton; **110r,** NASA/SPL/Photo Researchers, Inc.; **111,** NASA/Science Photo Library/Photo Researchers, Inc.; **112,** NASA and The Hubble Heritage Team.

Chapter 4
Pages 116–117, Loke Tan; **117r,** Richard Haynes; **118t,** Richard Haynes; **118b,** Florence Museo delle Scienze/AKG London; **120all,** Andy Crawford/Dorling Kindersley; **121l,** VLA/NRAO/Smithsonian Astrophysical Observatory; **121ml,** W. M. Keck Observatory/Smithsonian Astrophysical Observatory; **121mr,** Jeff Hester and Paul Scowen/Smithsonian Astrophysical Observatory; **121r,** Marshall Space Flight Center/NASA; **122l,** Yerkes Observatory Photography; **122r,** Courtesy of the NAIC - Arecibo Observatory, a facility of the NSF; **123t,** NASA; **123bl,** David Nunuk/Science Photo Library/Photo Researchers, Inc.; **123br,** JPL/NASA; **124,** NASA; **125,** Richard Haynes; **126t,** Richard Haynes; **126b,** Dorling Kindersley; **129,** Mark Thiessen/Corbis; **133,** Luke Dodd/Science Photo Library/Photo Researchers, Inc.; **136,** Ariel Skelley/Corbis; **137,** Anglo-Australian Observatory/Royal Observatory Edinburgh; **137inset,** AURA/STScI/NASA; **141,** Frank Zullo/Photo Researchers, Inc.; **142all,** Celestial Image Co./Science Photo Library/Photo Researchers, Inc.; **143t,** David Malin/Anglo-Australian Observatory; **143b,** Celestial Image Co./Science Photo Library/Photo Researchers, Inc.; **144t,** David Malin/Anglo-Australian Observatory; **144m,** David Malin/Anglo-Australian Observatory; **144b,** Royal Observatory, Edinburgh/AATB/Science Photo Library/Photo Researchers, Inc.; **146l,** Dorling Kindersley; **146m,** NASA; **146r,** SOHO/ESA and NASA; **147l,** R. Corradi (Isaac Newton Group) and D. R. Gonçalves (Instituto de Astrofísica de Canarias); **147m,** Bill & Sally Fletcher/Tom Stack & Associates, Inc.; **147r,** Celestial Image Co./Science Photo Library/Photo Researchers, Inc.; **148,** NASA; **152,** American Institute of Physics; **153,** Jean-Paul Kneib/Observatoire Midi-Pyrénées, France/Caltech/ESA/NASA; **154,** Richard Haynes; **156,** NASA.

Pages 158t, NASA; **158b,** JPL/NASA; **159b,** JPL/NASA; **159t,** NASA; **160,** JPL/NASA; **161,** NASA, **162t,** Pat Rawlings/NASA; **162–163b,** NASA/JPL/Cornell; **163t,** Pat Rawlings/NASA; **164,** Tony Freeman/PhotoEdit; **165t,** Russ Lappa; **165m,** Richard Haynes; **165b,** Russ Lappa; **166,** Richard Haynes; **168,** Richard Haynes; **170,** Morton Beebe/Corbis; **171,** Richard Haynes; **173t,** Dorling Kinderlsey; **173b,** Richard Haynes; **175,** Image Shop/Phototake; **178,** Richard Haynes; **185,** Richard Haynes; **188,** NASA; **189,** Reto Stockli/GSFC/NASA; **190t,** G.Antonio Milani/SPL/Photo Researchers, Inc.; **190b,** Royal Observatory, Edinburgh/AATB/Science Photo Library/Photo Researchers, Inc.; **192,** NASA; **193,** Hubble Heritage Team/NASA.